BRITISH BIRDS

BRITISH BIRDS

BY

F. B. KIRKMAN
B.A. (OXON)

EDITOR AND PART AUTHOR OF THE "BRITISH BIRD BOOK," ETC.

AND

F. C. R. JOURDAIN
M.A. (OXON)

AUTHOR OF "EGGS OF EUROPEAN BIRDS"; PART AUTHOR OF THE
"PRACTICAL HANDBOOK OF BRITISH BIRDS"
"BRITISH BIRD BOOK," ETC.

THOMAS NELSON AND SONS LTD
LONDON EDINBURGH PARIS MELBOURNE
TORONTO AND NEW YORK

THOMAS NELSON AND SONS LTD
Parkside Works Edinburgh 9
3 Henrietta Street London WC2
312 Flinders Street Melbourne C1
5 Parker's Buildings Burg Street Cape Town

THOMAS NELSON AND SONS (CANADA) LTD
91–93 Wellington Street West   Toronto 1

THOMAS NELSON AND SONS
385 Madison Avenue New York 17

SOCIÉTÉ FRANÇAISE D'EDITIONS NELSON
25 rue Henri Barbusse Paris V᷍

———

*First printed May **1930***
Reprinted 1932, 1935
New and Revised Edition 1938
*Reprinted 1941, 1942, 1943, 1944, **1948, 1950***
1953

PREFACE

THIS work contains the coloured plates, two hundred in number, issued in the *British Bird Book* (edit. Kirkman), 1910–13. The text is new. Its object is to provide, in a compact and convenient form, the best available information sufficient to identify all British species except the rarest—their nests, their eggs, and their utterances. Notes on their habitat and geographical range have been added, chiefly as an aid to identification, and these have been brought up to date.

The systematic attempt here made to describe the songs and notes of each species has encountered two main difficulties, neither of which can at present be overcome.

The first is the paucity of information about the utterances of even some of our commonest species. Complete accounts demand a great deal of time and patience, and this can rarely be given under the existing conditions of the study. One has to be content if one gets good first-hand observations, incomplete though they be.

The second difficulty is the absence of an adequate descriptive medium. The voice organ of the bird, placed at the lower end of the windpipe, is a very different instrument from the human, and attempts to convey the sounds it produces by means of our written language must necessarily lack scientific precision. How lacking in precision they can be is illustrated by our use of the labial " p " in rendering bird notes, regardless of the fact that, being without lips, the bird is incapable of uttering the sound the symbol represents for us. In the absence of an avian phonetic we have to be satisfied if our descriptions suffice to aid, if not to ensure identification. Where possible, descriptive comparisons have been added and preferred to renderings in letters. In many cases more than one description or rendering has been given, each by a different observer, and it is instructive to note the differences. Considerable caution has been exercised in statements as to what particular utterances express, the occasion of the utterance being given where there is doubt as to the nature of its meaning.

The scientific nomenclature adopted follows the rules laid down by the Fifth International Zoological Congress as applied in the *Practical Handbook of British Birds* and by the B.O.U. Committee on Nomenclature. Where subspecies are clearly recognized trinomials are given, it being obviously incorrect, as a general rule, to give a description as specific which may in part not apply to the whole species, but only to one or more of its local forms.[1]

Where the scientific (Latin) name of the species or subspecies is followed by the author's name in brackets—*e.g.* (Linnæus)—this signifies that the generic name (the first of the two or three Latin names) is not the one originally used by the author named in the bracket. Linnæus, for example, named the House-sparrow *Fringilla domestica* ; it is now called *Passer domesticus*, and is therefore followed by (Linnæus) and not Linnæus.

The classification adopted follows generally that of Professor Hans Gadow in Bronn's *Thier-Reich : Vögel II.*, with slight alterations to include the results of modern research.

Mr. Jourdain is responsible for the notes on *Range and Habitat*, *Nest and Eggs*, and *Food* ; Mr. Kirkman for *Usual Notes*. Both share responsibility for the *Descriptions* of the birds.

The sources consulted will be found acknowledged in the footnotes.

Those who desire to consult larger works are referred for geographical range and distribution and for descriptions to the *Handbook of British Birds* (5 vols. now in progress), edited and published by Witherby, and for " behaviour " (habits and instincts) to the *British Bird Book*, 4 vols., edit. F. B. Kirkman (Jack). The latter collects the published information up to 1913. Since that date much has been added, but it is scattered through a vast number of smaller books and periodicals. This additional material is incorporated in the present book, but only in so far as it falls within its scope. A much smaller (pocket size) book on the same lines as the present, but narrower in scope, is *British Birds*, by F. B. Kirkman (Nelson).

PREFACE TO NEW EDITION

EVERY effort has been made to bring up to date the information given in the following pages in so far as permitted by the limits of space and by the limited purpose of the book as defined at the beginning of the Preface to the First (1930) Edition. In order to render the work more complete brief notices have been added of those forms omitted from the body of the book on account of their rarity. Several of the sections on Usual Notes have been re-written.

---

[1] Binomial : *Corvus corax*. Trinomial : *Corvus corax corax*, the first name being that of the genus, the second of the species, the third of the subspecies, the last being added to distinguish various local forms or races—*e.g.* the typical *Corvus corax corax* from *Corvus corax hispanus* (Spain), etc.

THE CLASSIFICATION ADOPTED IN THIS WORK[1]
(*With slight modifications*)

CLASS : AVES

(The accent indicates that the preceding syllable is to be stressed. The i" in ' idæ " or " inæ " is pronounced as in " did.")

I. *Order :* **Pass'eriformes.** *Family :* (1) Cor'vidæ (Crows) ; (2) Fringill'idæ (Finches, Buntings) ; (3) Ploce'idæ (Sparrows) ; (4) Alaud'idæ (Larks) ; (5) Motacill'idæ (Wagtails, Pipits) ; (6) Certhi'idæ (Creepers) ; (7) Troglodyt'idæ (Wrens) ; (8) Cincl'idæ (Dippers) ; (9) Turd'idæ (Thrushes, Chats, Redstarts, Robin, Nightingale, Warblers) ; (10) Prunell'-idæ (Hedge-sparrow) ; (11) Sturn'idæ (Starlings) ; (12) Oriol'idæ (Orioles) ; (13) Bombycill'idæ (Waxwing) ; (14) Par'idæ (Tits) ; (15) Sitt'idæ (Nuthatches) ; (16) Panur'idæ (Bearded-Tit) ; (17) Lani'idæ (Shrikes) ; (18) Muscicap'idæ (Flycatchers) ; (19) Hirundin'idæ (Swallows).

II. *Order :* **Corac'iiformes.** *Family :* (1) Pic'idæ (Woodpeckers) ; (2) Apod'idæ (Swifts) ; (3) Caprimul'gidæ (Nightjars) ; (4) Strig'idæ (Owls) ; (5) Coraci'idæ (Rollers) ; (6) Merop'idæ (Bee-Eater) ; (7) Upup'idæ (Hoopoe) ; (8) Alcedin'idæ (Kingfisher) ; (9) Cucul'idæ (Cuckoos).

III. *Order :* **Charad'riiformes.** *Family :* (1) Columb'idæ (Pigeons) ; (2) Pterocl'idæ (Sand-Grouse) ; (3) Alc'idæ (Auks) ; (4) Lar'idæ (Gulls) ; (5) Burhin'idæ (Thick-Knees) ; (6) Glareol'idæ (Pratincoles) ; (7) Charadri'idæ (Snipe, Plovers, Sandpipers, Godwits, etc.).

IV. *Order :* **Gru'iformes.** *Family :* (1) Gru'idæ (Crane) ; (2) Otid'idæ (Bustards) ; (3) Rall'idæ (Rails).

V. *Order :* **Gall'iformes.** *Family :* Phasian'idæ (Grouse, Pheasants).

VI. *Order :* **Accip'itres.** *Family :* (1) Vultur'idæ (Vultures) ; (2) Buteon'idæ (Eagles, Kites, etc.) ; (3) Falcon'idæ (Falcons).

VII. *Order :* **An'seriformes.** *Family :* Anat'idæ (Swans, Geese, Ducks).

VIII. *Order :* **Cicon'iiformes.** *Family :* (1) Arde'idæ (Herons) ; (2) Ciconi'idæ (Storks) ; (3) Ibid'idæ (Ibis) ; (4) Phœnicopter'idæ (Flamingo) ; (5) Phalacrocorac'idæ (Cormorants) ; (6) Sul'idæ (Gannets).

IX. *Order :* **Procellar'iiformes.** *Family :* (1) Procellar'iidæ (Petrels) ; (2) Diomede'-idæ (Albatros).

X. *Order :* **Colym'biformes.** *Family :* (1) Podiciped'idæ (Grebes) ; (2) Colym'bidæ (Divers).

[1] In the main we follow Hans Gadow in Bronn's *Thier-Reich* : Vögel II, with a few minor modifications.

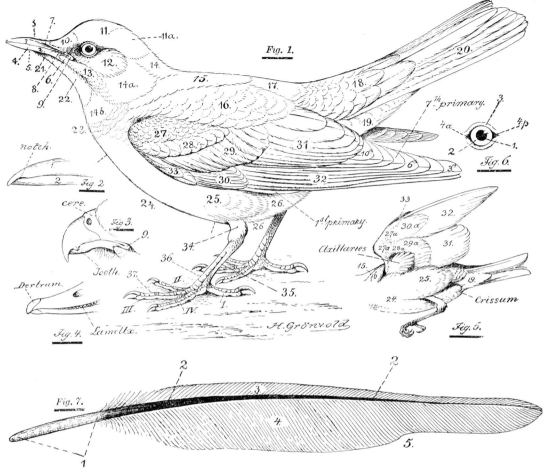

Fig. 1.
Fig. 2.
Fig. 3.
Fig. 4.
Fig. 5.
Fig. 6.
Fig. 7.

7th primary.
1st primary.
Axillaries
notch.
cere.
Tooth.
Dertrum.
Lamellæ.
Crissum
H. Grönvold

FIG. 1.

1. Upper mandible (often, but incorrectly, called maxilla) of the beak (L. *rostrum*).
2. Lower mandible.
3. Ridge (L. *culmen*).
4. Cutting edge (L. *tomium*; pl. *tomia*). The word Commissure, referring to the line of junction between the two mandibles, is also used.
5. Angle of the lower mandible, a projection present in many birds, sometimes called gonys.
6. Lores, space between bill and eye.
7. Nostrils (L. *nares*).
8. Rictal or gape bristles (L. *rictus*, opened mouth).
9. Flanges, margins of gape.
10. Forehead (L. *frons*), adj. *frontal*.
11. Crown (L. *vertex*).
11a. Nape (L. *nucha*), adj. *nuchal*.
12. Ear coverts or auriculars (L. *auricula*, ear).
13. Malar region or cheek (L. *mala*).
14. Hind-neck (L. *cervix*).

14a. Side of neck.
14b. Fore neck.
15. Back (L. *dorsum*), adj. *dorsal*.
16. Scapulars (feathers over scapulæ or shoulder-blades).
17. Rump (L. *uropygium*).
18. Upper tail coverts (L. *tectrix*, a covert; pl. *tectrices*).
19. Under tail coverts.
20. Tail feathers (*rectrices*, so called because they direct flight).
21. Chin (L. *mentum*).
22. Throat (L. *gula*), adj. *gular*.
23. Pectoral band or gorget. See Breast.
24. Breast (L. *pectus*), adj. *pectoral*.
25. Flanks, sides.
26. Belly (L. *abdomen*).
27. Lesser or minor wing coverts (L. *tectrices minores*).
28. Median or middle wing coverts (L. *tectrices mediæ*).
29. Major or greater coverts of secondaries (L. *tectrices majores*).
30. Major coverts of primaries (L. *tectrices majores*).
31. Secondaries; known also as cubitals

(supported by the cubitus or ulna), ulnar quills (*remiges secundarii*; L. *remex*, oarsman).

32. Primaries; known also as manuals (supported by the *manus* or hand), hand quills (*remiges primarii*). They are the large flight quills.

33. Bastard wing (L. *ala spuria* or *alula*).

34. Tibial feathers, covering the tibiotarsus, or shortly tibia, which, with its accompanying degenerate fibula, corresponds to the human leg between the ankle and knee. At its lower end the tibia fuses in adult birds with the three upper or proximal tarsals (ankle bones). Hence the double name—tibiotarsus, called "thigh" in error. See next, 35.

35. Tarso-metatarsus, or shortly metatarsus (or tarsus), formed by the fusion of the five lower or distal tarsals (ankle bones), and the three middle metatarsals (instep); popularly "leg" or "shank," but is actually the part of the foot from the base of the toes to near the top of the ankle. The back of the metatarsus is called the planta (sole). The bird walks on its toes.

36. Scutellations on front of tibio-tarsus.

FIG. 2.—As in Fig. 1.

Cere (L. *cera*, wax), wax-like skin which covers the base of the upper mandible in some species—*e.g.* Hawks and Eagles.

Tooth, not to be confused with the tooth in the ordinary sense. No existing birds have teeth.

9. As in Fig. 1.

FIG. 4.

Nail or hook (*dertrum*).
Lamellæ, tooth-like serrations, developed especially in Ducks and Geese, and used for sifting when feeding. *Adj.* lamellated.

FIG. 5.

As in Fig. 1. It shows the under wing coverts (Lesser, 27*a*; Median, 28*a*, etc.), the axillaries (L. *axilla*, armpit), and the vent (*crissum*).

FIG. 6.

1. Pupil. 2. Iris; *pl.* irides. 3. Eyelid.

FIG. 7.

1. Barrel (L. *calamus*, reed), which is hollow and transparent.
2. Shaft (L. *rhachis*), filled with pithy matter. The term quill, which has no connection with the Latin *calamus*, is rightly applied to the barrel and shaft taken together.
3. Outer web or vane (L. *vexilla*).
4. Inner web or vane.
5. Emarginate, having the margin broken by a notch.

GENERAL ALPHABETICAL LIST OF TECHNICAL TERMS, INCLUDING THOSE IN THE PRECEDING LIST

(The figures refer to the corresponding figures in the drawings and in the preceding list.)

Abdomen (belly), 1. 26.
Aftershaft (*hyporhachis*), a supplementary and, as a rule, relatively small feather attached to the inner and lower surface of the main shaft.
Alar bar, a bar (white, black, etc.) across the wing (L. *ala*).
Albinism, with plumage abnormally white. Cf. Melanism.
Angle (*gonys*), a projection on the under part of the lower mandible of certain species—*e.g.* the larger gulls, 1. 5.
Apex, the distal end of a feather, beak, toe; adj. *apical*. Cf. Distal.
Auricula, auriculars (ear coverts), 1. 12.
Axillaries, Fig. 5.

Back, 1. 15.
Barrel, 7. 1. The hollow transparent lower end of the quill.
Base, the root or proximal part; adj. *basal*.
Bastard wing, 1. 33.
Belly, 1. 26. Also abdomen.
Breast, 1. 24.
Brood (A.S. *brid*, that which is hatched or produced by means of warmth; a young bird), the nestlings collectively; to brood, cover the young with the wings. Cf. Incubate.
Cera, cere, 3. Wax-like skin on base of upper mandible.
Cheek, 1. 13. See Mala.

LIST OF TECHNICAL TERMS

Chin, **1. 21.**

Commissure, line of junction between the two mandibles.

Compressed, pressed together from the sides or laterally. Cf. Depressed.

Contour feathers (*pennæ, plumæ*), all which are externally visible, and so determine the contour of the body. They include the wing and tail quills. Cf. Down feathers.

Coverts, **1.** 18, 19, 27–30 ; **5.**

Crown, **1. 11.**

Cubitals, cubitus (secondaries), **1. 31.**

Culmen, **1.** 3. Ridge of the beak.

Cuneate, wedge-shaped.

Cutting edge, **1.** 4.

Decurved, curved downwards.

Depressed, pressed down vertically. Cf. Compressed.

Distal, the end distant from the centre or axis of the body—*e.g.* the tip of the beak is its distal end. Cf. Apex.

Dorsal, dorsum (back), **1.** 15.

Down feathers (*plumulæ*), soft feathers hidden below the contour feathers, except when the latter are absent, as on the neck of certain Vultures where the down feathers form a ruff. In nestling birds the Downs may be of two kinds : the pre-pennæ, which are replaced by contour feathers, and the pre-plumulæ, replaced by adult down feathers.

Eclipse. The male in the Duck Family (*Anatidæ*) is said to undergo an "eclipse" from late June or July to late September or October, when he assumes a plumage resembling the female's.

Emarginate, **7.** 5. Notched.

Erythrism, the abnormal replacement of other colours by red ; adj. *erythristic.*

Family, division of an Order.[1]

Flanks, **1.** 25.

Fledgling (Middle English *flegge,* " ready to fly,"), the young bird from the time it is ready to fly till the completion of the growth of its wing quills and tail. See Nestling.

Forehead, **1.** 10 ; adj. *frontal.*

Gape bristles, **1.** 8.

Genus ; pl. *genera,* division of a Family.[1]

Gonys (bend), **1.** 5. See Angle.

Gorget, pectoral or breast band or patch of colour, **1.** 23.

Graduated, applied to tail of which the feathers diminish gradually in length on each side, as in the Woodpecker. See Cuneate.

Gula, gular (throat), **1.** 22.

Hackles, lanceolate feathers, as on the neck of fowls. See Lanceolate.

Hallux, the first or hind toe.

Hind-neck, **1.** 14.

Incubate (L. *incubare*), to sit on eggs ; *subst.* incubation. Cf. Brood.

Iris, *pl.* irides, **6.** 2.

Lamellæ (serrations). See under Fig. **4** in the preceding list.

Lanceolate, elongated and pointed. See Hackles.

Local, term applied to a species found only in certain localities within its range.

Lores, **1.** 6. Space between beak and eye.

Mala, malar region (cheek), **1.** 13.

Mandibles, **2.** 1–2. The two mandibles compose the beak.

Mantle, term for the feathers of the back (Fig. 1, 15), the scapulars (Fig. 1, 16) and wing coverts taken collectively.

Manuals (primaries), **1.** 32.

Melanism, with plumage abnormally black.

Metatarsals (metatarsus). See preceding list under **1.** 35.

Nail (dertrum), **4.**

Nape, **1.** 11*a.*

Neck, side of, **1.** 14*a* ; fore-neck, 14*b.*

Nestling, the young bird before it is ready to fly. See Fledgling, and next two terms.

Nidicolæ (L. *nidus,* nest ; *colere,* to inhabit) or Altrices, nestlings hatched in a helpless condition and unable to leave the nest for several days. Cf. Nidifugæ.

Nidifugæ or Præcoces (L. *nidus,* nest ; *fuga,* flight), nestlings able to quit the nest and run the day on which they are hatched. Cf. Nidicolæ.

Nostrils, **1.** 7.

Order, division of a Class.[1]

Pads, underparts of the toes.

Passage migrants, birds that visit our shores in spring or autumn on their way to other countries, north or south.

Pectinated (L. *pecten,* a comb), having teeth like a comb—*e.g.* the middle claw of the Heron's foot is pectinated.

Pectus (breast), pectoral, **1.** 24.

Primaries. See preceding list under **1.** 32.

Proximal (*proximus,* next), the end next the centre or axis of the body. Cf. Distal.

Pupil, of the eye, **6.** 1.

Pyriform, pear-shaped.

Quill, barrel and shaft together, **7.**

Race, subspecies, a well-marked local form of a species.[1]

Rectrices (tail-feathers), **1.** 20.

---

[1] EXAMPLE : the raven (*Corvus corax*) is a *species* of the *genus* Corvus, which is a division of the *Family* Corvidæ or Crows, which in turn is a division of the *Order* Passeres of the *Class* Aves or Birds. Triple terms—*e.g. Corvus corax corax, Corvus corax varius, Corvus corax hispanus,* etc., are used to distinguish *subspecies* or local races. See footnote, p. vi.

Remex, remiges (quills), **1**. 31, 32.

Resident, term applied to a species or race present in the British Isles all through the year, though it may be represented by different individuals at different times, some being winter residents, others summer residents or passage migrants or stationary.

Rictal bristles (gape bristles), **1**. 8.

Ridge of the beak, **1**. 3.

Rump, **1**. 17.

Scapulars, **1**. 16. Feathers over shoulder-blades.

Secondaries. See preceding list under **1**. 31.

Shaft, **5**. 2. Part of the quill filled with pithy matter. See under Fig. **7**, 2, in the preceding list.

Shank, properly metatarsus. See preceding list under **1**. 35.

Sole (back of the metatarsus), **1**. 35.

Species, division of a Genus.[1]

Specuium (L. *speculum*, a mirror), applied to the metallic alar bar of the Duck tube. See Alar.

Stationary, term applied to species, races, or individuals that remain throughout the year in the British area—*e.g.* the Raven.

Summer residents (or visitors), birds which arrive usually between the end of March and the end of May from winter quarters in Southern Europe or Africa, and remain with us to breed, departing south generally in September, October, or November.

Superciliar (*super*, above, *cilium*, eyelid), just above the eye.

Thigh, properly tibiotarsus. See preceding list under **1**. 34.

Throat, **1**. 22.

Tibial feathers, **1**. 34. Feathers on the tibiotarsus.

Tibiotarsus or tibia, part between ankle and knee. See under **1**. 34, in the preceding list.

Toes, **1**. 36, 37.

Vagrants, birds that are casual visitors to our shore.

Vane, **7**. 3–4.

Vent (crissum), **5**.

Web, **7**. 3–4.

Winter residents (visitors), birds that arrive from September onwards from summer quarters in the Arctic regions or from Northern and Central continental Europe to pass the winter with us, departing north in the spring or early summer.

---

[1] See footnote on previous page.

ALPHABETICAL CONTENTS

* Indicates that the reference is to the page only, there being no plate of the species.

P before a reference indicates that the descriptive text is to be found on a page other than that opposite the corresponding plate.

For the list of the Notes of Additional Species see end of volume.

ALPHABETICAL CONTENTS

BRITISH BIRDS

Order: Passeriformes. Family: Crows—Corvidæ

PLATE 1.—RAVEN

Corvus corax corax Linnæus

I. Description.—Like a gigantic Carrion-Crow, but with heavier bill and more rounded tail. Length about 25 in. Colour, black, with purplish and blue gloss. In the field best recognized by its deep bass bark, " Pruk ! pruk ! " frequently uttered, and by its size.

II. Range and Habitat.—As a species is Palæarctic and Nearctic. Our British birds belong to a race which is found over the greater part of the Continent, except in the Mediterranean region, the Faeroes, Iceland, etc., where it is replaced by other races. In the British Isles it is found in hilly districts and rocky coasts, chiefly in Lakeland, Wales, and the Devonian peninsula ; also in smaller numbers on the south coast and in the Pennines ; and not uncommonly in Scotland and West Ireland. Other races are found in Asia and North America. It is sedentary throughout its range.

III. Nest and Eggs.—Chiefly on rocks inland or sea cliffs, also, but less frequently, in trees, rarely in ruins. Nest built of sticks, heather twigs, stems, sometimes seaweed, earth, etc., thickly lined with hair, wool, fur, dry grass, etc. Eggs : usually 4–5, sometimes 6, rarely 7, but 3, 2, and even 1 recorded from old birds. Colour, greenish, but ranging to clear blue or greyish, usually blotched and spotted with brown and black, underlying spots ashy grey. Occasionally markings almost absent ; red type also rarely met with, in which all blue and green is absent. Average size of 100 eggs, 49.8 × 33.5 mm. (1.96 × 1.32 in.). Laying begins February–March. Incubation period, 21 days. One brood. (Plate 180, f. 8.)

IV. Food.—Practically omnivorous ; largely carrion, occasionally injured or sick sheep, rodents, birds, reptiles, amphibians, fish, mollusca, crustacea, worms, insects, spiders, etc. Also eggs, fruit, and grain.

V. Usual Notes.—The commonest note of the Raven is the deep bark described in I. above. Captive birds have been heard to utter what might pass for a song : a succession of croaks, filing notes, cork-drawing pops, clacks of the mandibles, and trills. Its imitative capacity is well known. It has other notes incompletely studied : (1) a ringing " korronk " (usually by the male) ; (2) " toc, toc, toc " (in flight) ; (3) " clucks " and " worts " (driving off trespassers) ; (4) repeated " kiks " and " piks " (call notes).[1]

[1] For these and others see *British Birds* (Mag.), xx. 288 (H. A. Gilbert) ; xiv. 26–33 (Stanley Lewis).

PLATE 1.—RAVENS : A. W. Seaby.

Plate 2.—HOODED-CROW

Corvus corone cornix Linnæus [1]

I. Description.—Like the Carrion-Crow, but mantle and under parts grey. Length, 19 in. Hybrids between Hooded- and Carrion-Crows show all stages of intergradation.

II. Range and Habitat.—Takes the place of the Carrion-Crow in the Faeroes, Scandinavia, Denmark, East Germany, Poland, Hungary, Italy, to Russia and Western Siberia; with local races in Corsica, Sardinia, the Balkan Peninsula, Cyprus, Egypt, Iraq, Persia, etc. In the British Isles it is resident in Ireland, North Scotland, and the Isle of Man, its range overlapping that of the Carrion-Crow in Scotland, where interbreeding takes place. In England it is a winter visitor from Northern Europe, chiefly to the east side. A bird of the moorlands and wilder districts as a rule.

III. Nest and Eggs.—Like the Carrion-Crow, but in treeless districts often nests on or near the ground. Both sexes build. Eggs: 4–5, sometimes 6, very rarely 7. Colour, generally greenish, but occasionally blue; sometimes almost covered with flecks of brown and grey, but at times unmarked or nearly so. A red type has occurred. Average size of 100 British eggs, 43.5 × 30.3 mm. (1.71 × 1.19 in.). Laying usually begins April, rarely in March. Incubation period, 19–20 days. One brood. (Plate 180, f. 6.)

IV. Food.—Largely carrion, and in spring eggs of all kinds, small mammals, wounded birds, frogs, dead fish, mollusca, echini, worms, and grain.

V. Usual Notes.—Like the Raven, the Hooded-Crow indulges in a continuous outpouring of varied sounds, which may pass for a song. Its croak is said to be less guttural than that of the Carrion-Crow, and, according to Naumann, two or three croaks uttered rapidly express alarm. But its utterances have still to be closely studied.

Plate 2.—CARRION-CROW

Corvus corone corone Linnæus

I. Description.—Length about 19 in. All black, with purple and green reflections; end of tail almost square.

II. Range and Habitat.—On the Continent chiefly confined to the west (Spain, France, the Low Countries, West Germany, Switzerland, North Italy, part of Czecho-Slovakia, etc.); replaced by an eastern race in Siberia. In the British Isles it is absent from Ireland, the Isle of Man, and North Scotland, but in other parts is generally distributed, except where exterminated by gamekeepers. Resident.

III. Nest and Eggs.—Normally nests singly in trees, in the Welsh hills in mere bushes, sometimes on cliff-ledges by the coast. Nest built of sticks, twigs, earth, etc., lined warmly with hair, and built by both sexes. Eggs: normally 4–5, occasionally 6, very rarely 7. Colour, greenish, ranging to clear blue, usually thickly flecked with brown and ash grey; sometimes unmarked or nearly so. Average size of 100 British eggs, 43.2 × 30.5 mm. (1.70 × 1.20 in.). Laying begins April. Incubation period, 18–21 days. One brood. (Plate 180, f. 4.)

IV. Food.—Carrion, small mammals from rabbits downward, wounded birds, eggs, reptiles, fish, amphibia, mollusca, crustacea, worms, insects, especially beetles; also some vegetable matter, walnuts, acorns, and maize, as well as small seeds.

V. Usual Notes.—The loud hoarse " kwarrp " of the Crow is a familiar sound even in our large cities. The anger note is different: a rapid double or treble rather high-pitched rasping screech. Nothing is recorded of its other utterances.

[1] There is little doubt that the Hooded- and Carrion-Crows are not distinct species, but well-marked geographical races (subspecies) of one species.

PLATE 2.—HOODED-CROW AND CARRION-CROW (*upper figures*); HYBRIDS BETWEEN THE TWO RACES (*lower figures*): H. Goodchild.

PLATE 3.—ROOK

Corvus frugilegus frugilegus Linnæus

I. Description.—Length, 19 in. Black, with violet and blue gloss. Bill longer and more pointed than in Carrion-Crow ; adults have conspicuous white bare skin round its base. In the young the base is feathered during the first year. The bare patch is assumed as the effect of a moult.

II. Range and Habitat.—From South Sweden, Denmark, Finland, and North Russia to mid-France, North Italy, the Danube valley, and the Crimea ; replaced by other forms from Western Asia to the Pacific. In the British Isles it is numerous and widely distributed in all except absolutely treeless districts, and is resident. Immigrant flocks also arrive on our east coasts in autumn from central and northern Europe. Absent from mountains and moorlands, preferring cultivation.

III. Nest and Eggs.—Nests in colonies, sometimes of great extent, in tree-tops, but has bred exceptionally on chimneys, church spires, and low bushes. Nest built of sticks and earth, lined variously with dead leaves, grass, straw, moss, roots, and occasionally wool or hair. Both sexes build. Eggs : usually 3–5, sometimes 6, while 7, and even 9 (once), have been recorded. Colour, greenish to greyish or bluish, spotted and flecked with varying shades of olive brown to black, and ashy grey. Reddish types have occurred in Ireland and Germany. Average size of 100 British eggs, 40 × 28.3 mm. (1.57 × 1.11 in.). Laying begins late March or April. Incubation, by hen only, 17–18 days. One brood. (Plate 180, f. 7.)

IV. Food.—About 70 per cent. vegetable matter (grain, seeds, fruit, roots, potatoes, walnuts, berries, acorns, field peas, etc.), insects (about 15 per cent.), earthworms, and occasionally small mammals, carrion, birds, eggs of all kinds, fish, mollusca, spiders, millipedes, etc.[1]

V. Usual Notes.—Rooks have a remarkable variety of notes which E. Selous has endeavoured to list,[2] the most common being the familiar caw ; and, as Gilbert White long ago pointed out, they " attempt sometimes in the gaiety of their hearts to sing, but with no great success." Booth states that the song resembles that of the Starling, but is more varied and louder.[3]

[1] Collinge, *Food of Some British Wild Birds*, p. 55, etc.
[2] *Bird-watching*, pp. 299–300. Among those given are : " chug-a," " choo," " how-chow," " tchar." [3] *Rough Notes*, i.

3

PLATE 3.—ROOKS: G. E. Collins.

PLATE 4.—JACKDAW, *Corvus monedula spermologus* (Vieillot)

SCANDINAVIAN JACKDAW
Corvus monedula monedula Linnæus

I. Description.—Length, 14 in. Colour, black, with blue green or purple gloss, nape grey. Often associates with Rooks, but easily distinguished by quicker wing-beats and high-pitched notes.

II. Range and Habitat.—Various races inhabit Europe, North and West Asia, and North Africa, but it is very local in the Mediterranean region. Resident and common in the British Isles, except North-west Scotland. The same race is found in France, the Low Countries, Germany, Spain, possibly also Marocco. Usually found in wooded districts or where cliffs exist. The Scandinavian race, with small white patch at side of neck and rather lighter below, has also occurred as a migrant.

III. Nest and Eggs.—Usually nests sociably in holes of trees, rocks, ruined buildings, or cliffs, but occasionally builds substantial open or domed nests in trees. Nest built of sticks, lined chiefly with wool, also hair, grass, etc. Eggs : usually 4–6, occasionally 7, and 8 very rare. Colour, pale greenish blue, shading to bluish white, spotted brownish black and ash grey. Average size of 100 British eggs, 35.7 × 25.5 mm. (1.40 × 1.0 in.). Laying begins late in April. Incubation period, 17–18 days. One brood. (Plate 180, f. 3.)

IV. Food.—Mainly insects and worms, but also young birds and frequently eggs, slugs, wheat, fruit, walnuts, etc.

V. Usual Notes.—The Jackdaw has two or three common notes that may be heard following each other in a lively sequence as it flies ; a " jack," sometimes with additions, a kind of " ky-ah " or " ka," and something like the generic croak. It has been heard uttering a cheerful prattling or chattering that may be described as a song.

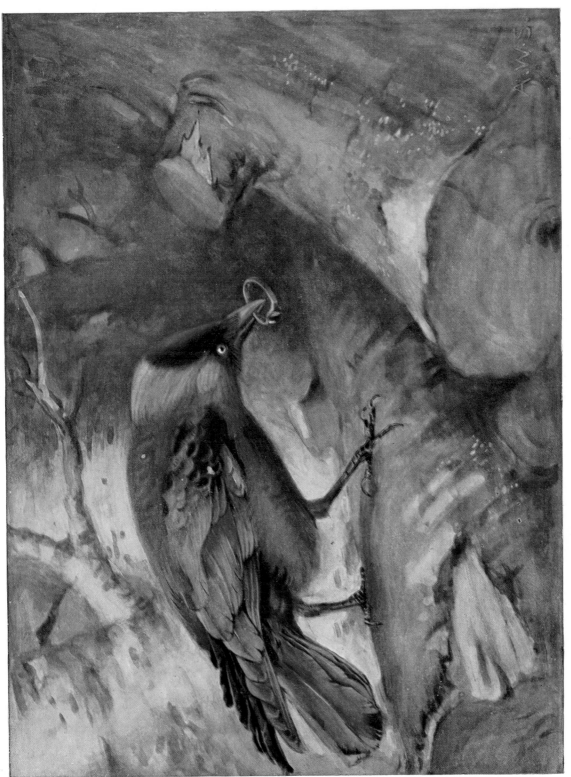

PLATE 4.—JACKDAW HIDING RING : A. W. Seaby.

Plate 5.—MAGPIE

Pica pica pica (Linnæus)

I. Description.—Length, 18 in. Easily recognized by its black and white plumage with green and purple reflections, and very long wedge-shaped tail.

II. Range and Habitat.—Widely distributed; resident in wooded localities in England, except where shot down by keepers, as in East Anglia. Rather local in Scotland and absent from north and north-west, Outer Hebrides, and northern islands. In Ireland introduced in seventeenth century. Now common wherever trees exist. On the Continent it is found through nearly the whole of Europe, North-West Africa, and temperate Asia; but races from Finland, France, Spain, North Africa, and parts of Asia have been separated.

III. Nest and Eggs.—Usually breeds high up in trees, but also not uncommonly in thorny hedgerows and bushes. Nest bulky, built of sticks, thickly lined with earth, on which a layer, generally of roots, is placed. A framework of sticks, usually thorny, forms a dome over the nest, with an opening as entrance. Eggs: usually 5–7, occasionally 8, and 9–10 recorded, as well as 3 and 4. Ground colour generally greenish blue, exceptionally greyish white, spotted and freckled freely with greyish brown and ashy. Erythristic, almost white, and blotched varieties have occurred. Average size of 100 British eggs, 34.1 × 24.3 mm. (1.34 × .95 in.). Laying begins latter part of April. Incubation, by hen, 17–18 days. One brood. (Plate 180, f. 1.)

IV. Food.—Insects (chiefly beetles and larvæ of moths), birds' eggs, and young small mammals, worms, carrion; also fruit, berries (acorns and holly berries), grain, etc.

V. Usual Notes.—The commonest cry of the Magpie has been described as "a hoarse rapid 'shushushushu'" (Witchell). It expresses alarm, if not other emotions. In the spring the birds may be heard chattering together "with a great variety of tone and emphasis." It is to this apparently that Naumann refers when he credits the Magpie with "a kind of song or chatter," adding that generally some "piping" notes are introduced; these correspond possibly to the "musical" "chōōk, chōōk" of English records.[1] The song of a captive bird sounded to the writer like "ka, ka, ka, ka; ko-wee-ou," the "ka's" being strident and the "ko-wee-ou" liquid.

[1] *British Birds* (Mag.), xviii. 122 (R. H. Brown).

5

PLATE 5.—MAGPIE : G. E. Collins.

PLATE 6.—JAY

Garrulus glandarius rufitergum Hartert
Garrulus glandarius hibernicus Witherby and Hartert
Garrulus glandarius glandarius Linnæus

I. Description.—Length, 14 in. Distinguished by its reddish-fawn back, conspicuous white rump, and patch of alternating white, blue, and black on wing. Under parts pale brownish buff, turning to rufous on flanks. Erectile crest whitish, striped with black. Iris pale blue. The Irish race has darker rufous on sides of head, ear coverts, and under parts ; also darker crest.

II. Range and Habitat.—The British race (*G. g. rufitergum*) is confined to England, Wales, and Southern Scotland : it is absent from the Isle of Man and the Hebrides, and is replaced in Ireland by the Irish race (*G. g. hibernicus*), which is local, but has recently increased its range. It is replaced by many other races on the Continent, North Africa, and Asia, and is confined to wooded districts. Sedentary wherever found, but migratory flocks from the Continent (*G. g. glandarius*) have occurred, sometimes in considerable numbers, on our east and south coasts.

III. Nest and Eggs.—Nesting sites are very varied : sometimes in undergrowth in woods or among outcrop from oak trunks, or in conifers, 5 to 60 feet from ground ; exceptionally in long heather. Nest neatly built of twigs, with inner lining of fine roots, occasionally hair. Eggs : usually 4–6, but 7 and 8 recorded of British form, and 3 only of Irish. Ground colour, pale sage green to olive buff, closely speckled with darker olive, and sometimes a black streak at the big end. A rare erythristic variety has occurred ; also a type with blue ground, unmarked or blotched, and some sets are thickly covered with brown speckles. Average size of 100 British eggs, 31.7 × 22.8 mm. (1.25 × .90 in.). Irish eggs (14) average 31.7 × 23.1. Laying begins from end of April to early in May. Incubation period about 16 days. One brood. (Plate 180, f. 2.)

IV. Food.—Young birds and eggs, mice, frogs, insects and their larvæ (chiefly beetles), and gall insects, worms, molluscs (snails and slugs) ; also grain, nuts, acorns, beech-mast, peas, potatoes, and fruit.

V. Usual Notes.—A startling outburst of high-pitched harsh screeches that suddenly possess a wood and whirl about it from end to end mark the presence of a Jay or Jays. These cries do not exhaust the bird's vocabulary, which includes a curious mewing note, also imitations of the utterances of many animals. Like other members of the Family, it has what may pass for a song.

6

PLATE 6.—JAY BY ITS NEST: G. E. Collins.

PLATE 7 —CHOUGH

Pyrrhocorax pyrrhocorax pyrrhocorax (Linnæus)

I. Description.—Length, 16 in. Black, with blue, violet, and green gloss ; feet and bill (which is curved), bright red. Bill straight at first and reddish or orange till first autumn moult.

II. Range and Habitat.—Now confined to Cornwall, Wales, Isle of Man, South-West Scotland, and Ireland, but chiefly on west and south-west. Most present breeding-places in Great Britain are in sea cliffs or near the sea, but in Man, Wales, and Ireland there are still nests some distance inland. Sedentary. Locally distributed in mountains of Europe, North Africa, but not north of the Baltic, and replaced by a larger race in the Himalayas.

III. Nest and Eggs.—Usually in holes in roof of sea caves or in crevice of cliff, but occasionally in buildings, especially when ruined or disused, and in " blow holes " near the coast. Nest an irregular mass of sticks, heather stems, furze, etc., lined thickly with wool, hair, etc. Eggs : usually 4–6, occasionally only 2 or 3, and 7 said to occur. Colour, white, creamy, or pale greenish, spotted and blotched with yellowish brown to sepia and ashy shellmarks, sometimes a black streak. Some sets distinctly reddish. Average of 100 British eggs, 39.4 × 27.9 mm. (1.55 × 1.09 in.). Laying begins end of April or early May. Incubation, by hen, 17–18 days. One brood. (Plate 180, f. 5.)

IV. Food.—Chiefly insects, especially beetles and their larvæ ; also worms, crustacea, spiders, molluscs, etc. Lizards and small mammals also said to be taken, and once recorded as attacking new-born lamb.

V. Usual Notes.—The usual cry of the Chough is described by different observers as " k'chare " or " ch-ē-ē-ē-ŏ." Other notes have been syllabled as " k'chouf " and " k'quouc." When excited it utters a rapid " kwuk-uk-uk-uk." According to Naumann, its song is a chattering warble not unlike that of the starling.[1]

[1] *Zoologist,* 1900, 498 (O. V. Aplin). Naumann, *Vögel Mitteleuropas,* iv. **51.** *Field.* June 1907, 870 (J. Walpole Bond). *Wild Life,* 1916, 172 (O. J. Wilkinson).

PLATE 7.—CHOUGHS: A. W. Seaby.

PLATE 8.—CROSSBILL

Loxia curvirostra curvirostra Linnæus
Loxia curvirostra scotica Hartert

I. Description.—Length, 6½ in. Recognized by crossed tips of bill. Male crimson with a touch of orange, but variable in depth, wings and tail dark brown. Female yellowish green, with wings and tail as in male. Juveniles brown above, lighter below, with dusty striations, later changing in male to greenish yellow and tawny orange before assumption of red plumage. The Scottish race has a deeper and more massive bill.

II. Range and Habitat.—The Crossbill inhabits coniferous forests in Europe, North-West Africa, Central Asia, and is also found in North America, but local races have been described from the Mediterranean region, Asia, and America. The Scottish form (*L. c. scotica*) is resident in Northern Scotland, and has occasionally wandered in winter to the Lowlands. The Continental form has established itself, owing to the planting of conifers, in East Anglia and possibly in Hants, and has bred in many parts of England, following irruptions from the Continent which take place at irregular intervals. In Ireland breeding has taken place in suitable districts following irruptions, but always subject to fluctuation, probably due to the cone crop.

III. Nest and Eggs.—Nests in conifers, generally Scots pine, usually not in dense forest, but on outskirts or in single trees, at varying heights, generally fairly high. Nest characteristic : a foundation of fir twigs on which is loosely fixed a cup of grasses, wool, etc., rather flattened and lined with grasses, rabbit's fleck, hair, or feathers. Eggs : 2–4, occasionally 5, greyish white, occasionally pale bluish or pinkish, with a few bold streaks of purple red or blackish and sometimes clouded. White varieties also occur. Average size of 84 English eggs, 22.2 × 16.1 mm. (.87 × .63 in.). Eggs of Scottish race slightly smaller. Laying begins in February and March, but some breed even late in December ; also in June and July. Incubation, by hen, 12–13 days. Apparently sometimes two broods. (Plate 181, f. 12.)

IV. Food.—Mainly seeds of coniferous trees, especially Scots pine and larch, also berries of hawthorn and rowan, apple pips, ivy berries, and insects, especially aphides and larvæ of lepidoptera.

V. Usual Notes.—The Crossbill's ordinary note, frequently uttered on the wing, is a double one, and has sounded differently to different observers ; among the renderings are " tsip-tsip," " gip-gip," and " whit-whit." It has also a deeper " tyoop, tyoop " (Jourdain), and a harsh " chack-chack-chack." The song is varied, being made up of " whits " combined with one or more other notes, including a wheezing " squeeze " and a full rising " burr."[1] According to the information available, it may be heard from March to November.[2]

---

[1] *British Birds* (Mag.), xxxi. 330 (L. S. V. Venables).
[2] *British Birds* (Mag.), xxix. 193 (H. G. Alexander).

PLATE 8.—CROSSBILLS, MALE (RED) AND FEMALE (GREEN), GOING TO THEIR
NEST : H. Goodchild.

PLATE 9.—GREENFINCH or GREEN LINNET

Chloris chloris chloris (Linnæus)

I. Description.—Length, 6 in. Plumage yellowish green, with bright yellow on primaries and base of tail. Bill stout. Female duller, with browner head and mantle ; young striped with brown above and below, with brown rump.

II. Range and Habitat.—Generally distributed over the British Isles and Northern and Central Europe, but replaced by other races in the Mediterranean region and Western Asia. It is only a visitor to the Shetlands and most of the Outer Hebrides. Both resident and migrant, arriving on east coast from the Continent.

III. Nest and Eggs.—Breeds in bushes and hedgerows ; sometimes many pairs nesting not far apart. Nest built of twigs and moss, with bits of wool and bents ; lined with bents, roots, and hair, occasionally with feathers. Eggs : usually 4–6, occasionally 7, or only 3, and 8 once recorded. Colour, pale purplish white or pale greenish, with a few red brown spots and streaks, chiefly at big end, and violet grey shellmarks. White or pale blue varieties also occur. Average of 100 British eggs, 20.2 × 14.5 mm. (.84 × .58 in.). Laying may begin late April, generally early May. Incubation, by hen, 13–14 days. Two broods at least. (Plate 181, f. 1.)

IV. Food.—Wheat, turnip seed, oats, and seeds of large numbers of weeds ; also in small quantities, beetles, aphides, ants, etc., while young are fed chiefly on insects and their larvæ, with a few macerated seeds.

V. Usual Notes.—The oft-repeated call of the Greenfinch once learnt is not likely to be confused with any other, but the descriptions given of it are not helpful : " a coarse wheeze " (Witchell),[1] " a monotonous long-drawn croak " (Johns).[2] A crooning " tzweerrr " is a possible rendering. Its other notes have been figured as " twit " and as " yell," the latter being often heard in autumn when the birds are in flocks. The song has usually three phrases, and, according to Naumann, runs thus : " tjoi, tjoi, tjoi, tjoi, tjoi—grrrrrr—kling, kling, kling, kling." It may be heard from February to August, and even later.[3]

[1] *Cries and Call-notes of Wild Birds.*
[2] *British Birds in their Haunts* (edit. J. A. Owen).
[3] Stanley Morris, *Bird Song*, 23.

9

A. W. SEABY

PLATE 9.—GREENFINCHES : A. W. Seaby.

Plate 10.—LINNET or BROWN LINNET

Carduelis cannabina cannabina (Linnæus)

I. Description.—Length, 5½ in. Distinguished from Twite and Redpolls by larger size, and from former by dark brown bill, brownish chestnut rump striated brown ; from Redpolls by white margins of tail feathers. Male has crimson on crown and breast in summer, chin and throat whitish, with streaks. Hen darker and lacks all red ; juveniles much like hen.

II. Range and Habitat.—Generally distributed over Europe, except in extreme north ; replaced by local races in the Mediterranean region and Atlantic Isles and in Western Asia. In the British Isles it is very widely distributed, but becomes scarce in West and North Scotland and only a straggler to the Western Isles, though breeding in the Orkneys. Flocks in autumn and moves southward, some migrating, while immigrants also arrive from the Continent.

III. Nest and Eggs.—Breeds sociably in gorse thickets on commons, but also singly in gardens, hedgerows, and plantations, occasionally among marram grass on sand-hills. Nest generally not far from ground, built of stalks, bents, moss, with a few twigs, and lined freely with hair and a little wool or a few feathers. Eggs : usually 4–6, but 7 recorded ; pale bluish white in ground colour, with a few spots and streaks of purplish red. Pale blue and white varieties without markings also occur. (.71 × .52 in.) Laying begins in April. Incubation period, 11–12 days. Two or more broods. (Plate 181, f. 8.)

IV. Food.—Mainly seeds of many species of weeds, but also turnip, rape, cabbage, flax, hemp, and hop ; also insects (beetles and moths with their larvæ), and in winter grain and berries.

V. Usual Notes.—The usual call of the Linnet is soft, liquid, difficult to figure. There is also a harsher " kek," or " knek," repeated. Both the soft call and certain less musical notes enter into the song, which may be heard more or less all the year.

PLATE 10.—COCK LINNET IN SUMMER PLUMAGE (*upper bird*) AND HEN: A. W. Seaby.

PLATE 11.—LESSER-REDPOLL

Carduelis flammea cabaret (P. L. S. Müller)

MEALY-REDPOLL, *Carduelis flammea flammea* (Linnæus)

I. Description.—Length, 4½ in. Our resident race is recognized by its small size, crimson forehead, black lores and chin, rosy throat, breast, and rump, dusty striated rufous brown back, and buff wing-band. Hen lacks pink on rump and breast, while in the juveniles it is altogether absent, as well as the black on chin and lores ; upper surface of juveniles greyish with dusky brown stripes, breast white, striped on throat and flanks. The winter immigrant Mealy-Redpoll is a larger bird with striated rump.

II. Range and Habitat.—The Redpolls have both a Palæarctic and Nearctic range. The British form (*C. f. cabaret*) is generally distributed over Great Britain and Ireland, and resident but less numerous in Southern England, and is practically indistinguishable from the birds breeding in the mountain ranges of Central Europe. The Mealy-Redpoll (*C. f. flammea*) is a winter immigrant to the British Isles in varying numbers, and breeds in Scandinavia, Finland, and North Russia, the Baltic States, and also in Asia, etc.

III. Nest and Eggs.—The Lesser-Redpoll nests in hedgerows, willow plantations, and occasionally in conifers at a good height, or even in tall heather. The Mealy-Redpoll breeds in low bushes or birch trees, generally at no great height. Both races tend to nest not far apart. Nest characteristic : foundation of small black twigs, roughly built of coarse bents and stalks, lined usually with white down, but at times hair and feathers are used. Eggs of Lesser-Redpoll usually 4–6, but 7 recorded ; Mealy-Redpoll, 5–7, but 8 recorded. Ground colour a characteristic dull rather deep blue, with some spots or streaks of brown, but occasionally quite unmarked. Average size of 100 British eggs of Lesser-Redpoll 15.7 × 12.2 mm. (.62 × .48 in.) ; 100 eggs of Mealy-Redpoll, 16.9 × 12.6 mm. (.66 × .49 in.). Laying begins in British Isles usually latter half of May, occasionally in April ; Mealy-Redpoll breeds later. Incubation period, 10–11 days (Lesser-Redpoll). Possibly a second brood sometimes reared. (Plate 181, f. 9.)

IV. Food.—Chiefly seeds of alder, birch, bulrush, and weeds of many species ; also insects, including small beetles, larvæ of lepidoptera, etc., and their eggs.

V. Usual Notes.—The call notes are metallic and high-pitched, easily recognized when once heard. Of the song there is no adequate description. The note of the rarer Mealy-Redpoll has been rendered by O. V. Aplin as " chizzzz," and its song as something like " chick-chick-chick-wee-wee." [1] Song periods, whether all the year or not, uncertain.

PLATE 11.—SISKIN

Carduelis spinus (Linnæus)

I. Description.—Length, 4½ in. Recognized by yellow and green plumage, black crown and chin, and dusty streaks on back and flanks. Hen greyer ; crown olive green with dusky streaks, chin dull white instead of black, and under parts all striped, except the belly. Juveniles still more striated.

II. Range and Habitat.—Resident in wooded parts of Scotland, Ireland, North England, and North Wales. Breeding records from South England probably due to escaped birds. Also in the forests of North Europe and Asia, and in the mountain forests of Central Europe. Otherwise winter visitor and immigrant to British Isles.

III. Nest and Eggs.—In its natural haunts breeds in conifers, usually high up and often near end of bough. The cases of nesting in Southern England are quite abnormal—in rose pergolas, bushes, in gardens, etc. Nest neatly built of small twigs, bents, moss, lichens, and wool, lined with roots, down, hair, and sometimes feathers. Eggs : 4–5, rarely 6, but 3 not uncommon. Ground colour, light blue to bluish white, with red brown streaks or spots, sometimes very dark. Average size of 53 British eggs, 16.4 × 11.9 mm. (.64 × .47 in.). Laying begins in early April. Incubation period (in confinement), 11–12 days. Double brooded. (Plate 181, f. 3.)

IV. Food.—Records scanty, but mainly seeds of trees, not only of conifers but also of deciduous trees, such as catkins of alders, and buds ; also seeds of weeds and insects, (larvæ of lepidoptera and aphides).

V. Usual Notes.—The Siskin's common note is not unlike the German name for the species, " Zeisig." The song is often uttered during the bird's nuptial flight, when it rises from its perch, circles with puffed-out plumage, wide-fanned tail, and rapid-beating wings. The composition of the song has not been closely described, but includes the " zeisig " above mentioned. Song period, all the year. [2]

---

[1] *Zoologist*, xx. 451 ; xxi. 69.   [2] Zander, *Vögel Mecklenburgs.*

PLATE 11.—LESSER-REDPOLLS (*three upper birds*) AND SISKINS (*two lower yellow-green birds*) : A. W. Seaby.

PLATE 12.—BRITISH TWITE
Carduelis flavirostris pipilans (Latham)
CONTINENTAL TWITE
Carduelis flavirostris flavirostris (Linnæus)

I. Description.—Length, 5 in. Much resembles Linnet in appearance, but beak always more or less yellow in summer and winter, and rump of male pink. No crimson on forehead or breast, as in Redpoll and Linnet, and chin buff. Female and juvenile have no pink on rump, which in the hen is like the mantle.

II. Range and Habitat.—The British race (*C. f. pipilans*) is confined to the north of England, Isle of Man, Scotland and the outlying islands, and Ireland. Also said to have bred in Wales and North Devon. The Continental race only breeds in Scandinavia and North Finland. In winter flocks move southward, and immigrants reach us from Scandinavia.

III. Nest and Eggs.—Frequently nesting in treeless districts, the Twite breeds generally among heather, but also often on or close to the ground, in corn crops, among stones or upturned sods, in holes, and among creepers. Nest, usually of bents and dead grasses with a few twigs or moss, lined with hair and wool, sometimes a feather or two. Eggs : normally 5–6, 3 or 4 exceptional and 6 normal in some districts, while 7 and 8 have been recorded. Colour, pale bluish or yellowish white, with a few brown streaks or spots, sometimes very dark. White eggs have occurred. Average size of 100 British eggs, 16.8 × 12.6 mm. (.66 × .49 in.) Laying begins in latter part of May. Incubation period, 13–14 days. Double brooded as a rule. (Plate 181, f. 10.)

IV. Food.—Seeds of many species of weeds, seedling turnips and cabbages ; also grain and insects.

V. Usual Notes.—A common note of the Twite is the " twaate " or " twite " which gives the species its name ; beyond this the records are too contradictory and vague to be of much use.

PLATE 12.—TWITE AND ITS NEST: G. E. Collins.

Plate 13.—BRITISH GOLDFINCH

Carduelis carduelis britannica (Hartert)

I. Description.—Length, 5 in. Easily recognized by the crimson, white, and black of the head and the bright golden yellow bar on the wing. Wing and tail quills black with white on tips, under parts mostly grey brown, back brown. Juveniles lack red, white, and black on the head, which is brownish, and have the upper surface streaked brown.

II. Range and Habitat.—A Palæarctic species inhabiting Europe, North Africa, and Western Asia ; but the British race, which is resident, is generally distributed, but commonest in Southern England, and scarce or absent in Northern Scotland and its island groups. Flocks in winter months and then wanders from place to place.

III. Nest and Eggs.—Usually breeds in gardens, avenues, shrubberies, or orchards, nesting sometimes at a good height on trees but also low down in hedges. Nest very neatly built of bents, moss, roots, and lichens, generally lined with down, sometimes wool and a few hairs. Eggs : usually 4–5, occasionally 6, or only 3 and 7 recorded. Ground colour, bluish white with a few streaks and spots of purplish brown and some ashy shellmarks. Some eggs unmarked, and a rare white variety has been met with. Average size of 100 British eggs, 21.3 × 14.8 mm. (.67 × .50 in.). Laying begins in May, but exceptionally late in April. Incubation, by hen, 12–13 days. Double brooded. (Plate 181, f. 2.)

IV. Food.—Mainly seeds of various weeds, especially thistles, chickweed, and ribroot ; small cone seeds also said to be taken. Insect food includes smaller beetles, larvæ of lepidoptera, diptera, and hymenoptera, also aphides.

V. Usual Notes.—The common note of the Goldfinch is a " twit " or " twitt-itt-itt." Also in German " stichlit " or " pickelnick." Repetitions of this and other notes make up its song, described by one of the older ornithologists as " not inelegant." It is heard more or less all the year, and very frequently during the breeding season. A close rendering has still to be made.

PLATE 13.—GOLDFINCH (HEN) FEEDING ITS YOUNG, THE MALE ALIGHTING:
Alfred Priest.

PLATE 14.—BRITISH BULLFINCH

Pyrrhula pyrrhula nesa Mathews and Iredale

NORTHERN BULLFINCH

Pyrrhula pyrrhula pyrrhula (Linnæus)

I. Description.—Length, 6 in. Recognized by black hood and white rump, contrasting with blue black tail and grey back and conspicuous in flight. Male has rose vermilion breast ; female has vinous brown breast and brown back. Young have white rump but lack black hood ; under parts pale brown. The northern race is a larger and more brightly coloured bird.

II. Range and Habitat.—Distributed over Europe, the Azores, and temperate Asia. The British race (*P. p. nesa*) is confined to the British Isles, where it is very general in Great Britain and Ireland, but becomes local in Scotland, and is probably absent from the islands as a breeder, except some localities in the Inner Hebrides. It is resident, but the northern race (*P. p. pyrrhula*) is an irregular winter migrant from the Continent, chiefly to the northern isles and east coast.

III. Nest and Eggs.—Nests in evergreens in gardens and woodlands, also in thick bushes and hedgerows. Nest built of twigs with moss or lichens, and lined characteristically with layer of fine black rootlets. Eggs : usually 4–5, occasionally 6, and 7 on record. Ground greenish blue with some purple brown markings, often forming a zone at big end, and at times some purplish cloudings. Variety with white ground and sometimes red brown spots or streaks occurs. Average size of 100 British eggs, 19.5 × 14.4 mm. (.77 × .57 in.). Laying begins late in April or early in May. Incubation by hen ; period, 13–14 days. Two broods. (Plate 181, f. 11.)

IV. Food.—Mainly buds in spring ; also seeds and berries of sycamore, birch, privet, lilac, heather, etc., and seeds of various weeds, and larvæ of lepidoptera and diptera as well as beetles.

V. Usual Notes.—The ordinary note of the Bullfinch is a soft flute-like " pee-ew " or " whee-ou," which may be followed by a softer " büt, büt " (Naumann). The song is a series of short, low notes, figured by Bechstein : " Si-üt-üt-üt-si-re-üt-üt-üt-üt-üt-si-re-üt-mi-üt-la." It may occasionally be heard outside the breeding season. The hen also sings, and is said by Petényi [1] to begin to do so as soon as the young are able to take care of themselves, continuing till the spring moult.

[1] *Ornithologische Fragmente.*

PLATE 14.—COCK (*upper bird*) AND HEN BULLFINCH. A. W. Seaby.

PLATE 15

BRITISH CHAFFINCH, *Fringilla cœlebs gengleri* Kleinschmidt
CONTINENTAL CHAFFINCH, *Fringilla cœlebs cœlebs* Linnæus

I. Description.—Length, 6 in. White patch on shoulders is conspicuous in both sexes. Male has slate blue crown and nape, mantle chestnut brown, rump greenish, throat and breast sienna brown. Female much duller, crown and nape yellowish brown, back olive green, throat and breast whitish brown with tinge of sienna. Young much like hen.

II. Range and Habitat.—A Palæarctic species, with ill-defined local races in some Mediterranean islands and also in Asia, but very distinct forms in the Atlantic island groups and North Africa. The British race (*F. c. gengleri*) has a browner pink breast and is widely distributed, and sedentary in the British Isles wherever any trees or bushes exist, but flocking and moving about in winter. The Continental race (*F. c. cœlebs*) is a mere straggler.

III. Nest and Eggs.—Placed in hedgerows, bushes, or trees, but usually 3 to 12 feet from the ground, very neatly and compactly built of grasses, moss, roots, wool, etc., externally decorated with lichens or bits of birch bark and even paper. Neatly lined with hair and sometimes a few feathers. Eggs : usually 4–5, occasionally 6 and 7, 8 and even 9 have been recorded. Ground colour, greenish or brownish stone, occasionally clear blue, with spots and streaks of dark purple brown, the former often with a " penumbra." Occasionally markings are absent, and a white variety has been recorded. Average of 100 British eggs, 19.9 × 14.6 mm. (.78 × .57 in.). Laying begins in April, often not till May. Incubation period, 11–12 days. Double brooded. (Plate 181, f. 7.)

IV. Food.—Seeds of many weeds and garden plants, seedlings, buds of fruit trees, grain, and fruit ; also insects (small beetles and larvæ, lepidoptera, especially noctuæ and larvæ, hymenoptera larvæ, orthoptera, also aphides), spiders, and eggs of snail.

V. Usual Notes.—The Chaffinch owes certain of its popular names to renderings of its familiar cry : " spink," " pink," or " twink." It has other notes that have yet to be closely studied—*e.g.* " whit," " chissick." The short oft-repeated song, a cheerful ditty ending with a characteristic little musical kick (if one may use so bold a metaphor), has usually three phrases, varying much in completeness. One rendering is " tschi-tschi-tschi," a mellow " tweet," " tee-choo-éo." For the ending Dr. Garstang gives " tissy-choo-éo." The song is heard more or less all the year, chiefly from end of February to early July. Some birds have a long-drawn wheezing note, suggestive of the Brambling and Greenfinch, which seems to replace the usual " spink." [1]

[1] For fluctuation in song tunes see *British Birds* (Mag.), xxviii. 366 (J. P. Burkitt) ; and *id.* xxix. 294 (J. J. Cash).

PLATE 15—COCK CHAFFINCH FEEDING THE YOUNG, THE HEN WAITING:
H. Goodchild.

PLATE 16.—BRAMBLING

Fringilla montifringilla Linnæus

I. Description.—Length, 6 in. White rump in both sexes. Male has throat and breast chestnut, and feathers of the head and mantle blue black, with ruddy brown edgings in winter ; breast, dull white. Female, brownish grey, mottled with brownish on head and mantle, lacks the rich chestnut on throat and breast and is generally duller.

II. Range and Habitat.—Winter visitor in varying numbers from Scandinavia, arriving on east coast, but has bred on at least two occasions in North Scotland. On the Continent its breeding range includes Scandinavia, Northern Finland, and Russia, as well as Northern Asia.

III. Nest and Eggs.—Usually nests in birches or conifers at varying heights. Nest much bulkier than Chaffinch's but similar, built of grasses, bents, etc., and covered with lichens or birch bark, lined thickly with hair or feathers. Eggs : usually 5–6, but 7 not uncommon, while 8 and even 9 are recorded. Not unlike those of Chaffinch, but often darker and greener, though similarly marked ; a type with clear blue ground occurs. Average size of 100 eggs, 19.5 × 14.6 mm. (.76 × .57 in.). Laying begins from mid May, but later in the high north. Incubation by hen ; period not exactly known. Apparently single brooded.

IV. Food.—Largely on beech-mast in England in winter ; also corn, berries of various kinds, nuts, seeds, insects and their larvæ.

V. Usual Notes.—Descriptions of the song of this bird differ greatly. Collett, the Norwegian ornithologist, writes of it as " sweet and melodious, consisting of several flute-like notes, somewhat resembling those of the redwing." [1] It is heard, according to him, only in the breeding season. The call usually heard at the breeding ground is a very monotonous long-drawn snoring or wheezing note, which is one of the most characteristic sounds of the Norwegian birchwoods.

[1] Jourdain says it recalls a Chaffinch's song, but is fuller and more vigorous.

PLATE 16.—BRAMBLINGS IN WINTER PLUMAGE : A. W. Seaby

Plate 17.—HAWFINCH

Coccothraustes coccothraustes coccothraustes (Linnæus)

I. Description.—Length, 7 in. Recognized by its huge beak with horny pads inside. General orange or tawny brown plumage, with blue black quills and black throat and lores. In hand the peculiar curled sixth to ninth primaries are distinctive. Female paler and greyer; juvenile has yellowish (not black) throat and barred flanks.

II. Range and Habitat.—A Palæarctic species, but replaced by local races in Northern Africa and Asia. In the British Isles it is sedentary, but subject to local movements, and now breeds in many localities in England and eastern Welsh counties, also in some parts of South Scotland. Said to have bred in Kildare, Ireland. Otherwise only scarce vagrant.

III. Nest and Eggs.—Breeds frequently in orchards, old wooded gardens, and blackthorns, hornbeams, or forest trees in wooded districts. Nest usually on horizontal bough, with layer of twigs as foundation and shallow cup lined with roots, hair, fibre, etc., on bents, lichens, and roots. Eggs: usually 4–5, occasionally 6, and 7 once recorded; 3 also occasional. Ground colour, blue to greyish green, boldly streaked with blackish brown and a few spots of the same colour, also ashy underlying markings. Scarce varieties are warm buff with rich brown markings, or slaty grey almost unmarked. Average of 100 British eggs, 24.2 × 16.5 mm. (.95 × .65 in.). Laying begins from end of April to early May. Incubation by hen; period, 10–11 days. Sometimes two broods. (Plate 181, f. 4.)

IV. Food.—Kernels and seeds of sloe, yew, hawthorn, hornbeam, beech, bird cherry, cherry, plum, bullace, laurel, ash, maple, and sycamore; also green peas and larvæ of moths. Young said to be fed on insects.

V. Usual Notes.—The information available is scanty. The common notes of the species have been described as a sharp click or clinking sound or " zick," and a harsh long-drawn whistle " zē-ip " repeated.[1] The most detailed analysis of the song is Seebohm's, " four simple whistles on an ascending scale, the first two at a slight interval, and the last two repeated rapidly, one after the other, the final one being somewhat drawn out." [2] It may be heard from about February to June.

[1] Stanley Morris, *Bird Song*, 23.   [2] *A History of British Birds.*

PLATE 17.—HAWFINCH (MALE): G. E. Collins.

PLATE 18.—CORN-BUNTING

Emberiza calandra calandra Linnæus

I. Description.—Length, 7 in. Distinguished by large size, heavy build, and thick bill, with palatal knob. General hue ochreous brown, upper parts streaked with dusky brown, under parts buffish white, streaked with brown on throat, breast, and flanks. Wing coverts margined with buff, forming a bar ; tail dark brown, edged paler brown. Yellower in autumn and winter.

II. Range and Habitat.—South Sweden and Europe south of the Baltic, North Africa, and Western Asia. Local races described from the Canaries, Corsica, and Siberia. Common along coasts of the British Isles, but local inland. Resident, but partly migratory, many birds moving southward and immigrants arriving in autumn.

III. Nest and Eggs.—Breeds in open country—downs, commons, grass fields, or in corn—sometimes on the ground or in gorse and bushes, occasionally a few feet above the ground. The nest is built of grasses and bents, with a few hairs in lining. Eggs : usually 3–5, occasionally 6, while 7 have been recorded. Ground colour, greyish white or pale bluish white to light sienna, boldly streaked and spotted with brown black, rarely without markings. Some sets richly marked with red brown on reddish ground. Average of 100 British eggs, 23.8 × 17.7 mm. (.93 × .69 in.). Laying begins late in May, but sometimes much later. Incubation by hen ; period, 12–13 days. Occasionally double brooded. (Plate 181, f. 13.)

IV. Food.—Chiefly cereals and seeds of weeds, also insects (chiefly small beetles and their larvæ, caterpillars, also odonata or dragon flies). Buds of sycamore and ivy berries also recorded.

V. Usual Notes.—The Corn-Bunting's song, uttered usually from a telegraph wire or hedge-top, is a not unmusical flow of little crackling notes that seem to issue from a throat too tired or too dry to give them ordered harmony. It has not the clean-cut formula of the Yellow-Bunting's ditty. The usual call is a " tsick," which, rapidly repeated, forms the first part of the song, " tsick-tsick-tsick-tsick." The end part has been compared to the jingling of keys, and may also be described as an incoherent stutter. The alarm note is " tseep " and " tseer." Song period, January to October, and occasionally later.[1]

[1] *British Birds* (Mag.), xvi. 292 ; xxii. 210 ; xxv. 293 (J. Walpole Bond) ; xxviii. 4 (Ryves) ; xxix. 193 (H. G. Alexander).

PLATE 18.—CORN-BUNTING : G. E. Collins.

PLATE 19.—REED-BUNTING

Emberiza schœniclus schœniclus (Linnæus)

I. Description.—Length, 6 in. Recognized by the black head and throat with intersecting white stripe, and ash grey rump tinged and striped with brown. Under surface white, flanks with dark stripes ; mantle blackish, feathers edged chestnut ; tail dark, but white on outer feathers. In hen, the head is reddish brown, with dusky stripes and yellowish white streak below and above the eye. In autumn the black of male becomes yellowish brown, and hen becomes browner ; young much like hen.

II. Range and Habitat.—Europe and Northern Asia, but replaced by other forms in countries bordering the Mediterranean and South-east Europe, as well as in Asia. In the British Isles it is generally distributed and partly migrating, many leaving for the south, while immigrants arrive on our east coasts. In the breeding season generally to be found in marshy ground.

III. Nest and Eggs.—Breeds in water meadows, alder and willow plantations, on the ground or on stumps. Nest built of grasses and bents with a little moss, lined with finer grasses and hair, occasionally flowers of reed. Eggs : usually 4–5, occasionally 6, while 7 has occurred in North Europe. Ground colour, brownish olive, ranging to greyish, reddish, or light green, with bold blackish brown streaks and a few spots, with suffused edges and ashy shellmarks. White and pale blue varieties, unmarked, or almost so, also occur. Average of 100 British eggs, 19.8 × 14.6 mm. (.78 × .57 in.). Laying begins end of April, often in May. Incubation period, 13 days ; male takes part. Generally double brooded. (Plate 181, f. 16.)

IV. Food.—Seeds of marsh weeds and grasses, also grain in autumn, and insects, including water-beetles, larvæ of moths, neuroptera and hemiptera (water boatman), etc.

V. Usual Notes.—The Reed-bunting's usual note, often uttered, sounds like " tcheee." The song, according to Naumann's rendering (anglicized), runs : " Tzya, teet, taee, tzisstziss—taee, tzeer, tzississ." There is considerable variation. Song period, February to end of July. Records of winter singing are apparently lacking.

PLATE 19.—REED-BUNTINGS IN SPRING, COCK (*upper figure*) AND HEN: A. W. Seaby.

Plate 20.—CIRL-BUNTING

Emberiza cirlus cirlus Linnæus

I. Description.—Length, 6½ in. Like Yellow-Bunting, but distinguished by the black throat and lores and olive green rump. Below black throat is a bright yellow band, then a sage green band ; reddish brown on flanks of yellow belly. Crown and nape olive green, streaked black ; mantle and wings chestnut. Female like that of Yellow-Bunting, but rump olive green ; throat yellow, striped dark brown.

II. Range and Habitat.—The Mediterranean region north to the south of England, France, South-West Germany, Croatia, and the Crimea, and south to North Africa, but Corsican and North African races have been separated. In Great Britain it is a local resident, common in the south coast counties, and in smaller numbers in Wales and inland counties to Salop and the Thames valley, occasionally also in Yorkshire and Essex. Largely, but not altogether, a downland species where some bush or tree growth exists.

III. Nest and Eggs.—Breeds generally higher than Yellow-Bunting, sometimes against trunks of trees, in bushes, hedges, etc., but also on ground on banksides. Nest has much moss in foundation, sometimes leaves ; built also of bents, lined with finer grasses and horsehair. Eggs : usually 3–4, sometimes 5 or only 2 ; distinguished as a rule by the greenish blue tint of ground and the blackish markings, more decided than in the Yellow-Bunting. Rare types are almost unmarked or lack the bluish ground. Average of 70 British eggs, 21.1 × 15.9 mm. (.83 × .62 in.). Laying begins in May. Incubation by hen, 11–13 days. Two or three broods. (Plate 181, f. 15.)

IV. Food.—Corn and seeds of many species of weeds and grasses ; also insects, including smaller beetles, grasshoppers, and larvæ of moths. Young fed on insects.

V. Usual Notes.—The Cirl's usual song is more trilled than the Yellow-Bunting's, with the " cheese " omitted. The usual cries are said to resemble those of the Corn- and Yellow-Buntings ; exact records are lacking. Song period : chiefly during the breeding season up to late August ; has been heard in every month of the year (E. W. Hendy).[1] An individual has been recorded as singing both the usual song and an alternative : " tistei " to begin with, then a louder " seear " repeated, and not unlike the notes of a descending Tree-Pipit.[2]

Plate 20.—LAPLAND-BUNTING

Calcarius lapponicus lapponicus (Linnæus)

I. Description.—In autumn male has blackish brown head, nape buffy chestnut ; mantle black, feathers edged rufous ; throat blackish, feathers edged buff ; under surface white, streaked on flanks. (Bright chestnut collar and black throat and crown only in breeding season.) Hen, lighter and browner than male, throat white, crown blackish, nape paler, collar of black and buff on throat. Young, brown, marked with black ; light stripe through eye round ear coverts ; under parts dull white, some stripes on flanks.

II. Range and Habitat.—Inhabits the fringe of the Arctic and Subarctic regions of the world, with local forms in Kamchatka and Alaska. In Europe it breeds in Norway, south to the Dovrefjeld, but is only a winter visitor on passage to the British Isles, chiefly to the northern and eastern coasts.

III. Nest and Eggs.—Does not breed in the British Isles, but nests in Arctic and Subarctic Europe in depressions on the ground, in sides of big grass tussocks, etc. Nest built of moss and bents, rather bulky, lined with finer bents and many feathers. Eggs : 5–6, sometimes 7, occasionally only 4. Ground colour, ranging from greyish to brownish, usually thickly clouded and blotched with chestnut, sepia, or ochreous brown, with a few dark streaks or spots. Average of 100 eggs, 20.6 × 14.9 mm. (.81 × .58 in.). Laying begins from early June. Incubation by both sexes ; period, 13–14 days. One brood.

IV. Food.—Chiefly seeds of various grasses and Arctic plants, but in summer insects, especially diptera.

V. Usual Notes.—The song of this species appears to be uttered usually when the bird is on the wing, and is said to be " as rich and clear as that of any of our songsters—not so shrill as that of the Lark, but far sweeter and more varied " (Wheelwright).[3] It " sounds best while the bird descends slowly, and without flapping of wings " ; it is " short, and of an extremely melancholy nature, but containing very pretty warbling runs, which are always represented in the same order " (Hagerup).[4] The usual cry is like the " tzirr " of the Snow-Bunting. The alarm notes are " wheee-ee," and, after the breeding season, a sharp " zip."[5] Song period not recorded.

---

[1] *Bird-watching*, p. 172.   [2] *British Birds* (Mag.), xvi. 188 (M. S. Curtler).
[3] *A Spring and Summer in Lapland.*   [4] *Birds of Greenland.*
[5] *British Birds*, ix. 230–238 (M. D. Haviland).

20

LAPLAND-BUNTING (MALE) : Winifred Austen.

PLATE 20.—CIRL-BUNTING (MALE) : G. E. Collins.

PLATE 21.—YELLOW-BUNTING OR YELLOW-HAMMER

Emberiza citrinella citrinella Linnæus

I. Description.—Length, $6\frac{1}{2}$ in. Distinguished by lemon yellow head, neck, and under parts, with chestnut rump. Greenish olive on nape and round ear coverts. Mantle and wing coverts dull red, striped black. White on two outer tail feathers. Female and young less brilliant, with crown dull olive brown, streaked black.

II. Range and Habitat.—Europe from about $65\frac{1}{2}°$ N. South to the Cantabrian mountains, Northern Italy and Bulgaria, but East European birds are generally separated as a local race. Generally distributed in the British Isles, but absent from Shetlands and some Hebridean isles as a breeding species. Resident, flocking in winter, when immigrants arrive from Northern Europe.

III. Nest and Eggs.—Usually nests by roadsides, on commons, or in hedges, either on the ground at the foot of the bush where grass and weeds are growing, or a foot or two above it. Nest neatly built of bents and dry grasses, sometimes a little moss in foundation, and lined with fine bents and horsehair. Eggs : usually 3–4, sometimes 5, rarely 6; usually greyish or purplish white, exceptionally pale reddish, streaked and pencilled with irregular lines of dark brown and a spot or two. Varieties of white, or even pale blue, without markings also occur. Average of 100 British eggs, 21.9×16.3 mm. ($.86 \times .64$ in.). Laying begins occasionally late in April, but usually in May. Incubation period, 12–13 days. Two or even three broods. (Plate 181, f. 14.)

IV. Food.—Largely vegetable matter, especially corn, but also seeds of many weeds and wild fruits, such as blackberry, also insects (beetles and larvæ, larvæ of flies, moths and larvæ, etc.), spiders, and eggs of land mollusca.

V. Usual Notes.—The familiar popular rendering of the song is a " Little bit of bread and no cheese," the last note being long-drawn ; it is sometimes omitted. To me the song sounds usually like " Tche-tche-tche-tche-tche-tche-tche-tche-e-e-se." The usual call is not unlike that of the Corn-Bunting, but less abrupt. The alarm note is " tsee." Song period, from February to August, and occasionally later.

21

PLATE 21.—COCK YELLOW-HAMMER : A. W. Seaby.

Plate 22.—SNOW-BUNTING

Plectrophenax nivalis nivalis (Linnæus)

I. Description.—Length, 7 in. In summer the male is white, except on the back, middle tail quills, and wings (part), which are chiefly black. In autumn upper parts largely tinged with chestnut and under parts with rufous buff. Hen has upper surface greyish brown, flecked with black ; in autumn, more like male. Young much like hen.

II. Range and Habitat.—The Arctic regions of the world, in Europe, south to 60°, in Norway, and in very small numbers in the mountains of North Scotland. To the British Isles it is mainly a winter visitor, usually near the coasts, but also occasionally inland, on open fields.

III. Nest and Eggs.—Nests out of sight under stones in screes on hillsides or under boulders ; in the Arctic regions, in crevices of rocks, also in or under wooden huts, in old tins, under driftwood, etc. Nest, bulky, built of dead stalks of weeds and grasses, moss, etc., lined warmly with grasses, hair, wool, and feathers. Eggs : usually 5–6, sometimes only 4, while 7 and even 8 have been recorded. Ground colour, buffish or bluish white, with streaks and spots of red brown, a few blackish markings, and ashy shellmarks. Some eggs thickly spotted or blotched red brown. Average of 100 eggs, 22.0 × 16.1 mm. (.82 × .63 in.). Laying begins late in May or early in June in Scotland. Incubation, by hen, 11–13 days. Sometimes two broods (D. N.-Thompson). (Plate 181, f. 17.)

IV. Food.—In summer, insects (diptera and larvæ, small beetles, and larvæ of moths), also seeds of grasses and alpine plants ; in winter, grain, seeds, sandhoppers, insect larvæ, and berries.

V. Usual Notes.—The Snow-Bunting's song " consists of loud and clear flute-like notes, combined with short stanzas, but has no definite melody " (Hagerup).[1] It has been described as " a lovely song, with no touch in it of a Bunting's scrape " (Trevor-Battye).[2] Naumann gives the chief cries as " tzirr," and a piping " feet." Song period not recorded.

[1] *Birds of Greenland.*
[2] *Icebound in Kolguev.*

PLATE 22.—SNOW-BUNTINGS IN WINTER PLUMAGE : Winifred Austen.

Family : Ploceidæ (Sparrows)

PLATE 23.—TREE-SPARROW

Passer montanus montanus (Linnæus)

I. Description.—Length, 5½ in. Much like male House-Sparrow, but smaller, with chocolate brown crown and nape, triangular black patch on white cheek, double wing bars of white, and more graceful appearance. Sexes alike.

II. Range and Habitat.—Distributed over Europe, Asia, and some of the islands off the coast of South-East Asia, but Asiatic birds have been subspecifically separated. In the British Isles it is local, but widely distributed, being absent from some counties on the west of Great Britain, and locally in small numbers resident in the islands off West Scotland and Shetlands, but not Orkneys. In Ireland very local, and confined to a few counties chiefly in the north. Resident.

III. Nest and Eggs.—Not invariably near houses, though common in some suburban districts. Nest frequently in holes of trees, especially pollarded willows, also in thatch, haystacks, quarries, nesting-boxes, or in foundations of old nests, etc. Nest of same type as House-Sparrow's, but smaller, and never built among open branches ; materials also similar. Eggs : usually 4–6, but 7 and 8 on record ; much smaller and glossier than House-Sparrow's ; variable, being often stippled with dark brown or chestnut, and with more brown in a series than House-Sparrow's. White varieties also recorded. One egg frequently lighter in colour than the rest. Average size of 100 British eggs, 19.3 × 14 mm. (.76 × .55 in.). Laying generally begins in May, but also said to take place in April. Incubation, by both sexes, 13–14 days. Two or three broods. (Plate 181, f. 6.)

IV. Food.—Seeds of weeds of many species, some corn ; also insects and their larvæ, spiders, etc.

V. Usual Notes.—According to Walpole Bond, the song is a grating " twit-it-it-it-chit." Heard from end of February to September. Its cry " chu-ip " corresponds to the House-Sparrow's " chirp " or " chilp." A second cry is " check," which may become a chatter ; a third, " tack," or " teck." (*British Birds* (Mag.), xxv. 332.)

PLATE 23.—HOUSE-SPARROW

Passer domesticus domesticus (Linnæus)

I. Description.—Length, 6 in. Distinguished by ash grey on crown and rump, black gorget, cheek-patch white, bluish black bill, chestnut nape and lores ; mantle striped black and chestnut. In hen, head and rump brown, mantle rufous streaked brown ; buff eye stripe, beak brown, under parts dull buffish white. In winter the grey and black of the cock are obscured by brown, the white by yellowish, and the beak becomes brown.

II. Range and Habitat.—Generally distributed over Europe and most of Asia, but local races have been separated from North Africa, Italy, and parts of Asia. In the British Isles it is generally distributed, except in mountains and moorlands, but very local in Outer Hebrides, and also in parts of Ireland. Resident.

III. Nest and Eggs.—Nearly always in the neighbourhood of houses ; in ivy or creepers, or hole in thatch or wall, under eaves, in spouting, also in upper branches of trees or tall hedges ; occasionally in foundations of rooks' nests or in cliffs. Frequently many pairs breed close together. Nest a large untidy mass of straw or rubbish of all kinds, domed, with circular side entrance, but in small holes merely lined freely with feathers, wool, etc. Eggs : usually 3–5, but 6 occasional, and 7 and 8 on record ; variable, often greyish white in colour, with numerous flecks of dark and light ash grey, varying to brown. Varieties occur in which the eggs are pure white, or white with all the colour concentrated at one end ; erythristic types have also occurred. One egg generally much lighter than the rest. Average size of 100 British eggs, 22.4 × 15.6 mm. (.88 × .61 in.). Laying usually begins in May, but breeding in winter exceptionally recorded. Incubation, chiefly by hen, 13–14 days. Several broods reared. (Plate 181, f. 5.)

IV. Food.—Varies according to locality. In towns, street refuse ; in farms, chiefly corn, seeds of weeds, etc. ; also many insects, especially when feeding young, including beetles, lepidoptera and their larvæ, hymenoptera, diptera, orthoptera, and aphides. In gardens, seedlings, fruit buds, and green peas are taken.

V. Usual Notes.—The House-Sparrow has a considerable vocabulary, which still remains to be closely studied. Among them the " chilp " is perhaps the most familiar. The alarm note sounds like " kwurk." Individuals utter sometimes a short continuous series of notes which might be regarded as a song. In autumn and winter flocks are often to be heard towards evening making a concerted chirping that is not unmusical.

PLATE 23.—TREE-SPARROW BUILDING ITS NEST: Alfred Priest.

TWO COCK HOUSE-SPARROWS COURTING A HEN: Winifred Austen.

PLATE 24.—SKYLARK, *Alauda arvensis arvensis* Linnæus
EASTERN SKYLARK, *Alauda arvensis intermedia* Swinhoe

I. Description.—Length, 7 in. Upper parts buffish brown, streaked with darker brown ; under parts pale buff, with brown streaks. Short erectile crest and buff stripe over eye. White edges to outer tail feathers, and hinder margin of the pointed wings shows buff in flight.

II. Range and Habitat.—The greater part of Europe, North-West Africa, and North and Central Asia, but in the Mediterranean region and Asia local races have been separated. In the British Isles it is widely distributed on open country, but avoids moorlands and forests, and is local in North-West Scotland. Local breeding birds move southward, and are replaced by autumn immigrant flocks. The Asiatic bird has occurred three times.

III. Nest and Eggs.—Nests on ground in corn, or pastures and edges of moors, occasionally on shingle. Nests in a slight hollow, building with bents and grasses and lining with finer materials, and at times some hair. Eggs : generally 3–4, sometimes 5, while 6 have been recorded. Ground colour, greyish white, occasionally a slight tinge of greenish, closely speckled all over with small spots of olive brown, in some cases forming a dark brown zone. Almost white and bluish varieties, very sparsely marked, have occurred ; also a rare erythristic type. Average of 100 British eggs, 23.7 × 17.0 mm. (.93 × .67 in.). Laying begins end of March, but usually in April. Incubation apparently by hen ; period, 11–12 days. Two or three broods. (Plate 181, f. 18.)

IV. Food.—Chiefly vegetable matter, seeds of many species of weeds, corn and leaves of seedling swedes, clover, etc. ; also earthworms and insects (beetles and larvæ, larvæ of moths and flies, orthoptera, hymenoptera, also aphides), as well as millipedes and spiders.

V. Usual Notes.—The Skylark's song, the " silver chain of sound of many links without a break," [1] is heard more or less throughout the year, but chiefly from the end of January to July. It is uttered as a rule in mid-air, also on the ground, or on some perch above it. It is stated the hen sings as well as the cock.[2] The song may last several minutes. The usual call note is a cheerful musical trill, heard often as the birds flit over the ground from place to place. One rendering is " tw-rup."

[1] George Meredith.
[2] Ussher and Warren, *Birds of Ireland*, p. 100.

PLATE 24.—SKYLARKS, COCK (*upper bird*), HEN, AND NESTLINGS: A. W. Seaby.

PLATE 25.—WOODLARK

Lullula arborea arborea (Linnæus)

I. Description.—Length, 5½ in. Much like Skylark, but smaller, with shorter tail, a conspicuous pale stripe above the eye passing backwards to the nape, smaller bill, and no white on outer tail feathers.

II. Range and Habitat.—Europe, from mid-Scandinavia southward, North-West Africa, and parts of Western Asia. Local races described from North-West Africa, Mediterranean Islands, and also from south-east of its range. In the British Isles it is a local resident, fluctuating in numbers, and chiefly confined to certain districts in Southern England and Wales ; only breeding occasionally in northern counties, and in Ireland now confined to co. Wicklow. Haunts open sandy country or hillsides thinly timbered with good cover.

III. Nest and Eggs.—Breeds in slight hollow in ground, sometimes quite exposed, at other times sheltered by grass, bracken, or heath. Nest small, neatly built of bents, sometimes a little moss in foundation, and lined with fine grasses and horsehair. Eggs : usually 3–4, occasionally 5, and 6 very rare. Ground colour, greyish white, finely speckled with reddish brown and ashy grey over the whole surface. Some sets have a zone of fine spots near the big end. White variety has occurred. Average of 64 British eggs, 21.5 × 16.3 mm. (.84 × .64 in.). Laying begins towards end of March or early in April. Incubation, by hen, 13–15 days. Two broods. (Plate 181, f. 19.)

IV. Food.—Principally insects (beetles and their larvæ, larvæ of moths, grasshoppers, and flies), small snails, and seeds of grasses and weeds or seedlings. Young fed on caterpillars and flies.

V. Usual Notes.—The Woodlark sings both when perched and soaring, also frequently on the descent ; it soars less high than the Skylark and in wide circles, but sings longer. The song is more flute-like ; it contains notes that have been compared to those of the Nightingale, and, unlike the song of the Skylark, it is broken by sudden pauses. Is heard throughout the year. The usual cries have been rendered as " too-lui-ee " and " wee-ou." Less common is one figured as " tscheeta-tscheeta." [1] Some individuals have been heard to sing at night. [2]

PLATE 25.—SHORELARK

Eremophila alpestris flava (Gmelin)

I. Description.—Length, 6¾ in. Has narrow line of black feathers along each side of crown, directed, like two horns, backward. In breeding season forehead, ear coverts, lores, and upper breast black, but in autumn feathers have brown edges. Crown, throat, and eye stripe yellow ; upper parts mixed browns ; under parts whitish ; wings and tail brown, with white on outer tail feathers and primaries. Hen, duller and horns shorter. Black and yellow absent from juveniles.

II. Range and Habitat.—Inhabits subarctic region of Old World and also a great part of North America. Other isolated forms are found in the mountains and deserts of North Africa, and in some mountain systems of South-East Europe and Western Asia. The Arctic form is a winter visitor, chiefly to our east coasts ; only a straggler to Ireland.

III. Nest and Eggs.—Does not breed in the British Isles. The North European race nests in hollow on open ground, sometimes sheltered by stone or grass ; built of stalks and grasses, lined with vegetable down or hair. Eggs : usually 4, sometimes 3 or 5, pale greenish white, thickly freckled all over with yellowish brown, and sometimes a dark streak. Average of 100 eggs, 22.7 × 16.2 mm. (.89 × .63 in.). Laying begins latter half May. Double brooded as a rule.

IV. Food.—In summer largely insects, especially small diptera and craneflies, also seeds of grasses, Arctic plants, and dwarf birch ; in winter more varied, and includes berries, grain, larvæ of lepidoptera, beetles and their larvæ, also sandhoppers and seeds.

V. Usual Notes.—The Shorelark's song is said to be inferior to those of the Skylark and Woodlark. It is uttered when the bird is on the wing or perched. To its clear musical call-note it owes the name of Bell-bird given it in Lapland.

---

[1] By E. W. Hendy. See his *Bird-watching* (pp. 45–47, 63) for a detailed description of the song.
[2] *British Birds* (Mag.), xvi. 126 (H. S. Davenport), also pp. 195–196.

SHORELARK (MALE) : Winifred Austen.

PLATE 25.—WOODLARK : Winifred Austen.

Family: Motacillidæ (Wagtails, Pipits)

PLATE 26.—GREY-WAGTAIL

Motacilla cinerea cinerea Tunstall

I. Description.—Length, $7\frac{1}{4}$ in. Distinguished by uniform slaty blue of upper parts and very long tail. In spring the male has a black throat, white stripes above and below the eye, sulphur yellow under parts, and white on outer tail feathers. Female has little or no black on throat. After autumn moult both sexes have white throats and buff eye stripe.

II. Range and Habitat.—Breeds in suitable localities in Europe, south from Scandinavia to North-West Africa, the Atlantic islands, and Northern and Western Asia, but local races have been separated for some of the Atlantic islands and Asia. In the British Isles it is resident or partial migrant, chiefly confined to the hilly parts of England, being absent from the flat, low-lying districts, or only met with breeding locally. In Scotland and Ireland it is more common, but is absent from the Outer Hebrides and Shetlands. Generally found near running water.

III. Nest and Eggs.—Usually in hole in wall, steep bank, or tree roots close to running water ; also under bridges and on lock gates, and sometimes away from streams. Nest rather large, built of coarse stalks, moss, leaves, and grasses, neatly lined with horsehair (often white), and a feather or two. Eggs : 5–6, in some districts 3 and 4 not rare, 7 also on record. Ground colour, generally buff or stone colour, faintly speckled, with sometimes dark hair-streak ; but varieties occur of pure white, with bluish ground and marked like Pied-Wagtail ; spotted and blotched with brown, and erythristic. Average of 100 British eggs, 18.9 × 14.2 mm. (.74 × .56 in.). Laying generally begins latter half of April, but sometimes earlier. Incubation by both sexes ; period, 13–14 days. Usually double brooded. (Plate 181, f. 22.)

IV. Food.—Chiefly insects, especially diptera and Ephemeridæ : coleoptera also taken ; small mollusca, crustacea, and stranded minnows also recorded.

V. Usual Notes.—The Grey-Wagtail's usual note may be figured as a sharp " tsiz-it " ; it bears a close resemblance to that of the other species here described, but once learned is said to be distinguishable. The song is not unlike that of the Pied and White forms, but held to be better. It has been described as a shrill " zee-zee-zee-zee " (E. M. Nicholson). Song period from March to June, and from September to January.[1]

[1] *British Birds* (Mag.), xxix. 194 (H. G. Alexander).

26

PLATE 26.—GREY-WAGTAILS, COCK (*upper figure*) AND HEN: A. W. Seaby.

PLATE 27.—PIED-WAGTAIL, *Motacilla alba yarrellii* Gould

WHITE-WAGTAIL, *Motacilla alba alba* Linnæus

I. Description.—Length, 7.30 in. Easily recognized by black, white, and grey plumage, long black tail with white outer feathers. In summer the male Pied-Wagtail is white on forehead and cheeks, but rest of head and back as well as gorget black, the hen being very dark grey on back ; in autumn both sexes have grey backs and white throats. The male White-Wagtail in spring has the back and rump grey instead of black, but in autumn can hardly be distinguished in the field from the Pied race, except that the tail coverts are grey instead of black. The female White has grey in the white of the forehead and black of the crown. Young have olive brown on upper surface and greyish gorget and crown.

II. Range and Habitat.—The White-Wagtail breeds in Iceland, Europe, Northern and Western Asia. Besides the British form (Pied-Wagtail) other local races inhabit Marocco and many parts of Asia east to Japan. The Pied-Wagtail is confined to the British Isles, where it is a very widely distributed resident, but absent in the Outer Hebrides and probably Shetlands, but is also known to breed in North-West France, occasionally in the Low Countries, and perhaps on the coast of South Norway. On the other hand, the White-Wagtail is a summer visitor and breeds occasionally in our southern and western counties.

III. Nest and Eggs.—Breeds in banksides, ivy, pollarded trees, sheds, holes in walls or thatch of buildings, etc.; even inside old nests of other species. Nest built of moss, dead leaves, bents, and grasses, lined with hair and a few feathers or bits of wool. Eggs : usually 5–6, occasionally 7, while 8 has occurred in the White form ; 9 to 11 also on record of Pied-Wagtail, but probably due to two hens. Ground colour, greyish white, usually freckled evenly with grey and leaden. Pure white sets also occur ; also sets with brown spots. Average size of 100 eggs of Pied-Wagtail (British), 20.1 × 15.1 mm. (.79 × .59 in.). Eggs of White-Wagtail are indistinguishable in size and colour, but an erythristic type has been recorded. Laying begins in late April. Incubation chiefly by hen; period, 13–14 days. Double brooded. (Plate 181, f. 20, 21.)

IV. Food.—Chiefly insects, especially diptera, but also smaller beetles, hymenoptera, larvæ of lepidoptera, small neuroptera, etc. Seeds and small fish fry occasionally taken.

V. Usual Notes.—The song of the Pied-Wagtail is a series of short phrases, exactly alike, that may continue for some minutes (Jourdain). It is recorded for all months except December.[1] The usual call sounds like a sharp " tchissik." The notes and song of the White form appear to be the same.

---

[1] *British Birds* (Mag.), xxix. 194 (H. G. Alexander).

PLATE 27.—PIED-WAGTAILS, COCK (*lower figure*), HEN, AND YOUNG: G. E. Collins.

PLATE 28

YELLOW-WAGTAIL, *Motacilla flava rayi* (Bonaparte)

BLUEHEADED-WAGTAIL, *Motacilla flava flava* Linnæus

I. Description.—Length, 6½ in. Distinguished from Grey-Wagtail by olive green of mantle and yellow eye stripe, with greenish grey crown. (The Blueheaded race has blue crown, white eye stripe, and white on chin.) Under surface yellow, wings and tail brown, outer tail feathers white. Female duller.

II. Range and Habitat.—Summer residents in the Palæarctic region; the Yellow-Wagtail breeding in the British Isles, and in small numbers on Heligoland, Holland, North France, while the Blueheaded race breeds in middle Europe from mid-Scandinavia to the Pyrenees, North Italy, etc., replaced by numerous other forms in the Mediterranean region, North Scandinavia, South-East Europe, and Asia. A few Blueheaded-Wagtails breed in England, chiefly on the south-east coast, while the Yellow-Wagtail is chiefly found in England and Wales, rare in Devonian peninsula, and local in Scotland (chiefly Clyde and Moray areas); in Ireland very local in north-west and not recently noted.

III. Nest and Eggs.—Breeds in grassy meadows, generally near water, but not always; also in cornfields. Nest in hollow on ground, generally in thick grass, built of roots, grasses, etc., lined thickly with cow or horse hair, sometimes one or two feathers. Eggs: usually 6, sometimes 5, and rarely 7; normally thickly covered with ochreous speckles, so that the ground colour is hardly visible, and at times a dark hair-streak. White, erythristic, and brown mottled types occur, and some sets have distinct blue grey ground. Average of 100 British eggs, 18.9 × 14.1 mm. (.74 × .55 in.). Laying begins end April, usually mid-May. Incubation chiefly by hen; period, 14–16 days. Two broods in south. Eggs of Blueheaded-Wagtail practically indistinguishable. (Plate 181, f. 23, 24.)

IV. Food.—Almost entirely insects, especially diptera; also said to take small land mollusca, and on passage, sandhoppers.

V. Usual Notes.—The ordinary usual note of these two races is a form of the sharp double note common to the Wagtails here described. It is figured variously as a ringing " chit-up " or " p'sip." The song is said to be like that of the Pied- and White-Wagtails, and inferior to that of the Grey, but an exact comparison has yet to be made. It appears to be confined to the breeding season, apart from records for September.[1]

---

[1] *British Birds* (Mag.), xxix. 194 (H. G. Alexander).

PLATE 28.—BLUEHEADED-WAGTAILS: A. W. Seaby.

YELLOW-WAGTAILS (*the cock is on the right hand*): A. W. Seaby.

PLATE 29.—TREE-PIPIT

Anthus trivialis trivialis (Linnæus)

I. Description.—Length, 6 in. Much resembles Meadow-Pipit, but is larger, and in the hand has curved hind claw shorter than the toe. It has a fuller song, delivered on descent from perch on tree. Upper parts clear brown, streaked with dusky, breast spotted, white or smoky white on outer tail feathers. Sexes alike.

II. Range and Habitat.—Summer resident to Europe and Asia, from Tromsö in Norway and Northern Russia in Europe to Northern Spain and Italy and mountain ranges in Greece ; also in Siberia to the Yenisei. Replaced by other forms in East Siberia, Japan, China, and the Himalayas. In British Isles : general in Great Britain, but rare in North Scotland, and only straggler to the island groups and Ireland.

III. Nest and Eggs.—Nests on ground in depression on bankside, under hedges, on sides of cuttings, etc., generally not far from trees or bushes, and is often found on outskirts of woods, or in open glades in wooded country. Nest well built of dead grasses and bents, a little moss and sometimes hair in lining. Eggs : usually 4–6, but 7 and even 8 have occurred. Variability extraordinary, types too numerous to describe : some erythristic, finely mottled, or blotched red brown ; others finely spotted, zoned, or blotched, and streaked with brown and grey of varying shades ; rare type pale blue, unmarked, or almost so. Ground colour is as variable as markings, pale greenish, creamy, reddish, grey, etc. Average of 100 British eggs, 20.7 × 15.5 mm. (.81 × .61 in.). Laying begins in second half May. Incubation, by hen, 13–14 days. Sometimes, but not always, double brooded. (Plate 181, f. 25.)

IV. Food.—Chiefly insects, including beetles, flies, bugs, hymenoptera, orthoptera, and also larval forms, also spiders and small seeds.

V. Usual Notes.—The Tree-Pipit generally takes flight from the branch of a tree, utters a few notes as it ascends to a brief height, and then sings while, on outspread wings and tail, it descends to its perch. It may begin and end its song without quitting its perch. The song is much superior to that of the Meadow-Pipit, but the attempts to syllable it are unsatisfactory. Some of its notes are very similar to those of the Canary. The usual call note has been rendered " srihb " (Naumann). It is a deeper and longer note than that of the Meadow-Pipit. Song period, from the date of arrival in April up to July.[1]

[1] *Zoologist*, 1851, p. 3,111 ; *British Birds* (Mag.), i. 371.

PLATE 29.—TREE-PIPITS' SONG FLIGHT: A. W. Seaby.

PLATE 30.—MEADOW-PIPIT

Anthus pratensis (Linnæus)

I. Description.—Length, 5 in. Upper parts, olive brown, mottled black ; throat, streaked black ; white on outer tail feathers ; hind claw almost straight and longer than toe. Rises from ground and sings cadence on wing ; alarm note squeaky. Sexes alike.

II. Range and Habitat.—Breeds in Iceland, Faeroes, British Isles, and Europe, south to the Pyrenees, Italy, and the Carpathians ; also in Western Asia. In the British Isles it is generally distributed, but northern birds migrate southward in autumn.

III. Nest and Eggs.—Breeds on moorlands, in marshes or rough pastures, nesting on ground, sometimes in hollow in side of tussock, or among rushes. Nest built of bents, lined finer grasses with some hair. Eggs : usually 4 or 5, occasionally 6, and 7 recorded from Scandinavia ; less variable than those of Tree-Pipit, almost covered with fine mottling of brown and grey, sometimes pale ochreous or greyish with dark hair-streak and scanty ashy markings. Blue type also occurs, unmarked or with a few ashy spots. Average of 100 British eggs, 19.7 × 14.6 mm. (.77 × .57 in.). Laying begins in second half April. Incubation, probably by hen ; period, 13–14 days. Double brooded. (Plate 181, f. 27.)

IV. Food.—Chiefly insects, including beetles and their larvæ, diptera and larvæ, hymenoptera, hemiptera, larvæ of moths, etc. ; also seeds, spiders, small land mollusca, and small earthworms.

V. Usual Notes.—This Pipit usually rises to sing in the air from the ground or a bush, and sings as it descends. The note on the ascent is " ze-ut " repeated ; on the descent, several " wheets " followed by the final trill, " tri-ze-ze-ze-ze." [1] The singer may begin and end its song perched. The song is much inferior to that of the Tree-Pipit, less varied and less musical. The bird has a squeaky alarm note, very different from that of the Tree-Pipit. Call note, " peet." Song period, from February to July, and sometimes outside the breeding season.[1]

[1] S. Morris, *Bird Song,* 44.

PLATE 30.—MEADOW-PIPIT FEEDING YOUNG CUCKOO : A. W. Seaby

PLATE 31.—TAWNY-PIPIT, *Anthus campestris campestris* (Linnæus)

I. Description.—Length, 6½–7 in. Distinguished by uniform buff under surface; rather larger than Tree-Pipit, and stands higher; throat white, and buff eyebrow; upper parts grey-brown, feathers dark in centre.

II. Range and Habitat.—Breeds locally in Europe from middle Sweden to the Mediterranean and its islands; also North-West Africa and Western Asia, but an Asiatic race has been separated. Has bred in the British Isles on the Sussex coast. Summer resident.

III. Nest and Eggs.—The only nest found in the British Isles was among sandhills with marram grass, but on the Continent it is found on the ground in barren open country, sometimes sheltered by grass tussock or bush. Nest neatly built of grasses and bents, lined with hair. Eggs: 4–5, rarely 6. Ground, greyish white with fine speckles, or more commonly rather bold spots and mottling of dark brown with ashy shellmarks. Erythristic variety also recorded. Average of 137 eggs, 21.9 × 15.7 mm. (.86 × .62 in.). Laying begins mid-April in south, June in Central Europe. Incubation period said to be 13–14 days. Probably double brooded.

IV. Food.—Mainly insects (coleoptera, diptera, orthoptera, etc.) and their larvæ; also larvæ of lepidoptera; spiders, but apparently not seeds.

V. Usual Notes.—Like the Tree-Pipit and the Meadow-Pipit, the Tawny-Pipit sings in the air. Its song is a series of clear metallic notes, with a slight fall, uttered over and over again. The usual call is figured by Howard Saunders as "a short 'whit,'" and by Naumann as "dillem" (flock call), and "didlihn" or "gridlhin" (pair call). Song period, May and June. Said to sing often by night as well as by day.[1]

PLATE 31.—RICHARD'S-PIPIT, *Anthus richardi richardi* Vieillot

I. Description.—Length, 7¾ in. Distinguished by large size, long straight hind claw, and long legs. Breast streaked, upper parts dark brown, feathers edged buff, white on outer tail feathers.

II. Range and Habitat.—Breeds in plains of Northern and Central Asia, while the race from Southern Mongolia and China to the Himalayas has been separated. Vagrant to the British Isles, which has occurred about a hundred times.

III. Nest and Eggs.—Does not breed in the British Isles. Nests on ground in open plains, sheltered by tussocks. Nest built of moss and bents. Eggs: 4–5, sometimes 6, variable. Ground varying from greyish to pinkish, closely mottled with fine spots of olive or reddish brown. Average of 28 eggs, 21.2 × 16.2 mm. (.83 × .63 in.). Laying begins early in June in Siberia. Double brooded.

IV. Food.—Chiefly insects and their larvæ (diptera, hymenoptera, orthoptera, and coleoptera, also occasionally lepidoptera), worms, and some vegetable matter.

V. Usual Notes.—The rendering of the usual note of this species, quoted from Gaetke in Naumann's work, is "rouf-r-r-rüp." (Anglicized except for the *ü*, which should be pronounced like the French *u*—phonetic symbol [y].) The bird, if startled, may utter only the "r-r-rüp." It is stated that the rendering is based on fifty years' experience of thousands of individuals. The note is uttered only in flight. There appears to be no record of the song.

PLATE 31.—ROCK-PIPIT, *Anthus spinoletta petrosus* (Montagu)

HEBRIDEAN ROCK-PIPIT, *Anthus spinoletta meinertzhageni* Bird

ALPINE- OR WATER-PIPIT, *Anthus spinoletta spinoletta* (Linnæus)

I. Description.—Length, 6½ in. Has smoky brown on outer tail feathers instead of white, upper parts olive brown with darker striations, under parts dull white, mostly striated dull brown; hind claw much curved. Alpine form has white on outer tail feathers and white eye stripe; hind claw straighter.

II. Range and Habitat.—The British Rock-Pipit is resident on the coasts of the British Isles, the Channel Isles, and perhaps North-West France. The Outer Hebridean race is very dark. The Alpine- or Water-Pipit visits us in winter, but breeds in the mountain ranges of Central and Southern Europe, while other local races are found on the coasts of Scandinavia, the Faeroes, various parts of Asia, and North America.

III. Nest and Eggs.—The Rock-Pipit is confined in the breeding season to those parts of our coasts and islands which have rocky shores or cliffs. The nest is made in any kind of hole or recess, sometimes hidden among sea plants or behind grass, sometimes in hole in ledge of rock. Exceptionally it has been known to breed in a boat. Built of grasses, bents, seaweed, and moss, lined fine bents and hair. Eggs: 4–5, exceptionally 6 in number. Ground, greyish white, thickly covered with fine olive brown and greyish spots, but ranging from rich deep brown to light grey with sparse fleckings; also sometimes with dark zone or cap. Erythristic variety also occurs. Average size of 100 British eggs, 21.3 × 15.9 mm. (.83 × .62 in.). Eggs of Alpine-Pipit are lighter as a rule in colour, and greyer, but differ little in size, and are usually found on banks in Alpine pastures. Laying in British Isles begins about mid-May. Incubation, by hen, about 14–16 days. Double brooded. (Plate 181, f. 28.)

IV. Food.—Almost entirely animal matter—insects (beetles, diptera and their larvæ, hymenoptera, aphides), also mollusca (slugs and snails), remains of fish, sandhoppers, etc.; rarely seeds.

V. Usual Notes.—Song said to resemble that of the Meadow-Pipit, but information is scanty. Call note, "phist."[2] Call of Alpine-Pipit, "pheest." Song period of Rock-Pipit, March to August.[3]

---

[1] Naumann, *Vögel Mitteleuropas*, iii. 75.　　　　[2] *British Birds* (Mag.), xxv. 301 (D. Lack).
[3] *id.* xxix. 194 (H. G. Alexander).

31

PLATE 31.—(*Upper*) RICHARD'S-PIPIT (*left hand*) ; TAWNY-PIPIT (*right*) ; (*Lower*) ALPINE-PIPIT (*left*) ; ROCK-PIPIT (*right*) :
H. Grönvold.

PLATE 32.—BRITISH TREE-CREEPER
Certhia familiaris britannica Ridgway
NORTHERN TREE-CREEPER
Certhia familiaris familiaris Linnæus

I. Description.—Length, 5½ in. Recognized by slender curved bill, graduated tail with pointed feathers, and habit of creeping spirally up trunks of trees. Upper surface brown with pale spots, rump rusty, lower parts white.

II. Range and Habitat.—The British race is confined to the British Isles, where it is resident, but other forms are distributed over the whole of the Palæarctic region and North America in wooded districts. The northern race occurs rarely in winter in Scotland.

III. Nest and Eggs.—Usually nests behind loose bark of tree, occasionally behind ivy, in crevices of buildings, and in the interstices of loose stone walls. Nest built on foundation of small birch twigs, and made of roots, grasses, moss, etc., lined freely with feathers. Eggs : usually 6, sometimes 5, and occasionally 7 or even 8 ; white, with small red brown spots, usually in zone near big end, and violet shell-marks. Unmarked variety also occurs. Average of 100 British eggs, 15.5 × 12.1 mm. (.61 × .47 in.). Laying begins latter half April. Incubation chiefly by hen ; period, 14–15 days. Sometimes double brooded. (Plate 182, f. 1.)

IV. Food.—Mainly insects : beetles, generally weevils, dermaptera (earwigs), also larvæ of moths, flies, and ichneumons. Spiders and their eggs are also taken freely : grubs from galls and a few seeds have also been recorded.

V. Usual Notes.—The Tree-Creeper's usual call note is a feeble " tsee " repeated ; also a sound figured by Naumann as " ssrih," by others as " zree " ; and a repeated " tsit." The song has been syllabled " Ticka-tce-tce-tce-tce-tce-ticka-ticka," and is usually uttered by the bird when pausing in its progress up a tree trunk. It is heard in and out of the breeding season, but chiefly from January to June.

PLATE 32.—TREE-CREEPER ABOUT TO FEED A CLUSTER OF YOUNG: A. W. Seaby

PLATE 33

WREN, *Troglodytes troglodytes troglodytes* (Linnæus)
ST. KILDA WREN, *Troglodytes troglodytes hirtensis* Seebohm
SHETLAND WREN, *Troglodytes troglodytes zetlandicus* Hartert
HEBRIDEAN WREN, *Troglodytes troglodytes hebridensis* Meinertzhagen

I. Description.—Length, 3½ in. Easily recognized by its small body, short upright tail, and characteristic shape. Upper parts rufous brown, more or less barred, chiefly on the rump, with dark brown, and also on tail and wings ; white spots on median coverts ; under parts lighter, more or less barred with dusky on belly and flanks ; pale stripe above eye. The St. Kilda form is decidedly larger, with big feet, and is greyer, with white and dark grey on primaries instead of white and dark brown. The Shetland Wren is a darker form than the common Wren, with a stout bill. The Hebridean Wren is an intermediate form hardly worth separation.

II. Range and Habitat.—Almost universally distributed, being found at high altitudes in mountains, and also in outskirts of large towns. Occurs over Europe and Northern Asia, but local races are found in Iceland, Faeroes, Shetlands, St. Kilda, Hebrides, and in the Mediterranean region, as well as in various parts of Asia, and is everywhere resident. In the British Isles it is generally distributed, except where the three local forms replace it.

III. Nest and Eggs.—Placed against a bank, among ivy, on up-turned root of tree, in old nests of other birds, stone walls, or holes of any kind ; built of whatever material is within reach, but usually largely of moss, though bracken and dead leaves are also often used ; domed, with circular entrance at side, and warmly lined with feathers when used for breeding. Eggs : normally 5–6, occasionally 4 or 7, but 8 to 11, 14, and 16 recorded on good authority ; white, occasionally unmarked, but generally fine red speckles, chiefly at big end. Average of 100 British eggs, 16.6 × 12.7 mm. (.65 × .50 in.). Eggs of St. Kilda Wren are larger —50 average, 18.3 × 13.6 mm. (.72 × .53 in.). Those of Shetland Wren intermediate. Laying begins late April. Two or more broods. Incubation period, 14–16 days, probably by hen. (Plate 182, f. 2 *a–b*.)

IV. Food.—Chiefly insects and spiders, including small beetles, larvæ of moths, craneflies and larvæ, Trichoptera larvæ ; also aphides and some seeds.

V. Usual Notes.—The usual notes of the species are the familiar scolding " trrrrr," and a combination of sharp " tooks," " tiks," and " trrks," rapidly repeated, that express high excitement in the presence of an enemy, such as an owl. The song, uttered from a conspicuous perch or while the bird flits from bush to bush, is amazingly loud and strident for the size of the singer. It may be heard throughout the year.

A.W.SEABY.

PLATE 33.—WREN FEEDING HER YOUNG: A. W. Seaby

PLATE 34.—DIPPER, *Cinclus cinclus gularis* (Latham)
IRISH DIPPER, *Cinclus cinclus hibernicus* Hartert
BLACK-BELLIED DIPPER, *Cinclus cinclus cinclus* (Linnæus)

I. Description.—Length, 7 in.   Recognized by white throat and chest, contrasting with dark brown upper surface and head ; breast chestnut, belly black, tail short.   The Irish race is darker on upper parts, with less chestnut, and brown black belly.   The black-bellied race lacks chestnut altogether.   Young have under surface cream colour, mottled grey.

II. Range and Habitat.—The British race is confined to the hilly districts of England, Wales, and Scotland, but is absent from the Orkneys and Shetlands as a breeder, and only found in two of the Outer Hebrides.   It is absent as a breeder from the country east of the Trent, Stafford, Gloucester, and scarce in Wilts.   The Irish race is widely distributed in Ireland.   Other races are found in the north of Europe and the mountain ranges of the centre and south, as also in Asia and North-West Africa, and the northern form has occurred as a straggler.

III. Nest and Eggs.—Built something on the lines of that of the Wren : a large domed structure of moss, affixed to a wall of rock or even building, sometimes against trunk of tree or under bank ; inner cup lined dead leaves of beech or oak ; entrance hole rather flattened and overhung.   Eggs : 4–5, 6 occasional ; pure white and pointed oval in shape.   Average of 100 British eggs, 26.2 × 18.1 mm. (1.03 × .71 in.); 50 Irish eggs, 25.7 × 18.6 mm. (1.01 × .73 in.).   Incubation, by hen 15–16 days.   Double brooded.

IV. Food.—Chiefly the larval forms of water beetles, neuroptera, trichoptera, larvæ of dragon flies, May flies, etc., hemiptera, as well as small water-snails, water-fleas ; also recorded as feeding on stranded small fish, and occasionally minnows.

V. Usual Notes.—The song of the Dipper is a cheerful meditative warbling that has in it something of the rippling music of the brook. The usual call is " chit, chit."   Song period, more or less all the year.[1]

[1] *British Birds* (Mag.), xvii. 225 (R. H. Brown), Records for every month.

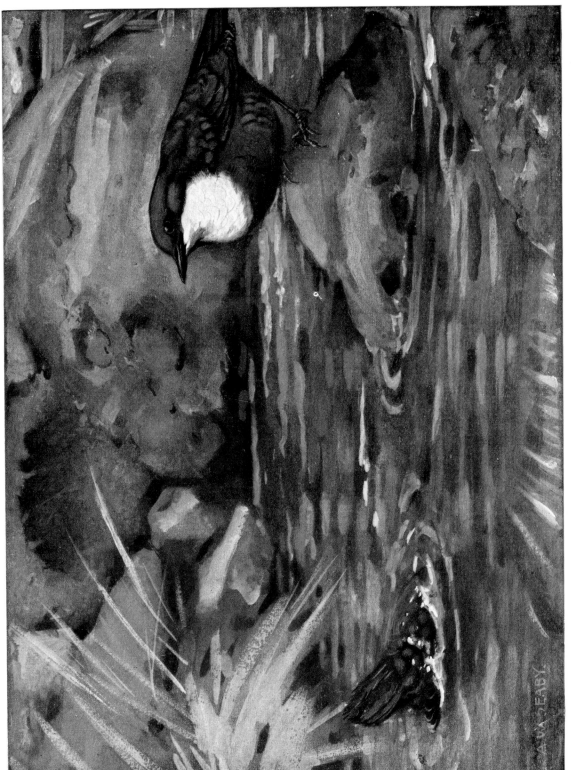

PLATE 34.—DIPPERS : A. W. Seaby.

PLATE 35.—MISTLE-THRUSH

Turdus viscivorus viscivorus Linnæus

I. Description.—Length, $10\frac{1}{2}$ in. Distinguished from Song-Thrush by larger size, spotted flanks, and white patches on outer tail feathers, conspicuous in flight. Upper parts greyish brown, under parts buff, turning to white on belly, with black fan-shaped spots on throat and neck and oval spots on breast and flanks.

II. Range and Habitat.—Found in wooded parts of Northern and Central Europe, but only locally South and North Africa, also in Asia to the Himalayas. The ordinary form is a resident in most parts of the British Isles where there are trees, but is absent from Shetlands as a breeder, rare Orkneys, and only at Stornoway in the Outer Hebrides. Now fairly general in suitable localities in Ireland.

III. Nest and Eggs.—Often places nest conspicuously on bare fork of tree, sometimes at a good height, less commonly lower down, and exceptionally on buildings, walls, etc. Nest big and substantially built of bents, grasses, moss, lichens, roots, and earth, lined dry grasses ; often conspicuous by bits of wool, paper, rags, etc. Eggs : usually 4, and only occasionally 5, but 6 on record. Ground colour, creamy, tawny, or even green blue, with blotches and spots of red brown, lilac shellmarks, and occasional blackish streaks ; sometimes blue without markings. Average size of 100 British eggs, 30.7×22.8 mm. ($1.21 \times .89$ in.). Laying begins February, but usually in late March. Incubation period, 13–14 days, by female only. Double brooded. (Plate 182, f. 3.)

IV. Food.—Chiefly berries and fruits, including those of yew, holly, rowan, ivy, hawthorn, rose, juniper, service tree, honeysuckle, mistletoe, ash, as well as cherry, apple, plum, damson, and black currants ; also insects (larvæ of beetles, moths and flies, ants, etc.), spiders, worms, mollusca (slugs), and has been known to kill nestling Blackbirds and Thrushes, also slow-worms.

V. Usual Notes.—The loud, familiar, oft-repeated strain of the Mistle-Thrush may be heard coming from a tree-top in all weathers and every season. It is sometimes uttered by the bird when on the wing. The usual alarm or anger note is a harsh scolding churr. Song period : more or less all the year, chiefly from January to May. Recently (1937) George Marples has described the song as consisting of three phrases, which may differ somewhat from bird to bird. He describes one full song thus : (1) "Mairi-do-it-quick-quick, quick ;" (2) "Teeawti-awti;" (3) "Pweee-pweee-pweee."[1]

[1] *British Birds* (Mag.), XXX. 305.

PLATE 35.—MISTLE-THRUSHES (*left hand*) AND FIELDFARE (*right*) : A. W. Seaby.

PLATE 36.—BRITISH SONG-THRUSH, *Turdus ericetorum ericetorum* Turton

CONTINENTAL SONG-THRUSH, *Turdus ericetorum philomelus* Brehm

HEBRIDEAN SONG-THRUSH, *Turdus ericetorum hebridensis* Clarke

I. Description.—Length, 9 in. Recognized by the olive brown back, fan-shaped black spots on whitish under surface, with striated flanks. The British race is more reddish brown on mantle, not so grey as the Continental form. The Hebridean form is darker than either and more heavily spotted on the breast.

II. Range and Habitat.—The British race is generally distributed in the British Isles, except on treeless moors, but is rare in the Shetlands, and replaced by the Hebridean form in the Outer Hebrides, and apparently also found in Holland. Resident in the British Isles, but moves southward in autumn. In Northern and Central Europe and Western Asia it is replaced by the Continental form, which is only a winter visitor to the Mediterranean region and is a passage migrant or winter visitor to the British Isles.

III. Nest and Eggs.—Breeds usually in bushes and hedgerows, often in evergreens in gardens, in ivy on walls or trees, in sheds, on banks, and occasionally on ground. Nest solidly built of grasses, twigs, roots, and sometimes moss, solidified with earth, and lined with smooth layer of dung or mud and rotten wood moistened with saliva. Eggs : usually 3–5, but 6 even to 9 on record ; normally blue with blackish spots towards big end, but exceptionally greenish, bluish white or pure white, sometimes unmarked or with reddish brown spots. Average size of 100 British eggs, 28.7 × 20.9 mm. (1.13 × .82 in.). Laying begins in March, and is general in April. Incubation period, 12–14 days, chiefly by hen. Several broods. (Plate 182, f. 5.)

IV. Food.—Chiefly snails and slugs, earthworms and insects (beetles and larvæ, moths, flies and larvæ, hymenoptera, earwigs, etc.), spiders, millipedes, and centipedes, berries and seeds of yew, holly, elder, rowan, birch, hawthorn, and various weeds ; also fruit (cherry, strawberry, currant, raspberry, mulberry, and fallen fruit, such as apples and pears).

V. Usual Notes.—The famous song is made up of separate parts divided by pauses ; each part contains usually a phrase or phrases repeated several times. These phrases have been variously rendered, according to the fancy of the listener. By some the bird is imagined to sing, " Did you do it ?—Did you do it ? . . ." In the next part it may give the answer, " You did—You did—You did . . . " ; or again, " I saw you—I saw you . . . " These renderings, crude though they are, suffice for recognition. The song is sometimes uttered when the bird is on the wing. The usual cries are " tchuck " and " Ptick " (the *p* scarcely sounded). In moments of excitement the " pticks " become a fusillade, " pticki-pticki-pticki-tick . . . " Song period : all the year, except during the moulting period in July-August.[1]

---

[1] For fluctuations in the song times, see *British Birds* (Mag.), xxviii. 364 (J. P. Burkitt).

36

PLATE 36.—SONG-THRUSH (*lower bird*) AND COCK BLACKBIRD: G. E. Collins.

PLATE 37.—FIELDFARE

Turdus pilaris Linnæus

I. Description.—Length, 10 in. Nearly as large as Mistle-Thrush, but recognized by chestnut brown back, contrasting with grey head, nape, and rump, with dark tail. Lores black, throat and upper breast buff, lower breast and belly white, throat striated black, with spots on breast and flanks.

II. Range and Habitat.—North Europe and Asia as far as the tree limit and east to the Lena valley, south to Germany (local), Austria, and Northern Hungary, but not in Rumania. Migrant, wintering chiefly in Southern Europe, and does not breed in Iceland. It is seen in the British Isles from September-October to April-May, chiefly in open country.

III. Nest and Eggs.—Breeds in colonies in woods of birch and conifers, nesting conspicuously at varying heights ; occasionally also on sheds, rocks, or on ground. Nest big and solidly built with grasses, solidified with earth and a lining of dry grasses over a mud cup. Mosses and lichens also used, but not extensively. Eggs : 5–6 as a rule, but 4, 7, and 8 recorded. Ground colour, deep greenish, varying to blue or yellowish, freckled and spotted reddish brown, and often much like Blackbird's. Average of 100 eggs, 28.8 × 20.9 mm. (1.13 × .82 in.). Laying begins in south in April and May, but much later in the north. Incubation chiefly, at any rate, by hen ; period, 13–14 days.

IV. Food.—Mollusca (snails, slugs, etc.), earthworms, insects (beetles, larvæ of flies, etc.), also berries and seeds of yew, holly, rowan, hawthorn, juniper, dog-rose, pyracanthus, rushes, and grasses ; grain, root crops in fields, especially where decayed, and fallen fruit also taken.

V. Usual Notes.—The song of the Fieldfare has been described as " a rather pretty low warble constantly interrupted by the usual harsh note" (Dresser). Jourdain states that the harsh notes dominate. The harsh note, heard when the birds are approached, is a sharp "tchak."

37

PLATE 37.—FIELDFARES : A. W. Seaby.

Plate 38.—REDWING, *Turdus musicus musicus* Linnæus
ICELAND REDWING, *Turdus musicus coburni* Sharpe

I. Description.—Length, 8½ in. Distinguished by broad white streak over the eye and rich red on flanks (not wing); breast as well as flanks striated; upper parts olive brown. Ground colour of breast buff, and belly white.

II. Range and Habitat.—Northern Europe and Asia, chiefly north of the Baltic, but on the east side south to East Prussia; replaced by a local race in Iceland. Migrant, wintering chiefly in Southern Europe. Is seen in the British Isles from September to May.

III. Nest and Eggs.—Does not breed in the British Isles. Where there are trees it breeds usually low down, near or on ground, occasionally, like Fieldfare, at some distance from ground. Though not a social breeder, nests may be found in a Fieldfare colony. North of the tree limit it breeds in low scrub. Nest much like that of Fieldfare, but smaller, lined dry grasses. Eggs: 5–6, occasionally 4; dark greenish ground, with fine speckles of brown, sometimes distinctly blue green ground. Average of 50 eggs, 25.8 × 18.7 mm. (1.01 × .73 in.). Laying begins in June as a rule, but varies according to latitude. Incubation, by both sexes, apparently 13 days. Frequently double brooded.

IV. Food.—Chiefly mollusca (slugs, snails, and fresh-water snails), worms, insects (beetles and larvæ, larvæ of moths and flies, earwigs, etc.), crustacea on shores, berries of yew, rowan, holly, hawthorn, *vaccinium*, and root crops in fields, especially if rotted.

V. Usual Notes.—A low sub-song may occasionally be heard in this country in the spring, before the birds migrate to their northern breeding-places. Heard by the writer in Yorkshire on April 12, it sounded like " a low rippling soliloquy, and went on without pause." The birds may be heard singing in concert, especially in their roost. The true song as heard in the breeding haunts consists of about five notes, repeated over and over again with deadly monotony, each male singing its little cadence in turn. Song period: the regular breeding season song begins in April. The usual notes heard on approaching the birds are a pretty liquid " twip " varied by sharp " tchiks."

38

PLATE 38.—REDWINGS MIGRATING: A. W. Seaby.

PLATE 39.—RING-OUZEL, *Turdus torquatus torquatus* Linnæus
ALPINE RING-OUZEL, *Turdus torquatus alpestris* (Brehm)

I. Description.—Length, 10 in. Recognized by blackish brown plumage, black-tipped bill, and white crescent on breast ; female browner, with narrower and duller crescent. Young have throat feathers tipped white, forebreast mottled black and brown, and rest of under parts spotted and barred with black and white.

II. Range and Habitat.—Mountainous and moorland districts of Devonian peninsula, Wales, the Pennines, and Scotland ; also locally in Ireland. Does not breed in Shetlands or Outer Hebrides. On the Continent nests in Scandinavia, but represented by allied races in mountains of Central and Southern Europe, Western Asia, etc. Absent from Iceland. Is a summer resident in the British Isles. The Alpine race, with white edges to feathers of underparts, is a straggler.

III. Nest and Eggs.—Breeds on sides of banks, by cart tracks in quarries, occasionally in bushes. Nest like Blackbird's, substantially made of grasses, sometimes with heather in foundation, lining of dry grasses. Eggs : normally 4, occasionally 5, and 6 on record ; like Blackbird's, and subject to similar variations, but usually more boldly marked Ground, greenish, ranging to creamy yellowish or deep blue, rarely unmarked, but generally with bold blotches and spots of red brown and ashy shellmarks. Some varieties quite erythrismal. Average of 100 British eggs, 30.3 × 21.5 mm. (1.19 × .84 in.). Laying begins end of April to May. Incubation period, 14 days ; shared by both sexes. Double brooded. (Plate 182, f. 6.)

IV. Food.—Chiefly berries and seeds of moorland berries in summer (bilberry, crowberry, blackthorn, rowan, etc.), also hawthorn and ivy, but occasionally fruit (cherry, raspberry, blackberry, currant, plum, gooseberry, strawberry, etc.) ; also earthworms, small mollusca, and insects (earwigs, flies and larvæ, caterpillars, etc.).

V. Usual Notes.—The usual alarm note of the bird when approached is a harsh " tschk " or " tchuck." Its song is heard in this country only during the breeding season. The following is the record of the song of a male bird, listened to repeatedly : it " consisted of three short monosyllabic whistles followed by a double whistle, also thrice repeated." The three preliminary whistles were sometimes omitted. As there was little variety, the performance soon became monotonous.[1]

---

[1] *Wild Life*, viii. (1916), 299 (R. Chislett). For a more complete account see W. Garstang, *Songs of the Birds* (1935).

PLATE 39.—RING-OUZEL SINGING TO HIS MATE: A. W. Seaby.

PLATE 40.—BLACKBIRD

Turdus merula merula Linnæus

I. Description.—Length, 10.1 in. Male recognized by black plumage, orange bill, and yellow eye rim. Female umber brown, with brownish bill and indistinct streaks on lighter breast. Immature birds are much like hen ; bill in male is black till second year. (See also Plate 36.)

II. Range and Habitat.—Generally distributed over all the British Isles, though scarce in the extreme north and north-west islands, and only absent from higher moorlands and mountains. Also general over Europe, North-West Africa, and Asia to the Himalayas at least, but in many places represented by local races, as in Spain, North-West Africa, Canary Islands, Azores, Balkan Peninsula, and perhaps Corsica and Sardinia, etc. Resident, but some move southward.

III. Nest and Eggs.—Breeds in bushes, ivy, hedgerows, or out-buildings ; also occasionally on ground or in trees. Nest well built and solidified with mud ; contains more moss than that of Thrush, and lined internally with dry grasses. Eggs : usually 3–5, but 6–8 on record. Ground, usually deep greenish, ranging to creamy or pale blue and even white ; rarely unmarked, but generally freckled with reddish brown and ashy, sometimes forming zone or cap at big end. Average of 100 British eggs, 29.4 × 21.6 mm. (1.15 × .85 in.). Laying begins in March and is general in April. Incubation period, 12–14 days ; by hen almost always. Several broods. (Plate 182, f. 4.)

IV. Food.—Fruits (apples, pears, strawberries, cherries, goose-berries, mulberries, currants, etc.), and berries of holly, rowan, ivy, hawthorn, blackberry, bird cherry, cotoneaster, etc., as well as seeds of many weeds ; also earthworms, insects (including beetles, larvæ of moths and flies, ants, earwigs, etc.), spiders, millipedes, small mollusca, etc.

V. Usual Notes.—The Blackbird's song is not composed of phrases repeated several times like that of the Song-Thrush ; it is a series of short warbles, with varied notes both good and indifferent, the best being flute-like sounds, not surpassed in the song of any bird. It is heard from February to the end of July, and from late August to October, and on mild days even later, but neither so often or so late as the song of the Thrush. Like the latter, the Blackbird has a pretty habit of singing as it flits from tree to tree. The usual cries are " tchuck," barely distinguishable from the corresponding note of the Thrush, and the familiar " mink," which in moments of excitement becomes a rapid " mink-mink-mink." The well-known alarm rattle is composed in part of the " tchucks." A common form of it is a rapid excited " tchuck-tchuck-tchuck - tchuck - toweetaweet - toweetaweet - tchuck - tchuck." The bird utters at times a Robin-like " ptsee." [1]

---

[1] For fluctuations in the song times see *British Birds* (Mag.)., xxviii. 365 (J. P. Burkitt).

PLATE 40.—HEN BLACKBIRD INCUBATING: G. E. Collins.

PLATE 41.—WHEATEAR, *Œnanthe œnanthe* (Linnæus)

GREENLAND WHEATEAR, *Œnanthe œnanthe leucorrhoa* (Gmelin)

I. Description.—Length, 6 in. Both sexes have conspicuous white rump. Male has upper parts mostly grey, a white strip passing round forehead and over eyes, lores and ear coverts black, wings dark brown, under parts buff, except belly, which is white. Female has upper parts and ear coverts brown, under surface buff. In autumn male resembles female. Young have back greyish brown, throat and forehead indistinctly barred brown.

II. Range and Habitat.—Haunts open downs, pastures, and waste lands, and in consequence only locally distributed in British Isles, though widespread. Migrant visiting Europe and Northern Asia to Alaska in summer, but represented by a larger race in Greenland, and an intermediate form in Iceland. Other races have been described from the Atlas Mountains, South Spain, Syria, and Western Asia. In southern part of range found only at high levels. The Greenland form is only a passage migrant with us. Winters in tropical Africa.

III. Nest and Eggs.—Usually in a hollow under stone, in a loose stone wall or stone heap, or in a rabbit hole ; built of grasses, lined finer bents, feathers, bits of wool, etc. Eggs : usually 5 or 6, occasionally only 4, and sometimes 7, rarely 8. Ground colour, pale blue, generally unmarked, but occasionally with fine reddish speckles, chiefly at big end. Average of 100 British eggs, 21.2 × 15.9 mm. (.83 × .62 in.). Laying begins end of April. Incubation chiefly by hen ; period said to be 14 days. Single brooded as a rule, but in some localities two broods are reared. (Plate 182, f. 7.)

IV. Food.—Chiefly insects, including smaller beetles, flies, hymenoptera (humble-bees and ants), moths and caterpillars, grasshoppers, etc. ; also spiders and small land mollusca.

V. Usual Notes.—The usual note of the Wheatear is a stony " chack," to which in moments of rising excitement is added a softer " weet." The song, said to be like the beginning of the Skylark's song, does not yet appear to have been analysed. It is often uttered as the bird makes a short flight into the air and down again ; also on the ground. It is heard from April to June, sometimes later.

41

PLATE 41.—COCK WHEATEAR (*upper bird*) COURTING HEN: A. W. Seaby.

PLATE 42.—BRITISH STONECHAT, *Saxicola torquata hibernans* (Hartert)
HEBRIDEAN STONECHAT, *Saxicola torquata theresa* Meinertzhagen
INDIAN STONECHAT, *Saxicola torquata indica* (Blyth)

I. Description.—Length, 5⅓ in. Male has head, throat, and back black, white patch on tail coverts (not tail), wing, and neck; breast orange chestnut, under parts buff. Female very different: head and mantle brown, with darker markings, under parts duller, little or no white on neck. Black of male turns brown in winter. Young much like female.

II. Range and Habitat.—The British race is resident, but very local; in England chiefly in maritime counties; commoner in Scotland, but still local, and only rarely breeds Outer Hebrides, a local race, and Orkneys, not in Shetlands. More general in Ireland. Haunts coasts, commons, and heaths, and is a partial migrant in inland sites. Represented by other forms on the Continent, North-West Africa, and Asia, but Portuguese birds are not distinguishable from British.

III. Nest and Eggs.—Usually under shelter of gorse bush or heather, on or close to the ground, built of moss, dead grasses and weeds, lined bents and hair, occasionally a few feathers. Eggs: usually 5–6, but 3, 4, and 7 have been recorded. As a rule the ground colour is a paler greenish blue than in the Whinchat, with generally a more or less defined zone of reddish brown speckles towards the big end. Average of 100 British eggs, 18.8 × 14.3 mm. (.74 × .56 in.). Laying begins end of March or early April. Incubation period, 14 days; by hen only. Double brooded. (Plate 182, f. 9.)

IV. Food.—Largely insects (small beetles and larvæ, diptera and larvæ, small butterflies and caterpillars of moths, earwigs, larvæ of hymenoptera); also frequently takes spiders; earthworms and eggs, as well as small lizards recorded.

V. Usual Notes.—The beautiful little song of the Stonechat is uttered when the bird is perched or in flight. The song flight has been described by W. H. Hudson: " To sing, the Stonechat flies up almost vertically from his perch on the topmost spray of a bush to a height of 40 or 50 or 100 feet, and at the highest point pours out a rapid series of double notes, the first clear and sharp, the next deeper and some-what throaty, then the clear again, the sound rising and falling rhythmically; and as he sings he drops rapidly a distance of a couple of feet, then flutters up and drops again and again." [1] It is heard from March till the end of June. There appears to be no record of the song outside the breeding season. The usual note heard when the nest is approached is a " chat " or " chack," like the impact of two stones, to which may be added a plaintive " tr'weet."

[1] *Nature in Downland*, 156.

PLATE 42.—STONECHATS; COCK SINGING, AND HEN WITH A SMALL LIZARD IN
HER BEAK: A. W. Seaby.

PLATE 43.—WHINCHAT

Saxicola rubetra rubetra (Linnæus)

I. Description.—Length, 5½ in. Distinguished at all seasons from Stonechat by white on basal part of tail and slighter build. Male has upper parts brown with black markings; throat and breast rufous, rest of under parts white, broad white stripe over eye, two white patches on wing as a rule. Female duller, with yellow buff eye stripe. Male in autumn much like female.

II. Range and Habitat.—Summer visitor to the British Isles, but somewhat locally distributed. Does not breed Shetlands; scarce Outer Hebrides and in Ireland; absent from many districts in south. On the Continent ranges north to 70° in Scandinavia, but does not breed in the southern Mediterranean countries, and is replaced by other races in Dalmatia, the Caucasus, and Western Asia.

III. Nest and Eggs.—Breeds in mowing grass or at foot of gorse or other bush on commons and cuttings. Nest built of moss and dead grasses, lined with finer bents and hair. Eggs : usually 5–6, sometimes only 4, but 7, 8, and 9 (once) on record. Colour, deep bluish green, sometimes blue, either unmarked or generally with fine red brown speckles, chiefly towards big end. A white variety has occurred. Average of 100 British eggs, 19.0 × 14.4 mm. (.74 × .56 in.). Laying begins second half of May. Incubation period, 13–14 days ; by female alone. Double brooded as a rule. (Plate 182, f. 8.)

IV. Food.—Chiefly insects, including beetles, craneflies and small diptera, caterpillars and moths, earwigs, etc. ; also spiders, earthworms, and small land mollusca.

V. Usual Notes.—There appears to be no adequate description of the song of the Whinchat; it is heard from April to the end of June; whether also heard outside the breeding season is not recorded. The usual note uttered when the bird is approached is " u-tick," therefore easily distinguishable from the usual monosyllabic " chack " of the Stonechat.

43

PLATE 43.—WHINCHATS: COCK SINGING, HEN CARRYING GRASS TO HER NEST: A. W. Seaby.

PLATE 44.—REDSTART

Phœnicurus phœnicurus phœnicurus (Linnæus)

I. Description.—Length, 5½ in. Male in summer has forehead white, throat and sides of face black, rump and tail coverts chestnut, back slate grey, breast chestnut, belly white. Female and male (in autumn) above brownish, under parts paler, breast and flanks rufous buff. Young mottled on upper and under surface.

II. Range and Habitat.—Summer visitor to Great Britain, but local and varying in numbers. Scarce in extreme north of Scotland, and rarely breeds in the islands ; status in Ireland now uncertain, but has bred in two counties. On the Continent it is generally distributed, except on the shores of the Mediterranean ; replaced by a local race in the mountains of North-West Africa and South Russia, as well as Western Asia. Haunts old woodlands, but is also at home in stone wall country where trees are scarce, and edges of moorlands.

III. Nest and Eggs.—In wooded districts usually nests in hole of tree or stumps at varying heights, sometimes in outbuildings, but in more open country often in loose stone wall ; also occasionally in old Swallows' nests and Woodpeckers' holes. Eggs : 5–7, but 8, 9, and even 10 on record. In colour, uniform pale blue, occasionally with fine red brown speckles. Average of 75 British eggs, 18.9 × 13.9 mm. (.74 × .54 in.). Laying begins usually about mid-May, occasionally earlier. Incubation period, 14 days ; chiefly by hen. Only exceptionally two broods. (Plate 182, f. 10.)

IV. Food.—Chiefly insects, including smaller beetles, smaller butterflies and moths, caterpillars, flies, larvæ of sawflies, etc. ; also spiders and small earthworms. According to Naumann, also takes elder berries, juniper berries, etc.

V. Usual Notes.—The song of the Redstart has been described by W. H. Hudson : " The opening rapidly warbled notes are so charming that the attention is instantly attracted by them. They are composed of two sounds, both beautiful—the bright, pure, gushing, robin-like note, and the more tender, expressive, swallow-like note. And that is all ; the song scarcely begins before it ends or collapses, for in most cases the pure sweet opening strain is followed by a curious little farrago of gurgling and squeaking sounds," and other notes scarcely audible. Whether the song is heard outside the breeding period (April–June) is not recorded. The usual cries are a sharp " tick," often rapidly repeated, and a soft " ptui," not unlike the corresponding note of the Willow-Wren.

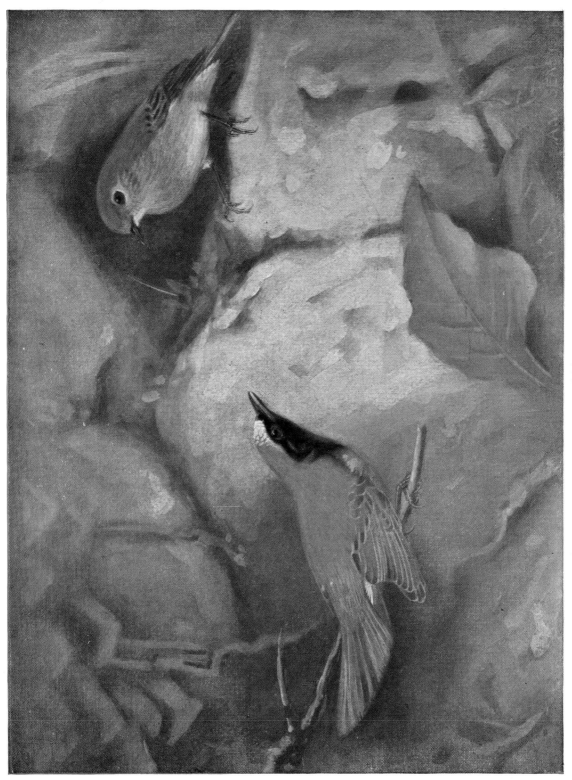

PLATE 44.—COCK REDSTART (*left*) DISPLAYING BEFORE HEN : A. W. Seaby.

Plate 45.—BLACK-REDSTART

Phœnicurus ochrurus gibraltariensis (Gmelin)

I. Description.—Length, 5¾ in. Male has cheeks, throat, *and breast* black; tail and rump chestnut, two middle feathers dark; white on outer edges of primaries and secondaries; belly white. Female and young sooty brown above, under side rather lighter.

II. Range and Habitat.—Generally an autumn visitor to the British Isles, but has been recorded as breeding in Southern England of late years. On the Continent it ranges from Denmark and the Baltic south to the Mediterranean and east to the Balkan Peninsula, wintering chiefly in Africa, and replaced by other races from the Caucasus to Eastern Asia. In Southern Europe a mountain-haunting species, but in the northern part of its range breeds in plains and villages.

III. Nest and Eggs.—In Central Europe usually breeds in holes of buildings or among rafters in sheds or under bridges, but in mountainous districts also in crevices of rocks. Nest often bulky, built of dry grasses, moss, etc., lined with hair and feathers. Eggs: 4–6, pure white, but faintly tinged; bluish eggs also on record, and also spotted with reddish. Average of 100 eggs, 19.4 × 14.3 mm. (.76 × .56 in.). Laying begins from middle of April. Incubation period, 12–13 days, chiefly, at any rate, by the hen. Double brooded.

IV. Food.—Insects mainly, especially small beetles and flies, but also ants, butterflies, and caterpillars. Naumann records spiders and millipedes, and says that berries are taken in hard weather. Saunders says crustacea are picked up on the coast.

V. Usual Notes.—According to Naumann the Black-Redstart's song resembles that of the Redstart, except for certain harsh or hissing sounds. The usual cries are also similar, but, according to the same authority, more strident.

Plate 45.—BLUETHROAT, *Luscinia svecica svecica* (Linnæus)

WHITE-SPOTTED BLUETHROAT, *Luscinia svecica cyanecula* (Wolf)

I. Description.—Length, 6 in. Blue throat with chestnut patch in middle; tail brown, but basal part chestnut. Female and young: dark band on throat, sometimes blue and chestnut traces; under surface yellowish white. Central European form has white spot instead of chestnut.

II. Range and Habitat.—An autumn visitor to the east coast of Great Britain and probably also on spring passage. Breeds in the high fjeld of Scandinavia, in Lapland, and eastward to the Yenisei; a second race (white-spotted) breeds in Central Europe, south to the highlands of Spain, which has also occurred with us; and other races in South Russia and Asia.

III. Nest and Eggs.—Nests on the ground on banksides, in birch scrub, or partially concealed by juniper or sallow; built of dry grasses and bents. Eggs: 6–7 as a rule, greyish green or occasionally blue green to blue, freckled over with fine speckles of red brown. Average of 100 eggs of the Lapland race, 18.5 × 14.0 mm. (.73 × .55 in.). Laying begins in June in Finmark. Incubation by hen; period about 13–14 days. Does not breed in the British Isles.

IV. Food.—Apparently mainly insects: diptera (mosquitoes and craneflies and their larvæ), smaller beetles, and various aquatic insects and larvæ, also " cuckoo spit " and small mollusca; a few seeds also recorded, and earthworms are said to be taken.

V. Usual Notes.—The Bluethroat's song is given in separate phrases like that of the Nightingale, which it resembles in some of its notes. Its most characteristic feature is certain bell-like utterances which have been compared to the sound made by striking a metal triangle. It has a song-flight comparable to that of the Tree-Pipit.[1] The usual cries are said to resemble the " tick " or " ptui " of the Redstart.

---

[1] For the song, see *Zoologist*, 1896, 426 (O. V. Aplin); *ibid.* 1861, 82 (P. and F. Godman); Seebohm, *British Birds*, i. 272.

PLATE 45.—1. BLACK-REDSTARTS ON THE GROUND (*the nearer bird being the cock*);
2. REDSPOTTED-BLUETHROATS ON TWIG (*the farther bird being the cock*): A. W. Seaby.

PLATE 46.—BRITISH REDBREAST OR ROBIN
Erithacus rubecula melophilus (Hartert)
CONTINENTAL REDBREAST, *Erithacus rubecula rubecula* (Linnæus)

I. Description.—Length, 5¾ in. Throat and breast orange red, margined with blue grey, belly white, upper parts olive brown. Juveniles lack red, and are mottled brown, spotted and streaked with buff. Continental birds have breast yellower and back rather lighter.

II. Range and Habitat.—The British Robin is a resident race, but there is a southward movement, and some cross the Channel. In the British Isles it is very generally distributed, except in the Shetlands, and is scarce in the Outer Hebrides. The Portuguese birds are apparently identical. The Continental race visits us on passage and is found throughout Europe up to 68° N., but is replaced by allied races on the Atlantic Isles, North-West Africa, Sardinia and Corsica, the Caucasus, and Persia. With us it is a bird of the lowlands, but in Southern Europe haunts mountain forests.

III. Nest and Eggs.—Frequently breeds on banksides, especially in country lanes, also in gardens, either in hollow on ground or in ivy, among outhouses, in stumps, and occasionally in boxes, old tins, or kettles. Nest variable in size, sometimes large, of dead leaves, moss, neatly lined with bents and hair, a few feathers only. Eggs : usually 5 or 6, but 3, 4, and 7 to 10 recorded. Ground, white or bluish white, sometimes almost covered with fine orange red freckles, or more distinctly spotted or zoned with red. Occasionally pure white, unmarked, or bold dark red spots. Average of 100 British eggs, 19.8 × 15.5 mm. (.78 × .61 in.). Laying begins about end of March, exceptionally earlier. Incubation, by hen, 13–14 days. Two or three broods. (Plate 182, f. 11.)

IV. Food.—Largely insects, including small beetles, moths, and caterpillars, flies and larvæ, earwigs, ants, gall insects, etc. Earthworms are freely taken, also eggs of slugs and snails ; seeds of many weeds, grain, berries of rowan, bilberry, and yew, as well as fruit (raspberry, currants, blackberry, and grapes from greenhouse).

V. Usual Notes.—One associates the song of the Redbreast chiefly with autumn and winter. There is in it a touch of quiet melancholy, reminiscent of the drifting fall of autumn leaves, that, once seized and mastered, makes recognition easy and immediate, even when, as sometimes happens, the bird utters but a few casual notes. The song is heard all the year, but not often in July and early August. The usual cries are a sharp " tik," sometimes rapidly repeated ; a long-drawn plaintive intense note, " ptzeee," uttered especially when the young are in danger ; also a " tsip " or " tsip-ip " or " tsis-ip," frequently heard during the winter territorial disputes, and also serving the hen as a begging note for food.

46

PLATE 46.—REDBREAST : A. W. Seaby.

PLATE 47.—NIGHTINGALE

Luscinia megarhyncha megarhyncha Brehm

I. Description.—Length, 6⅜ in. Upper surface russet brown, tail coverts and tail pale chestnut, under parts white, forebreast and flanks greyish brown. Young have upper parts rufous with buff spots, under parts whitish with dark edgings forming bars, tail chestnut.

II. Range and Habitat.—Haunts well-watered and wooded districts, usually in valleys. In Great Britain is confined to the south and west, rarely occurring east of the Severn–Wash line, but absent from the greater part of the Devonian peninsula. Sporadic to Yorkshire and North Wales, and absent as a breeder from Scotland and Ireland. On the Continent it ranges from the North Sea to the Mediterranean and Black Seas, but also breeds in North-West Africa. The Corsican, Persian, and Turkestan races have been separated. Summer visitor ; wintering in Africa.

III. Nest and Eggs.—Generally breeds in shrubberies, light woodlands or thickets, and double hedgerows. Nest generally on the ground, but at times a foot or two above it, bulky, built of large quantities of dead leaves of oak, etc. ; inner cup of grasses, with hair lining. Eggs : 4–5, occasionally 6 ; generally greenish or brownish olive and uniform in colour, sometimes more or less definite brown speckles. A rare variety is deep blue, unmarked, while bright terra-cotta eggs have also occurred, and others with very definite brown markings. Average of 100 British eggs, 20.9 × 15.6 mm. (.82 × .61 in.). Laying begins early in May. Incubation period, 14 days ; mainly by hen, but male said to take part. Single brooded. (Plate 182, f. 12.)

IV. Food.—Chiefly insects, including beetles, flies, caterpillars (especially those of tree-infesting species, such as *Tortrix*), and ants ; also earthworms, spiders, and to some extent berries and fruit, especially that of elder.

V. Usual Notes.—The Nightingale's song is heard by night and day. It is divided by pauses into separate strains, each strain being mostly a repetition of the same note or notes. The most characteristic are the " jug-jug-jug-jug," and still more so, " that marvellous *crescendo* on a single note, which no other birds attempt."[1] Perhaps the best advice to the learner is that of Warde Fowler, " To wait by a wood till he is fairly startled by a bird that puts his whole ardent soul into his song."[2] The song is heard from April till about the beginning of June, rarely later. The usual cries are a croak-like " krrrr," and a soft " weet."

[1] Warde Fowler, *A Year with the Birds*, 106.
[2] *Ibid.* 107. Attempts to figure the whole song are given in Naumann's *Vogel Mitteleuropas*, i. 16.

47

PLATE 47.—NIGHTINGALE: A. W. Seaby.

Family: Sylviinæ (Warblers)

PLATE 48.—WHITETHROAT

Sylvia communis communis Latham

I. Description.—Length, 5½ in. Male in spring has ash-grey head, upper parts ochreous brown, under parts whitish, throat pure white, forebreast rosy, wings and tail brown, wing coverts and secondaries edged rusty brown, outer tail feathers white. Female has head brown and is duller. Young like hen, but browner.

II. Range and Habitat.—A generally distributed summer visitor to the British Isles, but scarce or absent in the extreme north of Scotland, and only breeds exceptionally in the Outer Hebrides, while it is absent from Orkneys and Shetlands, except as passage migrant. On the Continent ranges to 65° in Scandinavia south to North-West Africa, and is replaced by an eastern race in Asia to the Yenisei. Occurring wherever there is scrub growth.

III. Nest and Eggs.—Breeds in bushes, bramble clumps, hedge bottoms, etc., generally not far from the ground; occasionally in rank grass, and often among nettles. Nest well-built and solid of dead grasses and bents, freely lined with horsehair, and decorated with bits of down, etc. Eggs: 4–5, occasionally 6, and 7 recorded; generally with greenish white or creamy ground, spotted with dark leaden or ochreous brown. In a large series erythristic varieties may be found, also white, unmarked or with leaden spots, and numerous other types with very varied markings, some being blotched and others capped or zoned. Average of 100 British eggs, 19.1 × 13.7 mm. (.75 × .54 in.). Laying begins early in May. Incubation period, 11–12 days; the male takes part in incubation. Two broods. (Plate 182, f. 14.)

IV. Food.—Largely insects, including smaller beetles, moths and caterpillars, flies and hymenoptera; also spiders and their eggs, aphides, and, in autumn, fruit (currants, raspberries, etc.), as well as peas.

V. Usual Notes.—When disturbed, the Whitethroat utters a scolding "churr" as it slips in and out of cover. More intense alarm is expressed by a repeated sharp "tcheck" or "tchuck." The song is a vigorous warble, varying considerably in quality. A rendering of one song listened to repeatedly by the writer runs: "Wee-to-wee, wee-ti-wee-ti, wee-tee-er, wee-ter," and shorter: "Wee-to-wee, wee-tee, wee-tee, wee-ter." The song is often uttered as the bird tosses itself out of a hedge or bush into the air, during which performance, to quote Gilbert White, it "uses odd jerks and gesticulations." It seems to be more bent on displaying its "grit" than its musical gifts. Song period, April to July, possibly later.

48

PLATE 48.—WHITETHROATS (*the lower figure being the male*): G. E. Collins.

PLATE 49.—LESSER-WHITETHROAT

PLATE 49.—LESSER-WHITETHROAT

Sylvia curruca curruca Linnæus

SIBERIAN LESSER-WHITETHROAT

Sylvia curruca blythi Ticehurst and Whistler

I. Description.—Length, $5\frac{1}{4}$ in. Head and back blue grey, no chestnut on wings, smaller than Common-Whitethroat. Sexes alike : outer web of outer tail feathers white, throat pure white, tinged pinkish buff on breast, and buffish brown on flanks ; wings grey brown, partly edged paler ; feet lead-coloured.

II. Range and Habitat.—Summer visitor to Great Britain, but avoids Cornwall, the western Welsh counties, and is local in the four northern English counties. In Scotland it has only bred exceptionally, and is only a straggler to Ireland. Haunts hedgerows, gardens, and wooded districts. On the Continent ranges to about 65° N., south to the Mediterranean, and east to Persia and the Urals, but is replaced by other forms in various parts of Asia and South-East Russia, and is absent from Spain, except on passage ; winters in North Africa.

III. Nest and Eggs.—Breeds in hedgerows, thickets, and shrubs, usually within a few feet of the ground. Nest slighter than that of Common-Whitethroat, built of grasses and dead plant stalks, lined with horsehair or fine roots. Eggs : 4–5, sometimes 3, or 6 and 7 on record. Ground colour, whitish with bold markings and spots of dark brown and ashy grey, generally near big end and often in zone. Some eggs almost unmarked or quite white, others distinctly bluish. Average of 100 British eggs, 17.2 × 12.8 mm. (.67 × .50 in.). Laying begins early in May, exceptionally at end of April, but often later. Incubation period, 10–11 days ; male takes part. Two broods reared in many cases. (Plate 182, f. 15.)

IV. Food.—Chiefly insects and their larvæ, including small beetles, flies, ants, caterpillars ; also spiders and aphides. Fruit is taken to some extent, especially currants, and berries of elder, bramble, daphne, etc.

V. Usual Notes.—The song of this species is composed of a short low prelude followed by an outburst of high notes, all of the same pitch. When the bird is alarmed it utters a sharp " tcheck," which becomes a rattle in moments of excitement. It utters also, according to Witchell, the churring note. Song period, usually April to July ; it has been heard later.[1]

[1] *British Birds* (Mag.), i. 371.

PLATE 49.—LESSER-WHITETHROAT FEEDING YOUNG : G. E. Collins.

PLATE 50.—BLACKCAP

Sylvia atricapilla atricapilla (Linnæus)

I. Description.—Length, 5¾ in. Male has black cap ; rufous brown in female and young ; upper parts ashy brown ; under parts from chin to belly grey ; no white in tail, in which feathers have olive brown margins.

II. Range and Habitat.—Summer visitor to the British Isles, being widely distributed in England and Wales, but rare in Anglesey. In Scotland it is confined to the south, except locally on the east side, and has been recorded as breeding in the Inner Hebrides. In Ireland it is local and scarce, but widely distributed. A woodland bird, haunting deciduous woods with undergrowth. On the Continent ranges to 66° N. and south to the Atlantic isles and North-West Africa, east to Persia and West Siberia, but the Madeiran and Canarian races and perhaps some of the Mediterranean birds belong to other races. Winters chiefly in Africa.

III. Nest and Eggs.—Breeds in bushes, hedgerows, trailing honeysuckle on trees, bramble thickets, etc., usually higher up than Garden-Warbler. Nest rather flimsily built of dead grass stems, bents, etc., lined with finer bents and at times also horse-hair. Eggs : 4–5, sometimes only 3 or 6, slightly smaller on average than Garden-Warbler's, but at times indistinguishable ; usually with light buff ground and blotched and clouded with brown of varying shades and ashy shellmarks. Occasionally white, unmarked or nearly so ; also an erythristic type with pinkish ground and red markings. Average of 100 British eggs, 19.3×14.5 mm. (.76×.57 in.). Laying begins late in April, but generally not till May. Incubation period, 10–11 days ; both sexes take part. Probably a second brood is reared occasionally, but not regularly. (Plate 182, f. 16.)

IV. Food.—Insects, including small beetles, caterpillars, flies, hymenoptera, etc. ; also aphides and spiders. Fruit and berries form a large proportion of food later in season—cherry, currants, raspberry, strawberry, etc., and berries of rowan, daphne, ivy, holly, honeysuckle, privet, elder, blackberry, etc. ; also takes peas and has been seen to pick up worms.

V. Usual Notes.—If one hears floating down from a tree a bird song of the first order that is clearly not a Blackbird's, and is not divided into contrasted strains like the song of Thrush or Nightingale, one may be sure the singer is a Blackcap. The song is a short sweet warble, perfect of its kind. Its most characteristic phrase is the final, described as a " loud bright ' hee-ti-weeto-weeto.' "[1] It is heard from April to the end of July and sometimes later.[2] The usual cries are a sharp " tack," rapidly repeated in moments of excitement, and a churring note, like " tcharr." The species has a quite common sub-song, " an intermittent inward warbling . . ."[3]

[1] *British Birds* (Mag.), xx. 64 (E. Peake).   [2] *British Birds* (Mag.), i. 371.
[3] E. M. Nicholson, *Songs of Wild Birds*, 120.

PLATE 50.—BLACKCAPS (*the male being the nearer*) : A. W. Seaby.

PLATE 51.—GARDEN-WARBLER

Sylvia borin (Boddaert)

I. Description.—Length, 5⅞ in. Upper parts, wings, and tail uniform olive brown ; under parts greyish white, with tinge of buff on throat, breast, and flanks ; inconspicuous buff eye stripe. Sexes alike. Throat no lighter than breast. Feet lighter than in Blackcap.

II. Range and Habitat.—A summer visitor to Great Britain, avoiding West Cornwall and extreme west of Wales, and ranging in Scotland north to Perthshire. In Ireland it is very local, but has bred in all provinces. Usually met with in gardens and well-wooded districts. On the Continent ranges north to lat. 70° N., south to the Cantabrian Mountains and Albania, and east to West Siberia : wintering in Africa.

III. Nest and Eggs.—Breeds in shrubs and bushes in gardens or thickets and outskirts of woods ; occasionally in trees or tall fern. Nest built of grass stalks, rather stouter than Blackcap's, lined with fine bents and some hair. Eggs : 4–5, occasionally 3 or 6, and 7 said to have occurred. Ground, yellowish or whitish, with yellowish brown spots and blotches of various shades ; generally a " brand spot " or two. Some varieties are very pale, almost white ; an erythristic type has occurred, but very rarely, while some eggs have very rich dark brown markings. Average size of 100 British eggs, 20.1 × 14.7 mm. (.79 × .58 in.). Laying begins about mid-May, sometimes later. Incubation period, 11–12 days ; male takes part. Single brooded. (Plate 182, f. 17.)

IV. Food.—Insect food includes smaller beetles, flies, small caterpillars ; also aphides, spiders, and, it is said, occasionally worms. Fruit and berries also form a substantial part of diet—cherries, raspberries, and currants, also berries of ivy, privet, elder, honeysuckle, etc.

V. Usual Notes.—The Garden-Warbler's song is not unlike that of the Blackcap, but it differs in being, on the average, less mellow and in continuing without pause much longer, sometimes for several minutes. The cries are also not unlike those of the Blackcap : a sharp " tak " or " tek," a grating " tchurr " or " tcharr " ; also a plaintive " whit " or " bit," all used when the nest is approached. The song period, April to July, sometimes later.

PLATE 51.—DARTFORD-WARBLER

Sylvia undata dartfordiensis Latham

I. Description.—Length, 5 in. Tail long and fan-shaped ; upper parts blackish brown ; throat and under parts dark chestnut red, feathers on throat tipped with white ; wings and tail dark brown, white on outer web of outer tail feathers. Orbital ring and iris red in adult, yellow in young. Females and young lighter, not so black.

II. Range and Habitat.—In England a local resident confined to the gorse-grown commons and heaths of the southern counties, from the Thames valley southward, but in small numbers also in East Anglia, and recorded exceptionally north to Salop and perhaps Staffordshire. The British race is confined to England, but very closely allied, if distinct, races are found in the Channel Isles, France, Spain, North-West Africa, Corsica, and Sardinia.

III. Nest and Eggs.—Breeds generally in gorse, but in some districts also in long heather, as a rule about 18 in. from the ground, but occasionally in old gorse and then higher. Nest built of stalks and bents, lined with finer grasses and in some cases with horse-hair ; also usually a feather. Gorse spikes and spiders' cocoons in frame of nest. Eggs : normally 4, sometimes only 3, and rarely 5, while 6 once recorded. Ground colour, white or faintly greenish, marbled and spotted with umber brown and ashy, sometimes forming a zone or cap. Though the pure red type does not occur in England, a type with chestnut spots on a white ground exists. Average of 100 British eggs, 17.5 × 13.2 mm. (.69 × .52 in.). Laying begins about 20th April. Incubation period, 12–13 days ; chiefly, but not entirely, by the hen. Double brooded. (Plate 182, f. 18.)

IV. Food.—Mainly insects, including small beetles, butterflies, and moths with their larvæ, flies (*Tipula*, etc.), spiders, and, according to Blyth, blackberries.

V. Usual Notes.—Its song is " a subdued liquid warble," which may continue for a considerable period. " Short bursts of song are often uttered on the wing." The alarm note is a scolding vibrant " pit-cha-cha," [1] and uneasiness is shown by repeated " tacks." Song period, every month, chiefly March to May.[2]

[1] E. L. Turner in the *British Bird Book*, ii. 44.
[2] *British Birds* (Mag.), xxix. 196.

PLATE 51.—GARDEN-WARBLER (*left hand*) AND DARTFORD-WARBLER (*right*) : G. E. Collins.

PLATE 52.—BRITISH GOLDCREST

Regulus regulus anglorum Hartert

CONTINENTAL GOLDCREST

Regulus regulus regulus (Linnæus)

I. Description.—Length, 3½ in. Upper parts olive green, with yellow crest bounded **by black** streak on each side ; that of male orange red in middle. Under surface of male dull white, **tinged** on throat and flanks with green ; in female, dull buff. Young lack the yellow crest.

II. Range and Habitat.—Haunts woodlands, with preference for conifers, and is a **generally** distributed resident, avoiding treeless districts and moorlands, and is rare or absent as a **breeding** species in Northern Scotland, the Outer Hebrides, Orkneys, and Shetlands. The British **race is** confined to the British Isles, but the Continental race is found in wooded parts of Europe **south** to the Pyrenees, Italy, Caucasus, and Asia Minor, with allied races in Atlantic and Mediterranean isles, Central Asia, and Japan. Occurs as passage migrant on our east coasts.

III. Nest and Eggs.—Generally the nest is affixed to the lower side of a branch of some **conifer,** less frequently on the upper side ; also in ivy on tree trunks or in furze bushes. Nest built of **green** moss and spiders' webs, lined with feathers. Eggs : usually 7 to 10 or 11, sometimes 12 ; **white** or light buff in ground, with fine brownish spots tending to form a zone or cap at the big end ; sometimes white unmarked. Average of 100 British eggs, 13.6 × 10.2 mm. (.53 × .40 in.). Laying begins usually latter part of April. Incubation period, 15–17 days ; apparently by hen. **Double** brooded. (Plate 182, f. 19.)

IV. Food.—Chiefly small insects and their larvæ, including small beetles, flies, hymenoptera, etc. ; also spiders and various blights and scales from trees.

V. Usual Notes.—The Goldcrest's song is composed of " two notes repeated five or six times, and ending in a rapid trill." [1] The little call notes are high-pitched, " like needle-points of sound." [2] One rendering is " tzit." Naumann gives to the species a second call note, " se-se-se " or " sre-sre-sre," which enters into the song. The bird has been heard to make " tiny little warblings **quite** unrelated to the song." [3] Song period, more or less from February to November.

FIRECREST

Regulus ignicapillus ignicapillus (Temminck)

(No Plate)

I. Description.—Length, 4 in. Resembles Goldcrest, but has a whitish streak over the eye and below it, also a distinct black streak passing through the eyes ; crest of male fiery red ; female yellow. Under surface lighter than in Goldcrest.

II. Range and Habitat.—Not confined to coniferous woodlands, but frequently found **among** deciduous trees. Autumn visitor to Great Britain, chiefly on east side : reported to have bred **once,** but confirmation required. On the Continent nests in Central and Southern Europe, also North-West Africa and Asia Minor. Allied race in Madeira.

III. Nest and Eggs.—Sometimes placed like Goldcrest's under branch of conifer, but also **against** tree trunk, or in bushes. Built of down or moss, according to locality, lined with feathers, etc. Eggs : 7–11 or 12. Ground colour, warm pinkish or reddish, with a tinge of yellow, and lightly marked. Average of 100 eggs, 13.5 × 10.3 mm. (.53 × .40 in.). Laying date varies, according **to** latitude, from April to May. Incubation period, 14–15 days. Double brooded.

IV. Food.—Chiefly small insects and larvæ, small beetles, flies, etc. ; also spiders and aphides.

V. Usual Notes.—According to Naumann the Firecrest's usual notes—a soft fine " tzit " **and** the " sre "—are much like the corresponding notes of the Goldcrest. The song is alike **but** shorter, lacking the cadence at the end ; it consists chiefly of repetitions of the " sre " **or** " **se.**" Song period, the breeding season and occasionally afterwards. [4]

[1] E. L. Turner in the *British Bird Book*, ii. 52, **11.**
[2] Lord Grey of Fallodon, *Charm of Birds*, 38.
[3] *British Birds* (Mag.), xx. 64 (E. Peake).
[4] *Vögel Mitteleuropas*, ii. 232.

PLATE 52.—GOLDCRESTS : A. W. Seaby.

PLATE 53.—WILLOW-WARBLER, *Phylloscopus trochilus trochilus* (Linnæus)

NORTHERN WILLOW-WARBLER, *Phylloscopus trochilus acredula* (Linnæus)

I. Description.—Length, nearly 5 in. Rather larger and brighter than Chiff-Chaff, with pale brown feet, and more yellow in plumage. Song also totally different, being a sweet descending scale. The northern race is indistinguishable in the field, but wing and tail slightly longer, and rather browner above.

II. Range and Habitat.—Widely distributed and common summer resident in the British Isles, scarce Cornwall, North Scotland, and Outer Hebrides, and absent from Orkneys and Shetlands. The northern race is a passage migrant to the east coast of Great Britain. On the Continent ranges from North Europe to the Cantabrian Mountains, but is scarce or absent from the Mediterranean area. Winters chiefly in Africa. Local races probably occur in Northern Europe. Found almost everywhere except moors and mountains.

III. Nest and Eggs.—Breeds in long grass in ditches, hedge bottoms, banks, or cuttings, normally on the ground, but exceptionally at some height above it in bush, sapling, or on wall among ivy or creepers. Nest built of green moss with some grass interwoven, sometimes bracken; domed, circular entrance at side, interior warmly lined with feathers. Eggs : usually 5–7, exceptionally 8 or 9 ; white, rarely unmarked, but usually with light or dark red spots or fine speckles, occasionally blotches. Average of 100 British eggs, 15.4 × 12.3 mm. (.60 × .48 in.). Laying begins normally early May, exceptionally late April. Incubation period, 13–14 days ; apparently by hen alone. In some cases double brooded. (Plate 183, f. 1.)

IV. Food.—Chiefly insects, including small beetles and larvæ, flies, smaller moths and caterpillars, etc. ; also spiders and aphides ; small worms also reported. Said to take elderberries and currants in autumn.

V. Usual Notes.—The Willow-Warbler's song, heard more frequently perhaps than any other in the breeding season, is a rippling warble, short, sweet, and somewhat plaintive, that gathers strength only to run gently down the scale and faint into silence. Once recognized it cannot be mistaken. Between the songs may be heard a subdued whispering sound corresponding to that of the Chiff-Chaff. It has been figured as " vip." [1] Individuals have been heard to utter modified forms of the Chiff-Chaff's song in addition to their own.[2] Song period, from end of March till August or later. Alarm note " hweet " and " whoo-it."

CHIFF-CHAFF, *Phylloscopus collybita collybita* (Vieillot)

SCANDINAVIAN CHIFF-CHAFF, *Phylloscopus collybita abietinus* (Nilsson)

SIBERIAN CHIFF-CHAFF, *Phylloscopus collybita tristis* (Blyth)

(No Plate)

I. Description.—Length, 4¾ in. Distinguished from Willow-Wren by blackish feet and characteristic song, " chiff-chaff," of two notes, repeated monotonously from trees ; also slightly smaller. Upper parts olive green, pale buff stripe over eye ; wings and tail brown, edged olive green ; under parts mostly dull white.

II. Range and Habitat.—Summer resident in British Isles, occasionally wintering, and scarce in Scotland north of Forth area, where it is only passage migrant, except locally on the west side and in Inner Hebrides ; general in Ireland. On the Continent is replaced by allied forms in the north, also in Siberia and the Canaries, but breeds in Central and Southern Europe to the Mediterranean. Scandinavian and Siberian races have occurred on east side of Great Britain.

III. Nest and Eggs.—Nest often in yew trees and evergreen bushes ; also in thick cover and bramble undergrowth in woods, etc. Nest rather bulky, of dead leaves, moss, and stalks, domed, with rather flattened entrance at side, and freely lined with feathers. Eggs : 5–6, rarely 7 ; white, sparsely marked with purplish spots, occasionally with brown. Average of 90 British eggs, 15.4 × 12.1 mm. (.60 × .47 in.). Laying begins early in May. Incubation period, 13 days ; apparently by hen. Single brooded as a rule. (Plate 182, f. 20.)

IV. Food.—Insects (including small beetles, flies, moths, and caterpillars, especially the Tineidæ) and eggs ; also spiders and aphides.

V. Usual Notes.—The song of the Chiff-Chaff is composed of a sequence of " chiffs " and " chaffs " in varying order. One individual listened to by the writer began every phrase with " chiff-chaff-chaff, chiff-chaff-chaff," but completed it with the notes in varying order and number—*e.g.* " chaff-chaff-chiff-chiff," or again, " chiff-chaff-chaff," or simply " chiff." A fact, rediscovered from time to time by field naturalists, but as old, at least, as the middle of the last century, is that the Chiff-Chaff is heard to utter between its phrases a few low muttered notes, figured by Naumann [3] as " hededet," by Bailly [4] as " frui-frui." Individuals have also been heard to utter notes like the " splintered fragments of a Willow-Warbler's song." [5] Song period, more or less from its arrival in March till end September.[6] Usual note a soft plaintive " hweet."

[1] *British Birds* (Mag.), xix. 51 (T. J. Beeston). Bailly (*Ornithologie de la Savoie*, ii. 438) mentions " un petit grognement " which follows the song. The present writer has heard the note more than once.
[2] *British Birds* (Mag.), xx. 153 (Bertram Lloyd).   [3] *Vögel Mitteleuropas*, ii. 105.
[4] *Ornithologie de la Savoie*, ii. 435 (1853). See also the *British Bird Book*, ii. 59.
[5] *British Birds* (Mag.), xvi. 161 (B. Lloyd). See also *British Bird Book*, ii. 60 ; Coward, *Birds of British Isles*, i., and *Ibis*, 1914, 304 (H. Lynes).
[6] Wintering birds heard singing February in Pembrokeshire (B. Lloyd, *in litt.*).

PLATE 53.—WILLOW-WARBLER BUILDING ITS NEST: G. E. Collins.

PLATE 54.—WOOD-WARBLER

Phylloscopus sibilatrix sibilatrix (Bechstein)

I. Description.—Length, $5\frac{1}{4}$ in. Slightly larger than Willow-Warbler, with distinct yellow eye stripe and sulphur yellow throat and breast, white belly, and yellow on flanks ; mantle yellowish green ; tail and wings brown, with yellowish green edges. Female duller.

II. Range and Habitat.—More local as a rule than the other Leaf-Warblers. Summer resident in England, more numerous in Wales, and absent from North Scotland, only straggler to the northern groups, and absent from Outer Hebrides. Very local in Ireland, but has bred in Galway, Wicklow, and Queen's County. On the Continent breeds in South Sweden, South Finland, but not south of Pyrenees, Alps, or Carpathians. A dubious Mediterranean race has been separated. Winters in Africa. A woodland-haunting species, absent from open country and moors.

III. Nest and Eggs.—Breeds on ground among dead leaves, bracken, and undergrowth in woods under trees. Nest built of dead bracken, grasses, or dead leaves, lined with fine dry grass ; sometimes a few hairs, but no feathers. Eggs : 5–7, occasionally 8 ; white in ground, spotted all over rather thickly with fine or bold deep brown markings, varying from chocolate to reddish brown, and some ashy shell-marks. Sometimes a zone of markings at big end. Average of 90 British eggs, 16.0 × 12.6 mm. (.63 × .49 in.). Laying begins latter part of May. Incubation period, 13 days ; apparently by hen alone. Two broods exceptional. (Plate 183, f. 2.)

IV. Food.—Insects (including small beetles, moths, and caterpillars), flies, and neuroptera (ephemera) ; also aphides. Berries said to be taken in autumn, but no evidence of fruit.

V. Usual Notes.—Gilbert White has described the Wood-Warbler's song as a " sibilous shivering noise in the tops of tall woods." Jourdain figures it, " ip, sip, sipp, sipsip, sipsipp, srrèèèèèè." It is sometimes preceded by a loud clear note repeated, " whee-ou." The latter sequence is also uttered separately, and may thus be regarded as a separate song. Song period, from its arrival in April to July, possibly later. The alarm notes are the plaintive " wheet," and another syllabled by Jourdain as " tee tee."

54

PLATE 54.—WOOD-WARBLER FEEDING ITS YOUNG : A. W. Seaby.

PLATE 55.—SEDGE-WARBLER

Acrocephalus schœnobœnus (Linnæus)

I. Description.—Length, nearly 5 in. Recognized by conspicuous buff eye stripe; crown dark brown, streaked russet; also dark stripes on russet back, rump markedly rufous. Under parts whitish, buff on throat, brownish on flanks, wings and tail dark brown with paler edges.

II. Range and Habitat.—Generally distributed summer resident near water on low ground in British Isles, becoming scarce in North Scotland, and very rare in Sutherland, absent from northern groups and Outer Hebrides, but has bred in Inner Hebrides. On the Continent from about 70° N. in Scandinavia and North Russia to South France, Italy, Bulgaria, and also Siberia east to the Yenisei. Winters in Africa and Asia Minor.

III. Nest and Eggs.—Breeds in rank vegetation in osier beds, ditches, etc., but also in bushes and even hedgerows; generally rather low, but exceptionally 5 to 10 feet from ground. Nest rather large, moss in foundation, untidily built of stalks and grasses, sometimes lined with feathers, at other times hair only. Eggs: usually 5–6, occasionally 4 only, and 7 recorded. Ground colour often so hidden by minute yellowish spots as to appear almost uniform; often a dark hair-streak. Some eggs have numerous darker greyish brown markings, and approach a light type of Reed-Warbler; a rare erythristic type also occurs, and white eggs have been found. Average of 100 eggs, 17.7 × 13.4 mm. (.69 × .52 in.). Laying begins latter part of May. Incubation period, 12–14 days; chiefly by hen, but male takes some part. Double brooded in some cases. (Plate 183, f. 5.)

IV. Food.—Insects (largely aquatic), beetles, flies, neuroptera; also spiders, aphides, small land mollusca, small worms, and in autumn elderberries.

V. Usual Notes.—The Sedge-Warbler sings in the rushes or bushes or in short Pipit-like song flights above them. The song is harsher but more varied than the Reed-Warbler's: the bird chatters " in a state of the intensest excitement, pitching up his voice into a series of loud squeaks, and then dropping it into a long-drawn grating noise, like the winding up of an old-fashioned watch." [1] That he mimics is disputed. The usual cries are not unlike those of the Reed-Warbler. Song period, from mid-April to mid-July; occasionally later. Sings at night as well as by day.

AQUATIC-WARBLER

Acrocephalus paludicola (Vieillot)

(No Plate)

I. Description.—Length, 4.9 in. Closely resembles Sedge-Warbler, but has a more yellow cast of plumage and conspicuous light band down middle of crown, bordered by two blackish bands on each side.

II. Range and Habitat.—An occasional visitor. Has occurred over twenty times in the southern counties of England, and three times in Scotland and Ireland. On the Continent its range extends over Central and Southern Europe, probably also to North-West Africa, but exclusive of Greece. Probably winters in Africa.

III. Nest and Eggs.—Not proved to breed in the British Isles. Not much definitely recorded; breeds in marshes among rank vegetation, and rather low down. Nest said to be smaller and deeper than that of Sedge-Warbler, built of grass stalks, down, etc., lined with hair or feathers. Eggs: 4–6, apparently closely resembling those of Sedge-Warbler. Average of 52 eggs, 17.1 × 13 mm. (.67 × .51 in.). Laying begins in May on the Continent. No details as to incubation, and has not yet been proved to breed in the British Isles.

IV. Food.—Mainly insects; beetles of many species, earwigs, diptera, etc.; also small mollusca.

V. Usual Notes.—This Warbler's song is like the Sedge-Warbler's, but shorter, more varied, less musical. Figured by Naumann, " Terrr-tettet, tettet, tzerrr-tüt-tüt-tüt-tüt, errr, yüp-yüp-yüp-yüp." (Anglicized, except for *ü*, which = French *u* in *plume*.) The usual cries resemble those of the Sedge-Warbler.

[1] W. Warde Fowler, *A Year with the Birds*, 2nd edit., 40.

PLATE 55.—SEDGE-WARBLER: A. W. Seaby.

PLATE 56.—REED-WARBLER

Acrocephalus scirpaceus scirpaceus (Hermann)

I. Description.—Length, 5½ in. Upper parts olive brown, inclining to rufous, especially on the rump ; wing quills and tail greyish brown, with olive brown margins ; under surface greyish or rufous buff, except throat and belly, which are white ; feet slaty brown. Closely resembles Marsh-Warbler, but differs widely in song and breeding habits. Sexes alike.

II. Range and Habitat.—Confined to marshes, wet ditches, and slow-flowing streams where reeds grow. Summer resident in suitable localities in England and Wales north to Cheshire, Staffordshire, and the Trent valley, and only sporadically in Lancashire and Yorkshire. Casual visitor to Scotland and Ireland. On the Continent breeds from South Sweden and the Baltic to North-West Africa, and replaced by other forms from South Russia and Palestine to Turkestan. Winters in Africa.

III. Nest and Eggs.—Usually breeds among reeds in or close to water ; also occasionally in rank vegetation or in lilac or other bushes, sometimes at a considerable distance from water. Nest rather cylindrical in shape, often built round stems of two or three reeds, of grasses, waterweed, reed flowers, etc., lined with grass heads, reed flowers, and some feathers, hair, etc., at times. Eggs : often 4, at times 5, rarely 6. Ground, greenish white, generally freely blotched and marbled with varied spots of olive and grey, ranging to brown of varying shades, and sometimes forming a zone. A scarce type is sparsely marked with a few ashy blotches on an almost white ground and approaches a variety of Marsh-Warbler's egg. Average of 100 British eggs, 18.3 × 13.6 mm. (.72 × .53 in.). Laying begins often not till June, but occasionally in latter half May. Incubation period, 11–12 days ; shared by both sexes. Proof of occasional second brood. (Plate 183, f. 3.)

IV. Food.—Chiefly waterside insects and their larvæ, such as flies, dragon flies, stone flies, and Mayflies, moths, and smaller beetles ; spiders and aphides also taken ; small land mollusca. Fruits and berries in late summer—currants, elderberries, bird cherry, dogwood, etc.

V. Usual Notes.—The Reed-Warbler's song, uttered by the bird either when clinging to a reed or flitting from one perch to another, has been described as " a long crooning soliloquy in accents not sweet, but much less harsh and declamatory than those of his cousin "[1] (the Sedge-Warbler). It is heard from the end of April to mid-July, and occasionally later.[2] May be heard singing at night. The usual notes are a sound like " tschetch " and a " charr " or " churr."

[1] W. Warde Fowler, *A Year with the Birds*, 2nd edit., 39.
[2] *British Birds* (Mag.), iv. 278 ; Stanley Morris, *Bird Song*, 64.

56

PLATE 56.—REED-WARBLER AT ITS NEST: G. E. Collins.

PLATE 57.—MARSH-WARBLER

Acrocephalus palustris (Bechstein)

I. Description.—Length, 5¼ in. As Reed-Warbler, but lacks rufous tinge; upper parts olive greenish, feet flesh colour. Song much superior to that of Reed-Warbler, and contains many imitations of other species, almost rivalling the Blackcap's in sweetness.

II. Range and Habitat.—Summer resident in the southern counties of England, west to Somerset and Dorset, north to Staffordshire, Warwick, Cambridge, and Huntingdon (but evidence for East Anglia not satisfactory), east to Kent. Haunts low-lying, moist wooded country, and avoids bare uplands and moors. On the Continent breeds from Denmark and the Gulf of Finland south to the Mediterranean on the west (evidence from Spain needs confirmation), and on the east to Bulgaria and the Caspian. Winters in South Africa.

III. Nest and Eggs.—Breeds among rank vegetation, especially meadow-sweet, in osier beds, spinneys, ditches, and occasionally in cornfields. Nest suggests that of a warbler (*Sylvia*), being slightly built of dry grasses, and fastened to supports by " basket handles," with a few hairs in lining; generally 2 or 3 feet from dry ground and not over water. Eggs: 4–5, sometimes 3 only, rarely 6. Ground, bluish or greenish white, boldly blotched with ashy and olive brown. Sometimes very pale and erythristic type has occurred. Average of 100 British eggs, 18.9 × 14.1 mm. (.74 × .55 in.). Laying begins about mid-June. Incubation period, 12–13 days. Both sexes take part. Single brooded. (Plate 183. f. 4.)

IV. Food.—Insects, chiefly marsh-haunting species; small beetles, flies, neuroptera, moths and caterpillars, etc.; also spiders and aphides. Fruits and berries in late summer (currants, elder, dogwood, and bird cherry).

V. Usual Notes.—The Marsh-Warbler's song is " more silvery, high-pitched, sweet, and varied than that of any other species of warbler." [1] The usual cries are like those of the Reed-Warbler. See above, § I. Song period, May to July and possibly later.

PLATE 57.—GRASSHOPPER-WARBLER

Locustella nævia nævia (Boddaert)

I. Description.—Length, 5½ in. Recognized by graduated and slightly barred tail and characteristic " reeling " note, like the metallic noise of a fisherman's reel in action. Upper parts olive brown with black brown markings, which tend to fall into lines; faint eye stripe; under parts pale brownish, with a few darker streaks on breast.

II. Range and Habitat.—Somewhat local summer resident in suitable localities in the British Isles, but is scarce in South-West Scotland, and breeds only in a few places north to Inverness and Elgin. Does not breed in the Scottish islands, except on Skye. On the Continent it breeds from South Norway and Finland to the Cantabrian Mountains, North Italy, and South Russia, but is replaced by another race in Siberia. Usually haunts marshlands and osier beds, but is also found on heaths and commons.

III. Nest and Eggs.—Breeds on commons among heather and on moorlands, as well as in marshes and osier beds, among undergrowth, and on outskirts of bramble thickets and plantations of young trees. Nest well concealed on ground or in rank grass above it, the bird usually leaving by a run through the tangle, built of dead grasses and bents. Eggs: usually 6, sometimes only 4 or 5, and 7 recorded. Ground colour, pinkish white, finely freckled all over with red specks, which sometimes form a zone at the big end. Exceptional varieties are very pale, or are marked with big purple red blotches. Average of 100 British eggs, 18 × 13.8 mm. (.70 × .54 in.). Laying begins in the south about mid-May or a little earlier, but not till late May in the north. Incubation period, 13–14 days; by both sexes, but chiefly by hen. Sometimes double brooded, especially in the south. (Plate 183, f. 6.)

IV. Food.—Chiefly insects (beetles, moths and caterpillars, flies, dragon flies, and Mayflies, etc.); also woodlice.

V. Usual Notes.—The reeling song (see above, § I.) may continue for some minutes, and seems to come from all quarters, owing to the bird's habit of turning its head about as it sings. The usual note is a sharp " t'whit " rapidly repeated. Song period, mid-April to September. [2] Sings at night as well as by day.

[1] *Zoologist*, 1906, 408–9 (Warde Fowler). See also *British Birds* (Mag.), xxvii. p. 63 (J. Walpole Bond).
[2] *British Birds* (Mag.), x. 94 (E. L. Turner).

PLATE 57.—MARSH-WARBLER (*left hand*) AND GRASSHOPPER-WARBLER (*right*) : Winifred Austen.

PLATE 58.—DUNNOCK or HEDGE-SPARROW
Prunella modularis occidentalis (Hartert)
HEBRIDEAN DUNNOCK
Prunella modularis hebridium Meinertzhagen
CONTINENTAL DUNNOCK
Prunella modularis modularis (Linnæus)

I. Description.—Length, $5\frac{1}{2}$ in. Head, neck, and fore-breast slate grey, streaked with brown ; back brown with rufous tinge, streaked blackish brown ; under surface dull greyish white, flanks pale brown, streaked amber brown ; wings and tail dusky brown, with paler margins ; beak slender. Female duller.

II. Range and Habitat.—The British race is a generally distributed resident in the whole of the British Isles, but is scarce in North Scotland and Orkneys, and absent from Shetlands. In the Outer Hebrides, where there are woods, it is replaced by a slightly different local race. The Continental race is a spring and autumn visitor to our east coasts, and is distributed over Europe from about 70° N. to the Mediterranean, but absent from many districts in the extreme south of Europe. Other races described from Portugal and Western Asia. Avoids open downs and moorlands.

III. Nest and Eggs.—Breeds in hedgerows, shrubberies, gardens, and edges of woods, nesting also in stick heaps, etc. Nest generally within a few feet of ground, built of moss, with some small twigs, and neatly lined with hair and bits of wool or feathers. Eggs : usually 4–5, occasionally 6 or only 3 ; clear deep blue, unmarked. Rare variety white, unmarked. Average size of 100 British eggs, 19.9 × 14.7 mm. (.78 × .57 in.). Laying begins usually in April, occasionally earlier. Incubation period, 11–13 days, but 15 also recorded. Two or three broods reared. (Plate 182, f. 13.)

IV. Food.—Insects (including beetles, caterpillars, etc.), earthworms, and spiders ; also seeds of numerous weeds and grains of corn.

V. Usual Notes.—The Dunnock's familiar song is a short, thin, but cheerful strain, sung from hedge-top or bush, and appreciated chiefly because heard at seasons when bird song is rare. The usual call is difficult to render ; it is perhaps best described in Gilbert White's words, " a piping plaintive noise." It is frequently to be heard in autumn. Song period, more or less all the year, with a break in July.

PLATE 58.—HEDGE-SPARROW : G. E. Collins.

Family : Sturnidæ (Starling)

PLATE 59.—STARLING, *Sturnus vulgaris vulgaris* Linnæus

SHETLAND STARLING, *Sturnus vulgaris zetlandicus* Hartert

I. Description.—Length, $8\frac{1}{2}$ in. Plumage glossy spangled, varying individually, some more green on head and others purple. Glossy black with metallic reflections of purple, green, and blue. Feathers of mantle tipped with buff ; those of flanks and belly spotted whitish. Dusky wing quills have rufous buff margins. Female less brilliant. Bill bright yellow in spring, in autumn blackish ; feet reddish brown. Metallic hues duller in autumn. Young have uniform greyish brown mantle and breast, throat and belly whitish.

II. Range and Habitat.—A widely distributed resident, formerly confined to certain districts, but now very general. Replaced in Shetlands, as well as Outer Hebrides, by a local resident race, but breeds in Orkneys, and now in Inner Hebrides. On the Continent breeds from North Europe south to the Pyrenees and Italy, but is replaced by other forms in the Faeroes, Azores, the Mediterranean region, and South-East Europe, as well as Asia. Has colonized the treeless islands of the north as well as wooded districts in the south, and also the industrial areas. Great numbers of Continental birds also arrive on our east coast in autumn.

III. Nest and Eggs.—Places its nest in almost any kind of a hole—in trees, buildings, ruins, or among ivy, and readily takes advantage of nesting-boxes, exceptionally making a rough open nest among thick branches of trees. In the Scottish isles it nests normally in holes in the ground, stone heaps, or under rocks. The nest is a very rough and untidy affair of straw as a rule, but stalks and grasses are sometimes used, lined chiefly with feathers, bits of wool, etc. Eggs : usually 4 to 6, occasionally 7 or even 8 ; very pale blue, sometimes bluish white or, rarely, white. Average size of 50 British eggs, 30.2 × 21.3 mm. (1.19 × .84 in.). Laying begins mid-April, exceptionally during the winter. Incubation period, 12–13 days ; both sexes taking part. Single brooded in most cases, but a proportion undoubtedly rear two broods. The eggs of the Shetland Starling average larger than those of the common species. (Plate 183, f. 8.)

IV. Food.—Varied, consisting largely of insects (beetles and their larvæ, larvæ of moths, earwigs, flies and larvæ especially of Tipulidæ, larvæ of hymenoptera, neuroptera, etc.) ; also spiders, centipedes, woodlice, smaller land mollusca (snails and slugs), crustacea (sandhoppers, small crabs, etc.), earthworms, marine worms, and occasionally eggs of small birds. Vegetable matter includes grain, fruit (cherries, damsons, mulberries, apples, pears, etc.), and seeds of asparagus, rowan, elder, acorns, holly, many species of weed, etc.

V. Usual Notes.—The Starling's familiar song is a curious medley of whistles, clicks, " twips," " guks," " quertsees," and other unpromising sounds, which, nevertheless, uttered in concert by hundreds or thousands of birds in their roost—reed bed, wood, or large building like the British Museum—compose a symphony, humble it may be, but greatly impressive and attractive, and with a power to stir emotion that may be denied to more subtle music. The usual cry is a harsh " kwrrrr " uttered when the bird is disturbed ; it is sometimes followed by a note like " whit, whit, whit." Intense alarm is expressed by a high-pitched metallic " kweek " or " kwik." The anger note is a petulant scream : " kwi-hi-hi." Song period, more or less all the year.

59

PLATE 59.—STARLINGS : A. W. Seaby.

PLATE 60.—ROSECOLOURED-STARLING

Pastor roseus (Linnæus)

I. Description.—Length, 8½ in. Recognized by conspicuous crest of pointed feathers ; head, wings, tail, and thighs black ; rest of plumage rose pink ; bill pink, black at base. Female duller, with smaller crest. Young lack crest, and pink is replaced by greyish brown.

II. Range and Habitat.—An erratic wanderer, migrating in vast flocks, and living socially where food is plentiful in South-East Europe and Western Asia, breeding irregularly west to North Italy and Hungary, east to Turkestan and Asia Minor. Casual visitor to the British Isles.

III. Nest and Eggs.—Does not breed in the British Isles, but has been found in various parts of Europe nesting in enormous colonies in quarries, among rocks, ruins, or broken ground, placing its nest in any kind of hole, and frequently deserting the district after a season or two if insect food becomes scarce. Nest, like that of Common-Starling, very carelessly made of straw, grasses, etc., lined with feathers, etc. Eggs : usually 4–5, sometimes 6–8 ; like those of Starling, but decidedly paler and usually glossy. Average of 80 eggs, 28.6 × 21.0 mm. (1.12 × .82 in.). Laying irregular, May to June. Incubation period short, between 11 and 14 days. Single brooded.

IV. Food.—Chiefly insects, especially orthoptera (locusts, grass-hoppers, crickets, etc.), beetles, flies, etc., and in summer, also where available, fruit (mulberries, currants, pears, gooseberries, cherries, figs, etc.), also berries of elder and privet.

V. Usual Notes.—The authorities have little good to say of the Pastor's song : harsh, sibilant, insignificant, ill-modulated ; not unlike the Starling's song with all its musical notes omitted ; a compound of " kritschs " and " tschirrs " and " etschs " and " retzs " and " tzwis " ; finally (says Naumann) like the squeaking of rats fighting in a corner. The usual cries are equally harsh, among the commonest being one rendered by Petényi[1] as " schrrr-tschorr-tschorr-scherr," a flock note. The alarm note is " tschirr." Song period, no record.

[1] *Ornithologische Fragmente.*

PLATE 60.—ROSECOLOURED-STARLINGS FIGHTING : H. Goodchild.

PLATE 61.—GOLDEN-ORIOLE

Oriolus oriolus oriolus (Linnæus)

I. Description.—Length, 9½ in. Male recognized by black wings (secondaries tipped yellow) and black tail (yellow on outer feathers); rest of plumage brilliant yellow; lores black; beak orange brown; feet lead; iris red. Female has upper parts mainly yellowish green, with wings and tail darker green; upper breast grey; rest of under surface white, turning to yellow on flanks, both striated. Young have iris brown.

II. Range and Habitat.—Irregular summer resident in very small numbers to south coast counties, and occasionally farther inland. On the Continent its summer range extends from South Sweden, and in Russia to 60° N., southward over Europe to the Mediterranean, and locally in the hills of North-West Africa; also Western Asia, but replaced by another form in Turkestan and India. Winters in Africa and Madagascar. A woodland-haunting species.

III. Nest and Eggs.—Breeds in parks, old gardens with big trees, forest with open glades, and patches of woodland, showing a partiality for oak trees. The nest is very characteristic, being hammock-like in shape, connected to a horizontal fork by being woven round it, built of fibre of some sort, grasses, sedge, bark, wool, etc., lined with grass heads, and frequently containing bits of paper. Eggs: usually 4–5, sometimes only 3 or 6; white or creamy in ground, with a few black spots with slight purple tinge at edge. A scarce variety is almost unmarked. Average of 100 eggs, 30.8 × 21.3 mm. (1.21 × .83 in.). Incubation period is said to be 14–15 days, and the male is said to take some part. Laying begins late in May in England, but earlier in Spain. Single brooded. (Plate 183, f. 9.)

IV. Food.—Chiefly insects in early part of the year (beetles, especially tree-haunting species such as cockchafer, larvæ of moths, flies, grasshoppers, humble-bees, and hemiptera). Later on also takes fruit (cherries, mulberries, currants, grapes, and figs), some berries (ivy and yew), occasionally spiders and small mollusca.

V. Usual Notes.—The Oriole's characteristic song is a loud, clear, and very musical whistle of four or five varied notes, rendered by the Dutch as " weal-a-woe," and uttered from the tops of lofty trees. In wooded parks the sound carries a long way, and the notes have something of the quality of the best part of the Blackbird's song, but once heard are unmistakable. In addition to the song the Oriole has a number of squawks and cat-like mews which are only audible at short range.

PLATE 61.—GOLDEN-ORIOLES (*the male being the upper bird*) : Winifred Austen.

Plate 62.—WAXWING

Bombycilla garrulus (Linnæus)

I. Description.—Length, 8 in. Recognized by long crest, brownish grey general colour, and scarlet waxy tips to secondaries ; chin and throat black, and black stripe from beak to nape ; tail tipped yellow ; under tail coverts chestnut. Sexes alike, but hen has less waxy tips on wings.

II. Range and Habitat.—Irregular autumn and winter visitor in varying numbers to the British Isles. Its breeding quarters lie in North-Eastern Scandinavia, North Finland, North Russia, and Siberia ; also in Canada. Another form apparently replaces it in Japan and South-East Siberia, and the American birds have been separated subspecifically. Haunts coniferous and birch forests.

III. Nest and Eggs.—Does not breed in the British Isles, but in arctic Finland and Russia nests in the scattered forests of birch and pine near the tree limit. The nest is built of twigs, grasses, and lichens, with sometimes hair or feathers in the lining. Eggs : usually 4 or 5, occasionally 6 ; greyish or greyish blue in ground colour, sometimes pale, and rarely with a warm tinge, with black spots or streaks and a few ashy shellmarks. Average of 100 eggs, 24 × 17.3 mm. (.94 × .68 in.). Laying begins in June. Incubation period (observed in confinement), 14 days. Probably single brooded.

IV. Food.—Mainly vegetable matter, but flies (chiefly crane flies) and Ephemeroptera (mayflies, etc.) also taken. Vegetable matter includes seeds of rowan, wild rose, hawthorn, privet, yew, holly, crowberry, cranberry, cotoneaster, juniper, bramble, mistletoe, and guelder rose ; also seeds of ash.

V. Usual Notes.—The song is said to be feeble, but adequate description is lacking. The usual note is a trill, a sequence of *s* and *r* sounds, not unlike the call of a tit.[1]

[1] Authorities : Dresser, Harvie-Brown, Seebohm, Naumann.

PLATE 62.—WAXWINGS : Winifred Austen.

PLATE 63.—BRITISH LONGTAILED-TIT
Ægithalos caudatus rosaceus Mathews
NORTHERN LONGTAILED-TIT
Ægithalos caudatus caudatus (Linnæus)

I. Description.—Length, 5½ in. (tail, 3½ in.). Recognized by long tail, and pink and black in plumage ; head white, striped on crown black ; eyelid orange red ; back black, mixed rose ; under parts white, with dusty striations on throat and breast, rest tinged grey ; wings and tail chiefly black, but show some white. Sexes alike. Young lack rose colour and have yellow eyelids.

II. Range and Habitat.—The British race is apparently found as a resident only in the British Isles, but in Western France (Brittany) a closely allied race is met with, which has been separated by some writers. Our bird is widely distributed over the British Isles where there is any cover, but becomes scarce on open moorlands and downs. Rare in extreme north of Scotland, and absent (except as straggler) from Orkneys, Shetlands, Outer Hebrides, etc. Over the greater part of Europe and Asia it is resident, divided into numerous races, but does not extend its range south of the Mediterranean Islands. The northern race is a rare vagrant.

III. Nest and Eggs.—Breeds usually in thorn bushes, thickets, or hedgerows, but also not infrequently against the trunk of forest trees or in orchards, sometimes at a considerable height from the ground. The nest is very remarkable, being domed in shape, with an entrance hole high up on the side, built chiefly of mosses, hair, and cobwebs, and completely covered with lichens, while the interior is lined with enormous numbers of feathers, which have been counted several times, and range from about 835 to over 2,000 in number. Eggs : usually 8 or 9 to 11, but all intermediate numbers up to 20 are said to have occurred. Ground colour, white, sometimes unmarked, but generally with fine red spots of varying extent and depth, occasionally a warm pinkish tinge in ground. Average of 100 British eggs, 14.2 × 11 mm. (.56 × .43 in.). Laying begins late in March. Incubation period apparently 15–17 days, but difficult to ascertain exactly. A second brood sometimes reared. (Plate 183, f. 10.)

IV. Food.—Almost entirely insects, small beetles, small moths, hymenoptera, etc. ; also spiders, scale insects, centipedes, and occasionally buds.

V. Usual Notes.—No song has been recorded. The ordinary note, heard as the birds wander in flocks, is a cheerful " tzee, tzee, tzee," followed at times by " tsirrip, tsirrip." The species has also a little harsh sharp alarm note.

PLATE 63.—LONGTAILED-TITS BUILDING THEIR NEST: A. W. Seaby

PLATE 64.—BRITISH MARSH-TIT, *Parus palustris dresseri* Stejneger

I. Description.—Length, 4½ in. No white patch on nape ; head (except cheeks) and throat glossy blue black, sides of head dull white ; upper parts greyish olive brown ; wings and tail mostly ash brown ; under parts dull white, with buff on flanks.

II. Range and Habitat.—The British race is confined to England and Wales, where it is rather local and scarce in some of the western counties, especially Cornwall, Anglesey and North Wales, and the Lake District. It is apparently absent from Scotland, and though said to have been formerly resident in four Irish counties, there are no recent records or specimens extant, though attempts have been made to introduce it recently. On the Continent it is represented by numerous local races over the greater part of Europe and Asia to China and Japan, but absent from most of the countries bordering the Mediterranean. Usually found in low-lying districts.

III. Nest and Eggs.—Usually breeds in a natural hole in the stump of a tree or in the trunk of a willow or alder, but will sometimes pick away the wood to enlarge the entrance ; also uses nesting-boxes occasionally. Nest built of green moss, with a thick pad of felted hair or down as lining. Eggs : 7–8, but 5 to 11 on record ; white, spotted chiefly at the large end and sometimes forming a zone, with red brown, on the average rather more heavily than the Willow-Tit, but still sparingly. Average of 47 British eggs, 15.6 × 13.2 mm. (.61 × .52 in.). Laying begins about the end of April. Incubation period, about 13 days ; apparently by hen. Perhaps sometimes double brooded. (Plate 183, f. 13.)

IV. Food.—Both insects and vegetable matter. Insects include smaller beetles, small hymenoptera (gall insects), and larvæ. Seeds and berries of beech, sunflower, rowan, and marsh thistle (*Cnicus*) also recorded.

V. Usual Notes.—Jourdain gives the song as " chit-a-bee-bee-bee-bee," Walpole Bond describes another song as beginning with " three to five ' see-ips ' " and ending with " some half-dozen ' chips.' " Usual call : a harsh " tchee tchee," or " tchee-tcheu," or even " let-be," often followed by the first song as described above. Song period, chiefly from January to July, but occasionally afterwards.[1]

For COAL-TIT *see page* 65.

PLATE 64.—BRITISH WILLOW-TIT, *Parus atricapillus kleinschmidti* Hellmayr
NORTHERN WILLOW-TIT, *Parus atricapillus borealis* Selys-Longchamps

I. Description.—Length, 4½ in. Closely resembles Marsh-Tit, but differs in lack of gloss on black of head and neck ; end of tail rounded when partly closed and not squared as in Marsh-Tit. Notes and nesting habits also differ, and edges of secondaries form ill-defined light line on wing.

II. Range and Habitat.—The British race is locally distributed over the greater part of Great Britain, and in Scotland seems to replace the Marsh-Tit altogether ; but owing to its resemblance to that species its distribution in England and Wales is imperfectly known. At present only from a few Welsh counties. In North Scotland confined to Moray area, and unknown in the islands. Not recorded from Ireland. Met with in wooded districts and river valleys ; in coniferous forest in Spey valley. On the Continent it is represented by many local races from the north of Scandinavia south to France, Italy, Bulgaria, etc., also across Asia, and in North America south to Mexico.

III. Nest and Eggs.—Bores a hole in very soft and decayed wood, leading into a neatly rounded chamber, more like the work of a Lesser Spotted-Woodpecker than a Tit. The nest is, as a rule, a very scanty affair indeed, consisting of a little down mixed with fragments of wood and, usually, no moss, forming a strong contrast to the much bulkier nest of the Marsh-Tit. Eggs : 7–8 as a rule, but 9 and 12 on record ; white, scantily marked with fine red brown spots, chiefly at the big end. Average of 31 British eggs, 15.8 × 12.3 mm. (.62 × .48 in.). Laying begins at the end of April in England. Incubation by hen ; period, about 13 days. Probably single brooded.

IV. Food.—Owing to the similarity of this species to the Marsh-Tit, food records are probably in some cases confused, and hardly any reliable material is available. Largely, at any rate, small insects found among undergrowth in marshy districts.

V. Usual Notes.—Mr. C. J. Alexander summarizes the Willow-Tit's notes as (1) " Deep plaintive note, sometimes prefixed by one or two thin notes. (2) Thin sharp notes, more frequently uttered than the corresponding notes of the Marsh-Tit. (3) Song, rich nightingale-like notes mingled with a soft musical warbling." Walpole Bond describes this song as a " deep, rich, melodious repetition of ' tchu.' "[2] Song period, January to June and July to December. Jourdain adds that he finds a long-drawn penetrating " chay-chay-chay " very characteristic of this species.

[1] *British Birds* (Mag.), xxiv. 1931, 320 (J. Walpole Bond).
[2] *British Birds* (Mag.), xxiv, 1931, 322 (Walpole Bond) ; *id.* xxv. 31, where a second song is described as a repeated lively " che-er " (Walpole Bond).

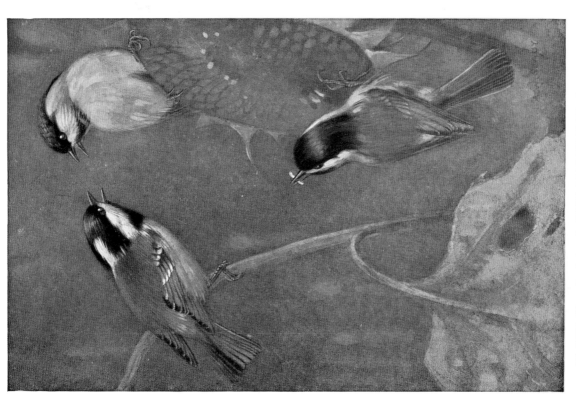

PLATE 64.—(*Left hand*) TWO MARSH-TITS ON A SUNFLOWER, ONE DISPUTING POSSESSION WITH A COAL-TIT; (*Right*) WILLOW-TITS : A. W. Seaby.

PLATE 64.—BRITISH COAL-TIT, *Parus ater britannicus* Sharpe and Dresser

IRISH COAL-TIT, *Parus ater hibernicus* Grant

CONTINENTAL COAL-TIT, *Parus ater ater* Linnæus

I. Description.—Length, 4¼ in. Recognized by conspicuous white patch on nape; head black, with white cheeks; upper parts olive grey, more brown in British than in Continental race; two white bars on wing; rufous tinge on rump; under parts dull white, reddish buff on flanks. The Irish race has patch on nape yellowish and tinge of yellow on cheeks, neck, breast, and belly.

II. Range and Habitat.—Resident in Great Britain, commonest where coniferous woods are present, and avoiding treeless districts and mountains. The Irish race is widely distributed and resident in Ireland, but many birds from the north-east coast are closer to the British form. The Continental race, which also occurs as an occasional passage migrant or straggler, breeds over the greater part of Europe and Northern Asia, but local races have been separated from North-West Africa and many islands and countries in the Mediterranean region, South Russia, and parts of Asia.

III. Nest and Eggs.—Frequently breeds in a mouse hole in a bank; sometimes in a stump or tree, and occasionally in a stone wall or in old nests of other birds. Nest built of mosses, with a very warm layer of felted hair or down, occasionally a few feathers. Eggs: usually 8–11, but 7 and 12 to 14 have been recorded. Colour, white, with red brown spots, sometimes forming a well-marked zone, at other times light and more distributed. Average of 100 British eggs, 15 × 11·6 mm. (·59 × ·45 in.). Those of the Irish Coal-Tit are very similar, but are often found in holes in banks faced with stones. Laying begins late in April. Incubation period, 17–18 days; chiefly by hen. Single brooded. (Plate 183, f. 11.)

IV. Food.—Largely insects, including beetles and their larvæ, larvæ and eggs of moths, larvæ of flies, hymenoptera and larvæ, etc.; also spiders and cocoons, aphides, scale insects, etc. Vegetable matter includes beech-mast, seeds of some conifers, nuts, seeds of thistle. Has been seen feeding on a carcass of a dog.

V. Usual Notes.—The Coal-Tit's song has two disyllabic forms, rendered by " chĭchēē, chĭchēē " and " wēēchŏ, wēēchŏ " (Peake). Selous renders the call-note " woo-tee " or " tooey." [1] Song period, more or less every month.

PLATE 65.—BRITISH BLUE-TIT, *Parus cœruleus obscurus* Pražak

CONTINENTAL BLUE-TIT, *Parus cœruleus cœruleus* Linnæus

I. Description.—Length, 4½ in. Readily distinguished by the light blue crown (edged white), wings and tail, the greenish back, and the yellow under parts; cheeks white, throat blue black, white wing bar, and black stripe running through eyes and round nape, which is dark blue with white nuchal spot.

II. Range and Habitat.—The British race is confined to the British Isles and apparently the Channel Isles (Alderney). It is very generally distributed wherever there are trees and hedgerows, avoiding only downlands and moors, but becomes scarce in North Scotland, and is absent from the north-west; not known to breed in the Orkneys, Shetlands, or Outer Hebrides. General in Ireland. The Continental race is an occasional visitor to our east coasts, and is widely distributed over the Continent of Europe and Northern Asia, but replaced by local races in the Mediterranean countries, North-West Africa, South Russia, and parts of Asia.

III. Nest and Eggs.—Breeds in holes of trees and walls as a rule, also takes readily to nesting boxes, and occasionally places its nest inside old nests of other species when holes are lacking, also in pumps, old tins, holes in banks, etc. Nest: moss and some grasses, with thick lining pad of felted hair or down and a few feathers. Eggs: usually 8–11, but all numbers up to 17 have been met with. Ground colour, white, sometimes quite unmarked, as a rule spotted sparingly or freely with red brown, occasionally blotches of colour. Average of 100 British eggs, 15·3 × 11·8 mm. (·60 × ·46 in.). Laying begins end of April. Incubation period, 13–14 days. Single brooded as a rule at any rate. (Plate 183, f. 15.)

IV. Food.—Although it does some damage to fruit in autumn, this is outweighed by its beneficial work in the destruction of injurious insects such as weevil, turnip flea, beetle, etc., larvæ of moths (especially the Tineidæ), larvæ of flies, hemiptera, and gall insects; also takes spiders, aphides, scale insects and plant lice, millipedes, etc. Attacks apples and pears in autumn, and takes grain, seeds of sunflower, poppy, Scots pine, beech, chestnut, and birch.

V. Usual Notes.—To the writer the song of the Blue-Tit has sounded like " Pwee, pwee-tee, tee, tee, tee, tee." It varies. A shorter form is " tit-tit-tittee." The alarm note, uttered by a bird with nestlings, sounded like " Pteep, pteep, pteep, trrrrrrr," this being followed by the scolding *r* note, more strongly articulated. The *r* note is also used by itself. The call note is much like the Great-Tit's. Song period, chiefly from February to May, but there are records for every month. [2]

[1] *Bird Life Glimpses*, 16.
[2] *British Birds* (Mag.), xx. 68 (Peake); S. Morris, *Bird Song*, 53.

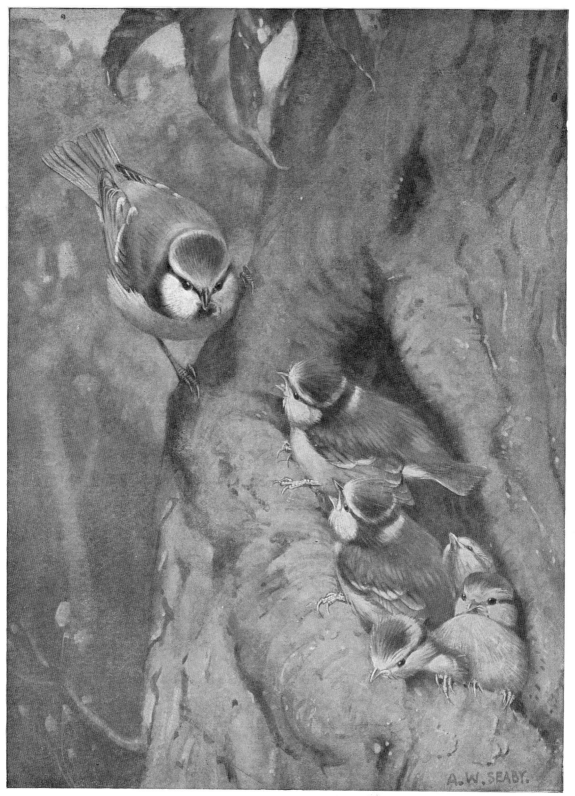

PLATE 65.—BLUE-TIT ABOUT TO FEED ITS NESTLINGS: A. W. Seaby.

PLATE 66.—BRITISH GREAT-TIT, *Parus major newtoni* Pražak

CONTINENTAL GREAT-TIT, *Parus major major* Linnæus

I. Description.—Length, 6 in. Recognized among other Tits by superior size, and black band from the black throat through middle of under surface. Crown glossy blue black, cheeks white; upper surface yellowish green, bluish grey on rump and tail ; under surface greenish yellow ; outer tail feathers mostly white, and white spot on nape ; wings grey blue and brown, with white bar.

II. Range and Habitat.—The British race is confined to the British Isles, where it is a generally distributed resident over all the wooded parts of the country, but becomes scarce in north of Scotland, and is absent from the extreme northern counties, Orkneys, Shetlands, and Outer Hebrides. The Continental race is an irregular visitor on passage, chiefly to the east coast and northern isles, and on the Continent breeds over the greater part of Europe, but is replaced by local races on the Mediterranean isles, North-West Africa, Greece, and Asia.

III. Nest and Eggs.—Normally breeds in holes of trees or walls, and readily takes to nesting-boxes ; occasionally in holes among rocks, and failing holes will breed inside old nests of other birds, in burrow of Kingfisher, or among accumulated rubbish in hedge. Nest consists of a foundation of moss and a few grasses, varying in size according to that of the hole ; the actual cup is formed of felted hair or down, and the eggs are covered during laying. Eggs : normally about 7 or 8 to 11, but all numbers up to 15, and once 17, have been recorded ; white, occasionally unmarked, but usually with red brown spots, varying in depth. Average of 100 British eggs, 17.9×13.5 mm. (.70×.53 in.). Laying begins end of April or beginning of May. Incubation period, 12–14 days ; apparently by hen alone. Nearly always single brooded. (Plate 183, f. 14.)

IV. Food.—Probably does more good than harm, but destroys many fruit buds in spring, and also eats holes in fruit (apples, pears, plums, etc.), as well as green peas. Insect food comprises beetles, moths and larvæ (especially the destructive winter moth), larvæ of flies, hymenoptera (humble-bees and bees), earwigs, etc.; also aphides, scale insects, spiders, and occasionally small land mollusca and worms. Other recorded articles of diet are wheat, chestnuts, nuts, and maize ; it has been known to kill a bat and small birds, eating the brains.

V. Usual Notes.—The Great-Tit's familiar ringing call has been figured in many various ways : *e.g.,* " Teacher, teacher, teacher, teach," or " Ching-see, ching-see, ching-see. It has another : " P'tsoo-ée, tsoo-ée, tsoo-ée." These notes may be said to rise to the dignity of a song. They vary much. The alarm note has been figured by Witchell, " Sha-sha-sha-sha-sha." The usual call can be imitated, he states, by " lightly flicking glass with the edge of a wet cork." [1] Song period, chiefly in spring, but records for every month.[2]

PLATE 66.—SCOTTISH CRESTED-TIT, *Parus cristatus scoticus* Prazak

Parus cristatus cristatus Linnæus and *Parus cristatus mitratus* Brehm

I. Description.—Length, 4¼ in. Recognized by its crest, long, black, white-tipped crown feathers. Sides of head white, with semicircular band of black extending downward and backward from eye ; throat and band from sides of neck black ; back, wings, and tail mostly grey or brown ; breast and belly white, flanks buff. Hen has shorter crest, and is duller.

II. Range and Habitat.—The Scottish race is confined to a few districts in Scotland which lie principally in the Moray area (Spey valley), though recently it has been reported as resident in the north-western part of the Tay area (Glengarry). It is resident here in coniferous forest. Stragglers from the Continent of two other races have been met with occasionally in England. On the Continent it is represented by local races from Scandinavia and North Russia to the Mediterranean and Middle Russia.

III. Nest and Eggs.—Breeds in holes excavated in rotten wood, generally in old stumps of pines, also in decayed alders and birches. Nests have also been recorded in iron fencing posts and Hooded-Crows' nests. The nest is made of moss, freely lined with hair of deer and hare, and occasionally a feather or two. Eggs : 5–6, occasionally 7, and 8 recorded once or twice ; much more heavily marked on an average than the other British Tits' eggs ; usually a zone of dark red spots at the big end. Poorly marked eggs are quite exceptional. Average of 100 British eggs, 16.2×12.7 mm. (.63×.50 in.). Laying begins at the end of April. Incubation by hen ; period, 13–15 days. Single brooded. (Plate 183, f. 12.)

IV. Food.—Little definitely recorded ; insects, chiefly caterpillars of moths ; also aphides. Small seeds and berries of juniper, etc., also taken.

V. Usual Notes.—Although it has been stated by some that the Crested-Tit has no song, this is hardly correct, for it does make use of a high-pitched double note, not unlike those of the other Tits. Jourdain notes that the characteristic cry of this species is a peculiar " churr," which generally functions as an alarm note. This churr is quite unmistakable ; the only other Tit which has a note at all like it is the Longtailed-Tit. Song period, not recorded.

[1] *Cries and Call Notes of Wild Birds,* 22–24.   [2] *British Birds* (Mag.), xx. 68 (E. Peake).

CRESTED-TITS: A. W. Seaby.

PLATE 66.—GREAT-TIT: A. W. Seaby.

Family : Sittidæ (Nuthatches)

PLATE 67.—BRITISH NUTHATCH, *Sitta europœa affinis* Blyth

I. Description.—Length, 5½ in. Distinguished by slaty grey upper parts, whitish throat, and rufous buff under parts. Black stripe runs through eye to nape, and sides of head below it are white ; flanks chestnut ; outer tail feathers patched with white.

II. Range and Habitat.—The British race is practically confined to England and Wales, being fairly common in the southern and central counties of England (except in the extreme west) ; also becomes very scarce along the western seaboard of Wales. In England north of the Trent it becomes decidedly scarce, but has bred in Cheshire and Yorkshire. In Scotland it is said to have occurred a few times only, and the one Irish record is no doubt due to introduction. On the Continent it is represented by other races from Scandinavia south to Spain and Marocco and the Mediterranean, also in Asia from the Caucasus and Asia Minor to Japan and China. It is a bird of old woodlands and parks, seldom seen except where big timber exists.

III. Nest and Eggs.—Usually breeds in a hole of a tree, occasionally in a wall, while nests have been recorded from haystacks and inside Sand-Martins' burrows. Nesting-boxes are also frequently occupied. The nest when inside a hole is partly filled up with flakes from the bark of Scotch pine ; or, in default of this, with birch bark or dead leaves of beech and oak. In a haystack it is a solid mass of clay. The entrance to the nest is generally reduced by plastering with clay. Eggs : usually 5–8, but all numbers from 9–13 on record. Ground colour, white, sometimes unmarked, but generally with chestnut brown blotches or spots and a few ashy shellmarks. Average size of 100 British eggs, 19.2 × 14.3 mm. (.75 × .56 in.). Laying begins about the end of April. Incubation period in two cases 13 and 17 days ; by hen only. One brood as a rule, exceptionally two. (Plate 183, f. 16.)

IV. Food.—Insects to some extent, but also seeds and berries. Among insects, small beetles, especially wood-boring and tree-haunting species, earwigs, flies, hemiptera, larvæ from oak-apple, etc., are recorded. Vegetable matter includes acorns, beech-mast, hazel nuts, yew berries, Portugal laurel berries, figs, peas, and maize, as well as small seeds. Small land mollusca and spiders also recorded.

V. Usual Notes.—The Nuthatch's loud mellow call has been figured as " Be quick, be quick, be quick," or " Tewit, tewit, tewit," to which is added in the breeding season a clear long-drawn note, also uttered separately. This whistle, writes Johns, is " rarely protracted into a bubbling sound " such as the bird might be supposed to make " if it were rattling a pea in its throat." [1] The male, in company with the female, has been heard making a soft flute-like " Twi, twi, twi." [2] Song period : January to June ; also, in mild weather, from September to December.[3]

[1] *British Birds in their Haunts*, 44.
[2] *British Bird Book*, ii. 218 (E. L. Turner).
[3] *British Birds* (Mag.), iv. 275 (Alexander) ; xx. 67 (Peake). See also *id.* xxv. 1931, 70.

PLATE 67.—NUTHATCH PICKING OUT THE KERNEL OF A NUT: A. W. Seaby.

PLATE 68.—BEARDED-TIT

Panurus biarmicus biarmicus (Linnæus)

I. Description.—Length, 6–6¾ in. Recognized by long rounded fawn-coloured tail, upper parts deep tawny, under parts greyish white with rosy tinge, under tail-coverts black. Male has bluish grey head with black moustache from eye to beak ; outer tail-feathers tipped white. Female lacks moustache and has head tawny, passing into greyish white ; back more or less lined with black.

II. Range and Habitat.—Now a very local species in England, and unknown in Wales, Scotland, or Ireland. Its main haunts are the Broad district in Norfolk, but it breeds in small numbers very locally in Suffolk, and apparently still at one locality in Devon. Former breeding-places in the Thames valley are now deserted, and an attempt to introduce it to Yorkshire failed. On the Continent it is found in the Low Countries, locally in France and East Spain, also in Italy ; but further east is replaced by an allied race which breeds from Hungary to Asia Minor and South Russia and across Asia to Manchuria. Haunts districts where there are vast expanses of reeds.

III. Nest and Eggs.—As a rule the nest is among thick sedges or reeds growing in water or on swampy ground, not far from the edge of the bed, and rather low down, about 18 in. or so from ground level. The nest is very characteristic and unlike any other, being built of flat dead portions of reed leaves, with a thick lining of flowering heads of reed, generally one or two feathers. Eggs : usually 5–7, but all numbers from 8–12 have been recorded ; but there is evidence that more than one hen may lay in a nest. Colour, white, with short streaks or lines and specks of liver brown, thinly distributed on the surface. Average of 106 eggs, 17.2 × 13.9 mm. (.67 × .54 in.). Laying begins early in April in some cases. Incubation period, 12–13 days ; both sexes taking part. Two or three broods. (Plate 183, f. 17.)

IV. Food.—During winter chiefly subsists on the seeds of reed, but larvæ of *Laverna phragmitella* are also taken ; *Succinea amphibia* and *Pupa muscorum* also recorded : while in spring and summer great numbers of small green caterpillars, small neuroptera and trichoptera, as well as flies are taken.

V. Usual Notes.—The species has no song. The call note is usually syllabled " ping-ping," which " though expressive is yet wholly inadequate to describe this vibrating sound ; it is like the ' singing ' of a bullet, or a pizzicato note on the violin." When alarmed, the birds utter a scolding " p'whut," like the sound made by " drawing a finger lightly across all four strings of a violin." [1]

[1] *British Bird Book*, ii. 229 (E. L. Turner).

PLATE 68.—BEARDED-TITS AND NESTLINGS (*the upper bird is the male*): Winifred Austen.

Family : Laniidæ (Shrikes)

PLATE 69.—REDBACKED-SHRIKE

Lanius collurio collurio Linnæus

I. Description.—Length, $7\frac{1}{2}$–8 in. Adult male has back red, crown and nape grey, with conspicuous black band running through the eyes across the forehead ; rump ashy grey ; middle feathers of tail black, outer black and white ; under parts white, with rosy buff tinge on breast ; wings mostly dark brown ; beak strong and hooked. Female much less brilliant : back dull brownish chestnut ; under parts dull white, with buff tinge on breast, conspicuously barred with semicircular black markings. Young have back barred with black on red or reddish grey.

II. Range and Habitat.—Summer resident to England and Wales ; commonest in south, and only occasionally breeds in Cheshire, Lancashire, Yorkshire, and Cumberland, being only regular south of the Trent valley in England ; only casual visitor to Scotland and Ireland (three occurrences only). It haunts wooded country, especially where there are numerous thickets and dense bushes. On the Continent it breeds from 64° N. in Scandinavia to the Cantabrian Mountains, Italy, Greece, and Northern Syria. In Corsica and Sardinia it also occurs, and apparently is replaced by a closely allied race in parts of Western Asia.

III. Nest and Eggs.—Breeds usually in bramble thickets or high hedges ; also in bushes in small plantations, etc. Nest bulky, with a good deal of moss in the foundation, as well as grasses, etc. ; neatly lined with hair and fine roots, usually rather low down. Eggs : 4–6, 7 rare, while 8 has occurred on the Continent. Eggs in a clutch are similar but vary in a series ; the ground colour varying from pinkish to pale greenish, creamy, brown olive, or white, and the markings, which usually form a zone, being red brown with the pink ground, or umber brown of varying shade in the other cases. White varieties and white with ashy blotches have been found. Average of 100 British eggs, 22.9 × 17 mm. (.90 × .66 in.). Laying begins latter part of May. Incubation period, 14-16 days ; by female only. Single brooded, but will replace lost clutches repeatedly. (Plate 183, f. 18.)

IV. Food.—Entirely animal and very varied, including carrion (small rabbits and hedgehogs), long- and short-tailed field-mouse, shrew, bank-vole, etc., many species of small birds and their young, including Chaffinch, Linnet, Yellow-Bunting, Meadow-Pipit, Yellow-Wagtail, Blue-Tit, Willow-Warbler, Whitethroat, Wren, House- and Sand-Martins ; also young of Blackbird, Thrush, Skylark, Sparrow, Moorhen, and "downy" young of Pheasant, Redlegged- and Common-Partridge. The normal food is, however, insects, especially bees (humble-bees), flies, beetles, earwigs, and grasshoppers. Earthworms and spiders also recorded, as well as frogs.

V. Usual Notes.—The Butcher-bird's song is described as a series of warbling notes ; there appears to be no detailed description. The bird is a great mimic. The familiar alarm note is " chack." The call note of the male to the hen is " chee-uck " repeated ; the call of the hen for food something like " chi-ee-i," or " chee-ay." [1] Song period, end April to June, possibly later.

[1] *British Birds*, x. 175-180 (J. H. Owen).

PLATE 69.—REDBACKED-SHRIKES IN THEIR LARDER (*the lower bird is the male*):
A. W. Seaby.

PLATE 70.—GREAT GREY-SHRIKE, *Lanius excubitor excubitor* Linnæus

SOUTHERN GREY-SHRIKE, *Lanius excubitor meridionalis* Temminck

I. Description.—Length, 9–9½ in. Recognized by grey upper parts, contrasting with black and white wings and tail, which is graduated ; broad black eye-patches ; under parts dull white ; bill and feet blackish. Female duller, with semicircular bars on under side. Immature birds have upper parts ash brown, with vermiculations and faint bars ; under side more barred than in female.

II. Range and Habitat.—Autumn visitor on passage to our east coasts, and has occurred in Ireland. On the Continent it breeds where there is conifer or birch growth, in Lapland and North Russia to mid-France, Switzerland, and Hungary ; also in Siberia, east to the river Ob ; but is replaced by other races in the Camargue, Spain and Portugal (once recorded) ; North Africa, the Canary Isles, as well as in South-East Europe and parts of Asia and North America. In Central Europe it haunts the edges of woods, isolated trees in open country, and small plantations.

III. Nest and Eggs.—Does not breed in the British Isles. In the north often breeds in a small pine, but in Central Europe breeds high in forest trees, such as oaks, or in orchards, sometimes well out on side branch. Nest large, built of twigs, heather stalks and moss, bents and stalks, lined with roots, hair, and feathers of many species of birds. Eggs : 5–7, but 8 and 9 on record ; resembling Magpie's in style of markings, being spotted and blotched all over with greyish olive and ashy shellmarks on a greyish or stone-coloured ground, and sometimes a tendency to a zone or cap of dark markings at the big end. Average of 117 eggs, 26.3 × 19.3 mm. (1.03 × .76 in.). Laying begins late in April in Central Europe, but in Lapland hardly before the end of May. Incubation period said to be 15 days, but confirmation required. Single brooded.

IV. Food.—Main food consists of small birds and insects. Among birds recorded as killed are Siskin, Redpoll, Bullfinch, Sparrow, Reed-Bunting, Skylark, Pied-Wagtail, Great-, Blue-, and Marsh-Tits, Robin, occasionally Blackbird, Thrush, and Fieldfare, and many other smaller species. Also field-mice, shrews, dead rabbits, frogs, etc. Insects include beetles, grasshoppers, caterpillars, wasps and bees, etc.

V. Usual Notes.—The song of this species consists partly of imitations of other birds' notes and of warbled notes, including the ordinary call, syllabled " trouü " (the *ü* pronounced as in French *plume*).[1] The note uttered when the nest place is invaded resembles the " chack " of the Redbacked-Shrike. The female is said to sing as well as the male. The song has been heard as early as 6th December in this country.

[1] Naumann, *Vögel Mitteleuropas*, iv. 129.

70

PLATE 70.—GREAT GREY-SHRIKE (MALE) WITH GOLDCRESTED-WREN IMPALED
UPON A THORN : A. W. Seaby.

PLATE 71.—SPOTTED-FLYCATCHER

Muscicapa striata striata (Pallas)

I. Description.—Length, $5\frac{1}{2}$ in. Recognized by its habit of perching on posts and making short excursions into the air in pursuit of flies. Upper parts mostly ash brown, with darker streaks on head ; under surface whitish, with dark brown streaks ; bristles on gape. Young conspicuously mottled on upper parts with whitish or buff.

II. Range and Habitat.—Summer resident in the British Isles ; very generally distributed in all sheltered and wooded districts, gardens, etc., but becomes rare in extreme north of Scotland, and only breeds exceptionally in the Orkneys, and not in the Outer Hebrides, but otherwise general in all suitable districts. On the Continent breeds from inside the Arctic Circle in Scandinavia and Archangel to the Mediterranean, also in North-West Africa in the Atlas and in Palestine, but is replaced by local races in the Balearic Isles, Corsica and Sardinia, and Western Asia.

III. Nest and Eggs.—Nests in ivy on walls, on branches of fruit trees, or on projecting beams or trellis ; also in niches on tree trunks, even on door hinges and on rock faces. Nest slight, built of mosses, cobwebs, lined with hair, etc. Eggs : 4–5, 6 and possibly 7 recorded. Ground colour, ranges from bluish green to greyish, with spots of reddish brown and ashy shellmarks, sometimes forming a cap. Varieties occur, blue or bluish white without markings, also an erythristic type with warm ground and rich red markings. Average of 100 British eggs, 18.5×13.8 mm. ($.72 \times .54$ in.). Laying begins about middle of May. Incubation period, $12\frac{1}{2}$–14 days ; both sexes taking part. Two broods sometimes, but not regularly reared. (Plate 183, f. 19.)

IV. Food.—Insects, chiefly flies, but also moths, butterflies, wasps, humble bees, small beetles and orthoptera ; exceptionally worms.

V. Usual Notes.—The Flycatcher's song is a low warble, heard once only by the present writer, and not often by others.[1] When alarmed by approach to the nest, the bird utters a note like " check " or " chick " or " teck." This may be preceded by another note, syllabled by Witchell " squee," which is also uttered separately. Song period, April to June.

[1] Records : S. Morris, *Bird Song*, 55 ; E. M. Nicholson, *Song of Wild Birds*, 117 ; *British Birds* (Mag.), xxxi. 269 (G. B. Gooch).

PLATE 71.—SPOTTED-FLYCATCHER AND ITS YOUNG : A. W. Seaby.

PLATE 72.—PIED-FLYCATCHER

Muscicapa hypoleuca hypoleuca Pallas

I. Description.—Length, 5 in. Adult male has upper parts black, forehead white, rump greyish, wings black, with large white patch ; tail black, three outer feathers have most of their outer webs white, except near tips. Female olive brown above, under parts buffish, white throat and belly ; tail as in male, but not so bright. Young have whitish or buff patches on wings.

II. Range and Habitat.—Summer resident to the British Isles, but chiefly confined in the breeding season to hilly and well-wooded districts with rapid streams, and occurs in small numbers in Devon, very numerously in Wales, especially the central and northern counties, again in numbers in Lakeland, and also in Northumberland and Durham, and locally in West Yorkshire. It has also bred in a good many of the southern Scottish counties, north to Inverness, and exceptionally in many English counties, though not all records can be accepted. It is only a casual visitor to Ireland, where it has occurred about sixteen times. On the Continent it breeds up to about 70° N. in Norway and about 60° in North Russia to France, Italy, Austria, and West Siberia, but is replaced by allied races in Spain, North-West Africa, and Siberia.

III. Nest and Eggs.—Breeds in natural holes of trees and stumps ; also in old buildings and in loose stone walls at varying heights. Nest loosely constructed of moss, strips of outer bark of honeysuckle, grasses, roots, etc., lined with hair and sometimes a feather or two. Eggs : usually 5–7, but 8, 9, and apparently 10 have been recorded ; in colour clear pale blue, and rather thin-shelled. Average of 100 eggs, 17.8 × 13.4 mm. (.70 × .52 in.). Laying begins about mid-May. Incubation period, 12–13 days ; by hen alone. Single brooded. (Plate 183, f. 21.)

IV. Food.—Mainly insects, chiefly flies, but also smaller beetles, butterflies and moths and their larvæ, earwigs, and ants. Has been seen on ground searching for worms and grubs ; also takes acarids.

V. Usual Notes.—The song of the Pied form has been rendered " Tchéetle, tchéetle, tchéetle, díddle-diddle-dee." The first three notes at times sound like " te-chéetle." The second half of the song is " a very delightful descending cadenza, but uttered so rapidly that it sounds more like a trill on some very delicate wind instrument. . . . Sometimes there is substituted for it a short warble which recalls a Robin's more mellifluous notes." [1] The usual note is a soft short " whit " or " wet," followed by a lower ; but exact information seems to be lacking. The sexes are said to have different alarm notes. Song period, from arrival in April on to mid-June at least.

[1] E. W. Hendy, *Bird-watching*, 70–72.

PLATE 72.—PIED-FLYCATCHERS (*the female is about to feed the young; the male is on the right*): A. W. Seaby.

PLATE 73.—SWALLOW

Hirundo rustica rustica Linnæus

I. Description.—Length, $7\frac{1}{2}$–$8\frac{1}{2}$ in. Head and upper surface glossy steel blue, forehead and throat chestnut red ; blue black band across lower throat, rest of under surface buff or creamy white ; tail dull metallic green, with white spots and a long streamer at each side. This character is absent in the young. Distinguished from House-Martin by long tail feathers and absence of white rump : toes not feathered.

II. Range and Habitat.—Summer resident in the British Isles, widely distributed, generally breeding near villages and farms. Scarce in North-West Scotland, rare in Orkneys, and still more so in Shetlands and Outer Hebrides ; also scarce in extreme west of Ireland. On the Continent it breeds from 71° N. in Norway over the whole of Europe, North-West Africa, as well as in West Siberia and Asia Minor to the Himalayas, but is replaced by local races in the Nile valley, Palestine, Eastern Asia, and North America.

III. Nest and Eggs.—In the British Isles the nest is almost invariably placed in a building of some sort, on the rafters or wall plate of a shed or deserted building, at an angle of a wall, in some districts not infrequently inside chimney stacks ; rarely in niche in roof of cave : bird has several times built an open nest among the branches of trees. Nests in lamp shades, etc., also recorded. Nest built of mud mixed with saliva, and stiffened with grass stalks ; open above, and freely lined with feathers. Eggs : usually 4–5, but 6–8 recorded, as well as broods of 2–3. Ground colour, white, with purplish or red brown spots, sometimes scanty and small, at other times larger, and often tending to form slight zone or cap with ashy shellmarks. White variety unmarked also occurs. Average of 100 British eggs, 19.9×13.7 mm. ($.78 \times .54$ in.). Laying begins about mid-May. Incubation period, 14–15 days ; probably by both sexes. Two broods in most cases ; three occasionally. (Plate 183, f. 24.)

IV. Food.—Mainly taken on the wing and almost entirely insects, including small beetles, many species of flies, winged ants and Chalcidæ, dragon flies, and occasionally butterflies and moths.

V. Usual Notes.—The song of the Swallow is a musical twittering, it is composed of variants of the usual call interspersed with little harsher trills, and is uttered by the bird whether perched or on the wing. The usual call or twitter has been variously described : " weet-a-weet," " feet-a-feet," and the like. When alarmed the bird utters a shrill double cry as it swoops down upon the intruder. Song period, from arrival end of March to departure in November.

PLATE 73.—SWALLOW ABOUT TO FEED YOUNG: G. E. Collins.

PLATE 74.—HOUSE-MARTIN

Delichon urbica urbica (Linnæus)

I. Description.—Length, $4\frac{3}{4}$-$5\frac{1}{4}$ in. Upper surface glossy dark blue, except rump, which is white ; wings and tail brown, with green reflections ; under parts all white ; tail forked, but much shorter than in Swallow ; toes feathered. No chestnut on throat or throat bar. Sexes alike.

II. Range and Habitat.—A summer resident in the British Isles ; more local than the Swallow, and more prone to nest in colonies. It is, however, widely distributed, though it rarely breeds in the Orkneys, and not in the Shetlands or Outer Hebrides, and is decidedly local in Ireland. On the Continent it ranges from 71° N. in Norway to the Mediterranean, and eastward to mid-Siberia. In North Africa and Southern Spain and apparently Greece, as well as in Central and Eastern Asia to Japan, it is replaced by other races. Breeds to rather higher altitudes than the Swallow.

III. Nest and Eggs.—Like the Swallow, the Martin depends chiefly on man to provide nesting sites, generally nesting on the outside walls of buildings, unlike the Swallow, which prefers interiors. Normally Martins' nests are built close under the eaves of houses, sometimes in enormous numbers and close together, shaped like a cup in section, but often almost roofed in. There are rare cases of Martins nesting inside sheds ; also many cases of nests on faces of cliffs, in sea caves, as well as inland. Nest built of mud moistened with saliva and mixed with bits of stalks, lined with feathers, bits of wool, etc. Eggs : 4–5, sometimes 6 ; pure white and glossy ; very rarely found with reddish spots. Average of 80 British eggs, 19.7 × 13.6 mm. (.77 × .53 in.). Laying begins latter part of May. Incubation period, 14–16 days ; shared by both sexes. Two or three broods. (Plate 183, f. 22.)

IV. Food.—Insects taken on the wing, including great numbers of small flies, small beetles, occasionally butterflies and moths ; also neuroptera.

V. Usual Notes.—The House-Martin's usual call is something like " chirr-up." Variations of this note compose the song, uttered by the bird in its nest, perched outside it, and on the wing. The alarm or anger note is a repeated " cheep cheep cheep cheer " (heard uttered when sparrow near nest). Song period, more or less from April to November.

74

PLATE 74.—HOUSE-MARTIN FEEDING ITS YOUNG : G. E. Collins.

PLATE 75.—SAND-MARTIN

Riparia riparia riparia (Linnæus)

I. Description.—Length, $4\frac{3}{4}$ in. Easily distinguished from the two preceding species by mouse colour or sandy brown of upper surface; under parts white, except pale greyish brown band across breast; wings and tail darker brown; small feather tuft above hind toe. Young have feathers of mantle edged buffish.

II. Range and Habitat.—A summer resident in the British Isles, somewhat localized by the necessity of finding suitable breeding places, but widely distributed and common locally. It is scarce in the extreme north of Scotland, and is rare in the Orkneys and Outer Hebrides, but has once bred in the Shetlands. On the Continent its range extends to 70° 30′ N. in Norway, south to North-West Africa, and east to Palestine and Siberia, as well as North America; but replaced by local races in Egypt, Turkestan, North-West India, and Siberia east to Japan.

III. Nest and Eggs.—Usually breeds in colonies in sand-pits, steep river-banks, cuttings, etc., making a horizontal burrow in sandy soil about arm's length, ending in a rounded chamber, where the nest is placed. Exceptionally the nest may be found in holes of walls, drain-pipes, and even in spouting or heaps of sawdust. Nest merely a collection of feathers, straw, and floating rubbish, picked up on the wing as a rule. Eggs: usually 4–6, sometimes only 3, or 7 occasionally; white, thin-shelled and glossless. Average size of 61 British eggs, 18×12.6 mm. ($.70 \times .49$ in.). Laying begins early in May. Incubation period not exactly known; about a fortnight. Double brooded. (Plate 183, f. 23.)

IV. Food.—Insects taken on the wing, especially small flies, but also certainly some Ephemeroptera (mayflies), and probably also beetles.

V. Usual Notes.—The notes are similar to those of the House-Martin, but no definite attempt to distinguish between the utterances of the two species has been made. The twittering song is pleasant enough, especially uttered by the birds in concert, when, after the breeding season is over, they flock to roost. Song period, same as that of the House-Martin.

PLATE 75.—SAND-MARTINS AT THEIR NEST-HOLES: G. E. Collins.

PLATE 76.—BRITISH GREAT SPOTTED-WOODPECKER

Dryobates major anglicus (Hartert)

NORTHERN GREAT SPOTTED-WOODPECKER
Dryobates major major (Linnæus)

I. Description.—Length, 9½–10 in. Smaller than Green- but much larger than Lesser Spotted-Woodpecker. Recognized by black on upper parts, white patches on cheek, sides of neck, and scapulars ; red on belly and under tail coverts. The male has crimson on the nape, which is lacking in the female. Wings black barred with white spots ; under parts dull buff, except where red ; middle tail-feathers black, others barred whitish and black. Young have the crown of the head crimson. Toes as in Green-Woodpecker.

II. Range and Habitat.—The British race is confined to Great Britain, where it is resident in the wooded parts of England and Wales, but is scarce or absent in the three northern counties. In Scotland it was formerly resident in the ancient Caledonian pine forests, but became extinct, and has gradually recolonized most of its ancient habitat by spreading from the Border counties and Lowlands, and has now been recorded as far north as Aberdeen, Elgin, Banff, and Spey Valley. It is absent from Ireland, and is replaced by the northern race in North Europe, which also occurs in autumn on the east coast from Shetland to Norfolk, and by other forms in Southern and Central Europe, North-West Africa, and many districts in Asia.

III. Nest and Eggs.—When undisturbed will nest year after year in the same tree, making a new hole below the old one where space permits. Hole is similar in character to that of Green-Woodpecker, but smaller. No nesting material used. Eggs : usually 5–6, occasionally only 3 or 4, while 7 and 8 have been recorded ; white, less transparent-looking than Green-Woodpecker's, and not so glossy. Average of 100 British eggs, 26.4 × 19.5 mm. (1.04 × .76 in.). Laying variable, but begins after mid-May. Incubation period, probably 16 days (Owen). Male takes part in incubation, and broods at night. Single brooded.

IV. Food.—Chiefly larval forms of wood-boring insects (beetles and their larvæ, moth larvæ, etc.) ; spiders frequently taken ; wood lice ; exceptionally young birds (House-Martins, Sparrows, and Blue-Tits). Vegetable matter includes hazel nuts, berries of rowan, beech-mast, pips of crab apples ; cherries also taken, probably for kernels.

V. Usual Notes.—No song. The note is a sharp " kik " or " chik," uttered, as a rule, singly (Naumann), and only used as an alarm note (Jourdain). In the breeding season the bird may frequently be heard " drumming "—*i.e.* making a rapid tapping or tattoo with the tip of its beak on dead timber. The instrumental music does duty for a song. Drumming period : December–April (E. M. Nicholson). The bird has also a loud rattle.

PLATE 76.—BRITISH LESSER SPOTTED-WOODPECKER
Dryobates minor comminutus (Hartert)

I. Description.—Length, 5¾–6 in. Recognized by black and white colouring. Much smaller than Great Spotted-Woodpecker. Unlike the latter, it has the middle of the back white, barred with black, and no scarlet under the tail. Wings rather similar. The male has the crown crimson, the female dull whitish, both with white patches on the cheek and side of neck. Middle tail feathers black, others barred black and white. Under parts whitish, streaked black on the flanks. Young like adults, but markings less defined ; some crimson on crown, and under parts buff, with short brown streaks. Toes as in other Woodpeckers.

II. Range and Habitat.—The British race is confined to Great Britain and apparently also Holland, where it is resident. In England it is local, but does not breed north of Lancashire and Yorkshire (except a single record from Cumberland), and is rare or absent from all the western counties of Wales. None of the Irish records are satisfactory. Usually found where old timber is left standing. On the Continent allied races are found in many districts from the tree limit in Scandinavia south to North-West Africa, the Mediterranean, and across Asia to Japan.

III. Nest and Eggs.—Bores its nest-hole only in very soft and decayed timber ; sometimes quite low down, at other times at a considerable height. Nest chamber almost spherical, not much below entrance, and sometimes with approach of some inches. No nest material. Eggs : 4–6 as a rule, but 7, 8, possibly even 9 recorded ; white and glossy, more transparent than those of the Wryneck. Average of 100 British eggs, 18.7 × 14.4 mm. (.73 × .56 in.). Laying begins sometimes in April, but usually in first half of May. Incubation by both sexes ; period, 11–14 days. Single brooded.

IV. Food.—Chiefly larvæ of bark-haunting and tree-boring insects, including beetles, moths, etc. ; also ants, larvæ of flies and gall insects ; spiders. Reported also as taking raspberries and currants.

V. Usual Notes.—No song. The usual note is a rapidly repeated " kink " or " keek." Like the preceding species, the bird makes a drumming noise by extremely rapid tapping with the tip of its beak on dead timber. This is heard in and out of the breeding season.

[1] *British Birds* (Mag.), xx. 69 (E. Peake).

GREATER SPOTTED-WOODPECKER (MALE) ABOUT
TO FEED NESTLINGS : A. W. Seaby.

PLATE 76.—LESSER SPOTTED-WOODPECKERS AT
THEIR NEST-HOLE (*the upper bird is the male*) :
A. W. Seaby.

Order : Coraciiformes.   Family : Picidæ (Woodpeckers)

PLATE 77.—BRITISH GREEN-WOODPECKER

Picus viridis pluvius Hartert

I. Description.—Length 12½–14 in.   Recognized by the bright green of upper parts, rich crimson crown to middle of nape, greyish green under parts ; black patch on side of head of male and crimson moustachial stripe ; rump yellow ; tail black, with greenish bars ; outer primaries chequered white.   Female has moustachial stripe black and less red on crown.   Young have head grey, tipped scarlet, under parts barred ; rump also barred.   Toes, two before and two behind ; iris white.

II. Range and Habitat.—The Central European form is resident in wooded districts of England and Wales, but is rare in the three northern counties, and local in Lancashire and Yorkshire, and only a vagrant to Scotland ; while it has not been recorded from Ireland for nearly eighty years.   On the Continent it is also found from France to East Prussia and south to the Alps and Jugo-Slavia, but is replaced in Northern Europe, the Mediterranean region, and parts of Western Asia by other forms.

III. Nest and Eggs.—Bores a hole into a tree trunk, which descends perpendicularly from the entrance and is enlarged and rounded at the bottom, which is about a foot below the entrance.   No nesting material is used.   Eggs : usually 5–6, occasionally only 4, while 7 and 8 have occurred ; glossy and transparent white in colour, generally rather pointed in shape.   At times they are stained yellow or red brown by secretions from the tree.   Average of 100 British eggs, 32.1 × 23.2 mm. (1.26×.91 in.).   Laying begins late in April, frequently later.   Incubation period, 18–19 days, and shared by both sexes, male during night.   Only one brood is reared.

IV. Food.—Largely insects found in bark of trees and on ground (ants and their larvæ, earwigs, arboreal beetles and larvæ, larvæ of moths and flies) ; also larvæ of gall insects, millipedes ; worms and remains of egg found in one case.   Has been known to kill young Thrush.   Vegetable matter also taken (acorns, pyracanthus berries, oats, seeds, apples, etc.).

V. Usual Notes.—No song.   The usual note is, as Gilbert White phrased it, " a sort of loud and hearty laugh ;" an ancient rendering of which has given to the bird one of its popular names, " yaffle."   It appears to be heard more or less throughout the year.   The bird has other notes that have still to be satisfactorily distinguished from the yaffle and its variations.   The species also occasionally "drums"—*i.e.* performs a loud, rapid tattoo with its beak on dead timber, but less so than the Spotted forms.[1]   In courtship, one of the pair, probably the male, has been heard uttering a soft " twee-twee-twee." [2]

[1] That the Green form " drums " has been doubted.   The evidence is supplied by Naumann, Voigt, Hudson (*Hampshire Days*), and by others.   [2] Bertram Lloyd (*in litt.*).

PLATE 77.—GREEN-WOODPECKERS, MALE (*left*) AND FEMALE, THE LATTER PROTRUDING HER TONGUE TO CATCH ANTS : A. W. Seaby.

PLATE 78.—WRYNECK

Jynx torquilla torquilla Linnæus

I. Description.—Length, 7 in. Recognized by its vermiculated plumage. Upper parts covered with intricate pattern of grey, brown, buff, and whitish, heavily marked with dark streaks. The erectile crown is barred with chestnut and spotted white. The brown wing quills are spotted with chestnut to form a chessboard pattern ; irregular dusky bars on greyish rounded tail ; under parts chiefly buff, deeper on throat and breast, with dusky bars and V-shaped striations. Toes, two in front and two behind, as in Woodpeckers. Young lack dark streaks on back.

II. Range and Habitat.—Unlike the Woodpeckers the Wryneck is only a summer resident, breeding chiefly in Southern England, and scarce in Wales. In England it is very local north of the Mersey-Humber line, and has not been known to breed in Northumberland or in Scotland, where it is only a vagrant, as also in Ireland. Only met with in wooded districts. Abroad it ranges over the greater part of Europe, but is replaced by allied races in Sardinia, North-West Africa, and Asia.

III. Nest and Eggs.—Breeds in all kinds of holes, frequently dispossessing Tits or other hole-breeders ; most generally in trees, but occasionally in burrow of Sand-Martin or hole in bank, in old shed, nesting-box, or hollow in decayed sleeper used as fence. No nesting material. Eggs : 6–10, but 5, 11, 12, and 14 on record. If eggs are removed, of course, much higher numbers can be obtained. Colour, white, larger and more opaque-looking than Lesser Spotted-Woodpecker. Average of 51 British eggs, 20.6×15.5 mm. (.81×.61 in.). Laying begins latter part of May. Incubation period, 12–14 days ; both sexes take part. Single brooded, but in hot summers may breed twice.

IV. Food.—Largely ants and their larvæ, beetles and moths (larvæ), etc.; also spiders, wood lice, and, according to Naumann, elder-berries.

V. Usual Notes.—The Wryneck's loud ringing " quee, quee, quee, quee " may be heard from the time of the bird's arrival in March on to mid-July, and also on migration southward in autumn. It hisses when disturbed in its nest-hole. The nestlings make a sound like the " jingling of silver coins." [1]

[1] *British Bird Book,* ii., 347 (E. L. Turner).

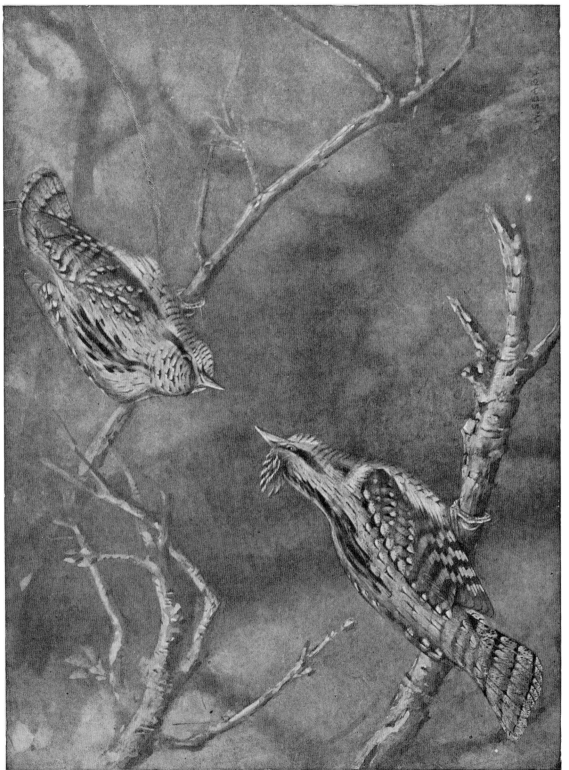

PLATE 78.—WRYNECKS QUARRELLING: A. W. Seaby.

PLATE 79.—SWIFT

Apus apus apus (Linnæus)

I. Description.—Length, 7–7½ in. Has all four toes directed forward. Distinguished on the wing from Swallows and Martins by larger size and long, narrow, scythe-like wings, equal to the body in length. General colour brownish black, except throat, which is dull white ; slight bronze green gloss on upper surface of body.

II. Range and Habitat.—Summer resident in the British Isles, widely distributed, localized by its breeding-places, which are not numerous ; absent as a breeder from northern islands and Outer Hebrides, and rare in Inner Hebrides. On the Continent it ranges north to lat. 70° in Norway, but is replaced by not well-marked races in the Mediterranean region, and also in various parts of Asia. Breeding places generally in buildings.

III. Nest and Eggs.—In the British Isles the usual breeding places are under eaves of preferably lofty houses, also in holes in thatch, a number of pairs generally breeding close together. Occasionally they will, however, breed in crevices among rocks, and in default of holes have been known to lay in House-Martins' nests. Nest is built of matter picked up on the wing, such as feathers, bits of straw, seed cases of trees, etc., and fastened together with the saliva of the bird. Eggs : 2–3, 4 occasional ; elongated in shape, dead white, and dull surfaced. Average of 100 British eggs, 24.9 × 16.3 mm. (.98 × .64 in.). Laying begins towards end of May. Incubation period, 18 days ; apparently by female alone, but both sexes found in nest hole. Single brooded.

IV. Food.—Taken on the wing entirely, and includes beetles, moths, flies, bees ; also aphides and frog-hoppers.

V. Usual Notes.—The familiar harsh screech heard as the bird speeds through the air is its only utterance, apart from the chattering of old and young in the nest.[1]

---

[1] Jourdain holds that the bird has an ordinary cry, and a special squealing cry used when racing with others.

PLATE 79.—SWIFTS: Winifred Austen.

Family: Caprimulgidæ (Goatsuckers)

PLATE 80.—NIGHTJAR

Caprimulgus europæus europæus Linnæus

I. Description.—Length, 10½ in. Recognized by its flattened head, enormous gape, with bristles; intricate variegated pattern of its plumage. General coloration ashy or silvery grey, streaked and barred with brown, chestnut, and buff; buff bar across wings. The male has conspicuous white spot on three outer primaries of each wing, and the two outer tail feathers on each side tipped with white; these are lacking in the female. Flies in twilight. Claw of middle toe pectinated, *i.e.* notched to form a comb-like structure.

II. Range and Habitat.—Summer resident in the British Isles, but locally distributed, as it avoids cultivated lands and haunts moors, commons, and woods. It does not breed in the Shetlands, Orkneys, or Outer Hebrides, but is found over the rest of Great Britain and Ireland in suitable localities. On the Continent it ranges from 63° N. in Scandinavia southward, but is replaced in the Mediterranean district, North-West Africa, South-East Europe, and parts of Asia by other races.

III. Nest and Eggs.—Breeds in open glades in woods with bracken, edges of heaths and moorlands, etc., laying on the bare ground, often near fragments of wood, dead leaves, bracken stalks, etc. Eggs: normally 2, a few cases of 3 and three of 4, possibly two hens. Ground, creamy white to greyish, beautifully marbled and blotched irregularly with ashy grey, yellowish brown, and some fine dark sepia markings. Occasionally white, almost unmarked or with a bold black blotch; bluish ground also occurs. Average of 100 eggs, 31.5 × 22.2 mm. (1.24 × .87 in.). Laying begins in latter half of May. Incubation period, 16–18 days; shared by sexes, but chiefly by female. Double brooded in the south, and probably generally. (Plate 185, f. 1.)

IV. Food.—As far as is known entire insects picked up on the wing, including beetles, flies, bees, moths; also frog-hoppers, aphides, dragon flies, and other neuroptera and orthoptera.

V. Usual Notes.—The Nightjar's well-known churring song is composed of two notes which alternate, one being in a lower key than the other. It is uttered when the bird is perched on a tree, also before it alights, or after it takes wing, and on the ground. The "churr" is followed by other notes difficult to describe. It may continue for some minutes. It is best heard just after sunset; is also heard before dawn, and occasionally in the daytime. The hen has been heard to utter on the nest notes not unlike the churring. Song period, from May to mid-August; again in September, before the bird's departure.[1] The usual note, uttered by the bird in flight, is "we-ip." The alarm note is "kwik, kwik, kwik." The food call to the chick, heard from birds in captivity, is "kourrr."[2] The birds make a clapping noise by smiting their wings together over the back.[3]

[1] T. A. Coward, *Fauna of Cheshire*, i. 257. [2] *Journal für Ornithologie*, 1909, 28 (Heinroth).
[3] For times of commencing each day its song, see *British Birds* (Mag.), xxviii. 259 (G. E. Ashmore).

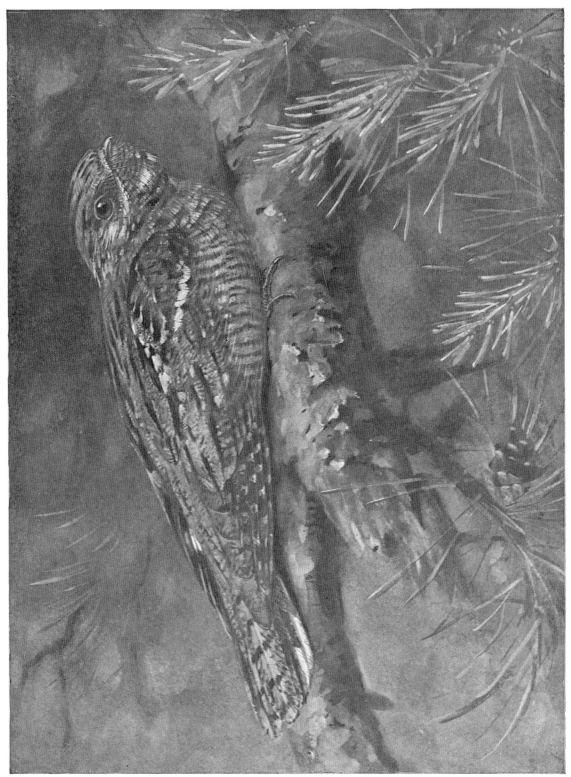

PLATE 80.—NIGHTJAR (MALE) IN FAVOURITE POSITION ON A BRANCH : A. W. Seaby.

Family: Strigidæ (Owls)

PLATE 81.—BARN-OWL
(Also known as WHITE-OWL, SCREECH-OWL)
(*Tyto alba alba* Scopoli)

CONTINENTAL BARN-OWL, *Tyto alba guttata* (Brehm)

I. Description.—Length, 13½–14 in. Distinguished from other British owls by buff and white coloration. The orange buff of the upper parts is delicately patterned with grey, white, and brown; facial discs white; rufous round eyes. Under parts white, with buff tinge on breast. Feet covered with white bristle-like feathers; middle claw serrated. Continental birds have under parts buff, with black spots.

II. Range and Habitat.—Thinly distributed resident in Great Britain and Ireland, but is scarce or absent in the northernmost counties of Scotland, and also absent from the Orkneys, Shetland, and, with possibly one or two exceptions, from the Outer Hebrides. The Continental or dark-breasted form also occurs irregularly in winter, chiefly on our east coasts. Abroad the white-breasted race is found in Western Europe, North Africa, and parts of South-West Asia, while other races represent it in Central Europe, west to East France, and north to South Sweden, and in other parts of Africa, Asia, Australia, and America. In the British Isles it is most likely to occur in agricultural or industrial areas.

III. Nest and Eggs.—Breeds either in natural holes in trees or in barns, ruins, church towers, rocks, or old buildings. No nesting material is used, but the regurgitated pellets are scattered about the eggs and form a bed for the eggs. Eggs: usually 4–6, but every number from 7–11 has been recorded; rather elongated in shape; white, without gloss. Average size of 100 British eggs, 39.4 × 31.5 mm. (1.55 × 1.24 in.). Incubation period, 30–31 days; by female alone. There is always an interval of at least a clear day between the laying of the eggs, but in some cases they are laid in pairs, with about one week's interval between each pair, causing great discrepancies in the size of young in the same brood. Apparently a second brood not infrequently reared.

IV. Food.—Mainly small mammals; long- and short-tailed field mice, bank voles, shrews form staple food, but house mice, young brown rats, moles, water voles, and long-eared bats are also taken, and there is one record of a young rabbit in a nest. Birds recorded include chiefly Sparrows and Starlings, but occasionally also Thrush, Blackbird, Greenfinch, Skylark, and Sedge-Warbler. A dead Jackdaw has also been found in a nest. Other food: frog, carp, and insects (chiefly beetles, but also moths).

V. Usual Notes.—"White-Owls often scream horribly as they fly along." Thus Gilbert White. He adds that the bird also snores and hisses "in a tremendous manner; and these menaces well answer the intention of intimidating; for I have known a whole village up in arms on such an occasion, imagining the churchyard to be full of goblins and spectres." Jourdain states that only the young snore. The species, when annoyed or alarmed, makes a snapping noise with its mandibles, the head being lowered and moved from side to side.

81

PLATE 81.—BARN-OWL HUNTING: A. W. Seaby.

PLATE 82.—LONGEARED-OWL

Asio otus otus (Linnæus)

I. Description.—Length, 14 in. Distinguished by long ear-tufts ($1\frac{1}{2}$ in.), iris orange yellow (not blackish as in Tawny- and Barn-Owls). Upper parts buff, with dusky streaks and vermiculations and paler mottlings ; wings and tail have dusky bars ; under parts mainly buff, with dusky striations, bars, and vermiculations. Female larger than male.

II. Range and Habitat.—Rather local resident in wooded districts in the British Isles, but does not breed in the Shetlands and Outer Hebrides, and quite exceptionally in the Orkneys. Abroad its range extends wherever there are woods over Europe, North-West Africa, the Azores, and Northern Asia, but it is replaced by allied races in the Canaries and in North America, and does not breed on some of the Mediterranean islands.

III. Nest and Eggs.—Usually met with in coniferous woods, which afford shelter in winter, nesting in open nests of other species, such as Crow, Raven, Wood-Pigeon, Heron, etc., or old squirrels' dreys, and occasionally among heather in open country or at the foot of a tree in a wood. Eggs : usually 4–5, occasionally 3 only, or 6, while there are records of 7 and 8 eggs. Colour, white, not so glossy as Wood-Pigeon's, but smooth. Average size of 100 British eggs, 40.9 × 32.6 mm. (1.61 × 1.28 in.). Laying begins about the middle of March. Incubation apparently by hen ; period, 25–28 days. Single brooded.

IV. Food.—Small mammals, including brown rat, bank vole, water vole, long- and short-tailed field mice, mole, and shrews ; one record of a rabbit. Birds include Greenfinch, Chaffinch, Sparrow, Brambling, Yellow-Bunting, Song-Thrush, Blackbird, Skylark, Swallow, Goldcrest ; also once Jay, and once young Pheasant. Insects taken are chiefly beetles.

V. Usual Notes.—The Longeared-Owl's song is composed of " flute-like repetitions of ' ooh, ooh,' uttered so softly that often they are a mere sigh. I have stood in the moonlight aisles of the great pinewoods in West Norfolk listening to the sighs of the Longeared-Owl, and I understood why men believed in pixies and ghosts and the restless dead." The same " ooh " is a warning or alarm note. The hunting cry is a mewing sound. The nestlings utter sounds like the " creaking of an unoiled hinge " ; they also hiss.[1] The species is credited with a " quacking " note (H. Saunders). It has been syllabled " kyak."

[1] The information here given is from Miss E. L. Turner's *Broadland Birds*, 84. For a fuller list see *British Birds* (Mag.), xxv. 361 (J. Walpole-Bond).

PLATE 82.—LONGEARED-OWL FEEDING ITS YOUNG: Winifred Austen.

PLATE 83.—TAWNY-OWL

(Also known as BROWN-OWL, WOOD-OWL)

Strix aluco sylvatica Shaw

I. Description.—Length, 15–19 in. Distinguished from the Barn-Owl by brownish plumage. The large head, superior size, and absence of ear-tufts, as well as the characteristic hoot (see below) distinguish it from Long- and Shorteared Owls. Most birds belong to a greyish type, streaked, mottled, and barred with various shades of brown. Under parts dull white, with dusky streaks and paler bars; wing and tail brown, barred darker. In the scarce reddish type, upper parts are reddish brown, similar otherwise. Female larger than male.

II. Range and Habitat.—The British race is confined to Great Britain, where it is a common and widely distributed resident in all wooded districts, but is scarce in the extreme north of Scotland, and absent from the Shetlands, Orkneys, Outer Hebrides, and also from Ireland. Abroad it is replaced by allied races as far as the tree limit extends north and south to the Mediterranean, North-West Africa, and east to Palestine and Persia.

III. Nest and Eggs.—The normal site for the nest is in a natural hole in a tree, but a few cases are known where this Owl has bred in barns, like the White-Owl, and it also breeds in rabbit holes, under sheltering rock on ground, in cliffs, and in old nests of Rook, Crow, Heron, Magpie, etc. No nesting material is used, but there are sometimes a few pellets about. Eggs: 2–4, 5 quite exceptional, and there are abnormal cases of 6 to 8 eggs on record. Colour, white, smooth and somewhat rounded in shape. Average of 100 British eggs, 46.7 × 39 mm. (1.83 × 1.53 in.). Laying begins towards the end of March. Incubation period, 28–30 days; share of sexes not certain, but apparently by female alone, male roosting apart. Single brooded.

IV. Food.—Largely mammals; brown rat, bank vole, long- and short-tailed field mouse, rabbit, water vole, mole, common, lesser, and water shrews—rarely squirrel, house mouse, or young leveret; also Sparrows and Starlings, occasionally other species such as Thrush, Mistle-Thrush, Blackbird, Bunting (sp.?), young Jackdaw, Little-Grebe, Chaffinch, Brambling, Great Spotted-Woodpecker, while feathers of Green-Woodpecker and body of Kestrel have been found in nests. Fish are occasionally taken; also frogs and once a toad; slugs and worms. One or two cases are on record of young Pheasants being taken. Insects are chiefly beetles and moths; occasionally also neuroptera.

V. Usual Notes.—The Tawny-Owl is best known as Shakespeare's " staring owl " that nightly sings " Tu-whit, tu-whoo, a merry note, while greasy Joan doth keel the pot." The rendering serves, but it is not exact. The note (or song) usually consists of a prolonged " hou," after which comes a long note that quavers to a full close. The usual call note is a sharp " ke-wick." Jourdain states that this species has also a number of lower conversational notes only audible at short distances. Song heard every month.

83

PLATE 83.—TAWNY-OWL MOBBED BY SMALL BIRDS: G. E. Lodge.

Plate 84.—SNOWY-OWL

Nyctea scandiaca (Linnæus)

I. Description.—Length, 21–26 in. Distinguished from the other Owls described by its great size, general white colour of plumage, almost unmarked in old males, but females are marked with broad bars of brown on crown, nape, mantle, and belly. Younger birds are generally still more barred. Irides golden yellow ; feet feathered to claws. Females larger.

II. Range and Habitat.—A winter visitor, chiefly to the north of Great Britain and Ireland, but has occurred in many parts of Southern England casually. Its breeding haunts are in the Arctic regions of both the old and new world, ranging south in lemming years to the high fjeld of Scandinavia, and not proved to have bred in Spitsbergen. It is a tundra breeding species.

III. Nest and Eggs.—This species does not breed in the British Isles. In the Arctic regions its nesting places are usually on hummocks in the tundra, giving a view over the surrounding country, always on moorland or even snowfield in the far north. Eggs : variable in number according to food supply, bird apparently not breeding in unfavourable seasons in some districts ; usually 7–9, occasionally 10–12 in number ; white. Average of 100 eggs, 57.3 × 45.1 mm. (2.25 × 1.77 in.). Laying varies according to latitude ; June in the high north, but earlier in the south. Incubation period, probably 32–34 days ; by female alone. Single brooded.

IV. Food.—In its breeding haunts feeds on lemmings, Arctic hares, etc., and birds (Ptarmigan, Ducks, Little-Auks, and small birds, such as Snow-Bunting). On migration and in winter it will take rabbits, mice, and many species of birds, including Ducks, game birds, Gulls, Coot, Little-Grebe, and many smaller species. Has been seen to attack a wounded Brent-Goose. Also some insects (beetles) and spiders found in castings.

V. Usual Notes.—Murie describes the " hoarse barking hoots " uttered by the male when attacking intruders on the nesting ground, and adds that the female joined in the outcry in a somewhat higher-pitched voice.

PLATE 84.—SNOWY-OWL WITH HARE : G. E. Lodge.

PLATE 85.—SHORTEARED-OWL, *Asio flammeus flammeus* (Pontoppidan)

I. Description.—Length, 14–16½ in. Distinguished by the very short ear-tufts (not always erected), absence of bars on under parts, which are buff, streaked with blackish brown. Upper parts buff, blotched and streaked with brown. Facial disc browner than in Longeared-Owl. Wings and tail pale buff, barred dark brown. Irides yellow. Female larger and somewhat darker.

II. Range and Habitat.—Very local and irregularly nesting resident in Great Britain, breeding in England occasionally in open moors and marshes south of the Pennines, and sparingly in the northern counties and in Scotland and many of the islands, but rare in the Shetlands, though not uncommon in the Orkneys. Almost world-wide, breeding sporadically over Europe, Asia, North and South America. The Hawaiian and an Asiatic race have been separated.

III. Nest and Eggs.—Breeds on the ground, among sandhills or on moors among heather, making a mere scrape for the eggs. In marshlands it may lay on swathes of reeds or in open space among sedge. Eggs : variable in number according to food supply, as is the case with other Owls ; normally about 5–8 or 9, but in vole years up to 13 and 14 on record. Colour, white, surface smooth. Average size of 100 eggs, 39.7 × 31.1 mm. (1.56 × 1.22 in.). Laying begins in latter part of April in the south, but much later in the north. Incubation by hen ; period, 24–28 days. Normally single brooded.

IV. Food.—Mainly small mammals, especially the short-tailed field mouse, which causes the " vole plagues," but also long-tailed field mice and occasionally young rats, bats, and young rabbits ; birds, including Meadow-Pipit, Twite, Thrush, Blackbird, Hedge-Sparrow, young Skylarks, young Lapwings, Dunlin, and Tree-Creeper (once), Snipe (once), Blackheaded-Gull (once), and Jack-Snipe (once). Beetles are also frequently taken.

V. Usual Notes.—When the nest or young is approached, the Shorteared-Owl has been seen to hover and swoop " hissing and making a spitting noise like an angry cat." [1] It also utters a sound like an angry bark or quack (Jourdain), " like the snappy bark of a Pomeranian, but rather more of a croak, figured ' mwaak.' " [2] No record of a song.

PLATE 85.—LITTLE-OWL, *Athene noctua vidalii* A. E. Brehm

I. Description.—Length, 9–9½ in. Distinguished from the other Owls here described by its small size and whitish spots on greyish brown ground of head and wings. Under surface dull white with brown streaks ; wing and tail brown with paler bars ; irides pale yellow ; toes not feathered, but with bristles. Female larger.

II. Range and Habitat.—An introduced species, now a widespread resident in many districts of England and Wales, in some places extremely common. It has now been recorded as breeding in all British counties (with the exception of some of the Welsh counties) south of Durham and Lancashire. Unknown in Ireland, and only a straggler to Scotland. The same form breeds in Western Europe, but is replaced by allied races in North Africa, Eastern Europe, and Asia, and it does not range north of the Baltic, except as a casual to Sweden.

III. Nest and Eggs.—Breeds most commonly where pollarded willows or old trees in hedgerows provide nesting sites, but frequently also nests in holes of buildings ; also in rabbit holes, and even among stacks of timber, etc. No nesting material ; eggs laid on floor of hole. Eggs : 3–5 as a rule, but where food is plentiful or in newly colonized districts up to 8, and possibly even 9 on record ; white, and rather dull in colour. Average of 100 British eggs, 35.2 × 29.2 mm. (1.38 × 1.14 in.). Laying begins in the latter part of April. Incubation period, 26–28 days ; by female alone. Single brooded.

IV. Food.—Very variable, differing according to the district. In some places almost entirely insects, especially earwigs, beetles, earthworms, etc. In others it is destructive to small birds, and at times does some damage to young game birds. Mammals include rat, long- and short-tailed field mouse, bank vole, house mouse, mole, common, water, and pygmy shrew. Birds : chickens, young Pheasants and Partridges (rarely), Blackbirds, Mistle- and Song-Thrushes, Starling, Sparrow, Greenfinch, Chaffinch, Skylark, Cuckoo, Lapwing, and Wood-Pigeon. Also frogs, earthworms, insects (earwigs and beetles in great numbers, moths, craneflies and sawflies), minnows, spiders, centipedes, millipedes, and blindworm.

V. Usual Notes.—The usual oft-repeated note sounds like " ku " or " ku-kee." The alarm note is " much like the bark of a toy terrier." [3] The bird has also a number of other notes ; one described by Jourdain as a yelling cry, uttered towards evening.

[1] E. L. Turner, *Broadland Birds*, 76.
[2] *British Birds* (Mag.), xviii. 226–230 (E. H. Armstrong and E. W. Phillips).
[3] Stanley Morris, *Bird Song*, 104.

85

LITTLE-OWL AT THE ENTRANCE TO ITS HOLE:
G. E. Lodge.

PLATE 85.—SHORTEARED-OWL SUNNING ITSELF ;
Winifred Austen.

PLATE 86.—ROLLER

Coracias garrulus garrulus Linnæus

I. Description.—Length, 13 in. Recognized by its cinnamon brown mantle and tertial feathers ; all the rest of the plumage is either light blue or blue green, with the exception of a little white on forehead and chin, and the dark primaries. No other of our birds shows such striking contrast in blues and brown. Sexes alike, bill black. Juveniles duller in plumage, with an admixture of brownish on head, breast, and tail.

II. Range and Habitat.—Only a straggler to the British Isles, occurring chiefly at migration times, and recorded over a hundred times from Great Britain as well as Ireland. Abroad it ranges from lat. 70° N. in Norway, but breeds only from South Sweden, to Marocco, Algeria, and Tunisia, and the islands of the Mediterranean and West Siberia, but is replaced by a slightly different race in Palestine, the Caucasus, Iraq, Persia, etc. In Europe mainly a forest species, but in the Mediterranean region more general.

III. Nest and Eggs.—Does not breed in the British Isles. The most usual breeding place is a natural hollow in an old tree, but in the Mediterranean region holes in ruins or old buildings, in steep mud banks, or among rocks are more favoured. Occasionally breeding in old nests of other species has been recorded. Little nesting material is used, but grass, feathers, and hair have been found in the nest hole. Eggs : 4–6, very rarely 7 ; pure white and glossy. Average of 100 eggs, 35.6 × 28 mm. (1.40 × 1.10 in.). Laying begins in mid-May in south ; late May in north. Incubation period, 17–18 days ; probably by both sexes. Single brooded.

IV. Food.—Largely insects, especially beetles, locusts, grasshoppers, earwigs and mole crickets, flies, caterpillars, and ants ; also small lizards, frogs, small birds, scorpions and centipedes, even 6 in. long. Fruit (figs, grapes, etc.) also taken in autumn.

V. Usual Notes.—During the breeding season, in fine weather, the male Roller " rises in the air with loud and harsh ' rack, rack-kack ' to a fair height, and proceeds to ' tumble ' or turn somersaults in his flight, after which he darts down with a harsh chatter, which Naumann writes ' raeh, raeraeh, rraeh, rrae,' returning at length to his perch " (Jourdain). It is to its antics during this nuptial flight that the species owes its name of " Roller." The usual call note is a high ringing " kraeh."

PLATE 86.—ROLLERS, ADULT (*foreground*), YOUNG (*background*) : Winifred Austen.

PLATE 87.—HOOPOE

Upupa epops epops Linnæus

I. Description.—Length, 10–12 in. Distinguished by its conspicuous crest, fan-shaped when erect, long, slender, and slightly decurved bill, and rich cinnamon buff plumage, relieved by black tips to crest and alternating bands of black and white on wings and tail. Rump and belly white. Female rather smaller and duller. Young have shorter bills. Note (from which it derives its name) very characteristic.

II. Range and Habitat.—Chiefly a passage migrant and straggler to the British Isles, but has undoubtedly bred in many of the southern counties of England. On the Continent it breeds in most of the countries of Europe south of the Baltic, and sparingly in South Sweden; also in Western Asia, but replaced by other races in Egypt, Central and Southern Africa, India, Ceylon, and Eastern Asia. In Europe its breeding-places are generally in well wooded and watered districts.

III. Nest and Eggs.—Always in a hole of some kind; often in a tree, sometimes low down and at other times high up, also in loose stone walls, stone heaps, and at times in drains or holes in buildings. Nest scanty, bits of straw and feathers, and, strange to say, frequently, but not always, excrement of animals, making the site very offensive. Eggs: usually 5–9, but 10 and 12 are said to have been found; elongated in shape and dull in texture, often uniform greyish white or yellowish olive, becoming stained as incubation progresses. Exceptionally deep blue; dark olive brown and white eggs have been recorded. Average of 100 eggs, 25.9 × 17.8 mm. (1.02 × .70 in.). Laying begins about end of April in south, but often not till late in May in north. Incubation period, over 20 days; by female alone. Probably single brooded. (Plate 185, f. 2.)

IV. Food.—Mainly insects, including beetles and larvæ, locusts and grasshoppers and larvæ, earwigs, moths and larvæ, flies, and ants; also spiders, centipedes, earthworms, and woodlice.

V. Usual Notes.—The bird owes its name to its usual note "poo-poo-poo," which it utters with its head bowed to the branch, its crest depressed, and the neck inflated. The neck is re-inflated after each treble call. The alarm cry is a harsh chattering, and a curious mewing call is not infrequently heard.

PLATE 87.—HOOPOES AT THEIR NEST-HOLE: Winifred Austen.

PLATE 88.—KINGFISHER

Alcedo atthis ispida Linnæus

I. Description.—Length, $7\frac{1}{2}$ in. This is another very strikingly coloured species, but recognizable at once by its small size and large head and bill, with short tail ; back, wings, and tail brilliant cobalt blue ; under parts chestnut ; throat white, bordered above on each side of neck and head by blue band, beyond which is a patch of chestnut behind the eye ; lores black ; crown barred blue ; bill black ; feet red. Female has orange on lower mandible.

II. Range and Habitat.—Resident in the British Isles ; not uncommon, but absent from swift-flowing streams, preferring slow-flowing rivers and brooks with mud banks. Scarce in Northern Scotland, and absent as a breeder from the Shetlands, Orkneys, and Outer Hebrides ; also scarce in Ireland. On the Continent it ranges north to Southern Sweden, and south to the Mediterranean ; replaced by allied races in North Africa and Asia east to Japan and south to India.

III. Nest and Eggs.—Nests at the end of a burrow bored by the bird almost horizontally into the perpendicular bank of a stream, about 2 ft. in length, and ending in a circular chamber. Occasionally the burrow may be found in a sand-pit at some distance from water, or among the roots of an upturned tree. The nest consists of fish bones, which are deposited round the eggs as incubation proceeds. Eggs : usually 7, though occasionally as few as 4 only, while 8 to 10 are on record ; pure glossy white and almost spherical in shape. Average size of 100 British eggs, 22.6×18.7 mm. ($.89 \times .73$ in.). Laying usually begins towards the end of April, exceptionally at the end of March. Incubation by both sexes ; period, 19–21 days. Two broods occasionally reared.

IV. Food.—Mainly small fish, especially minnow and stickleback ; also gudgeon, miller's thumb, fry of pike, roach, etc. ; also frog and newt recorded ; tadpoles, mollusca, worms, and water insects (beetles, larvæ of dragon fly, flies, and water boatman). On the coast crustacea (shrimps, prawns, and sandhoppers) as well as small rock fish.

V. Usual Notes.—B. B. Rivière gives three notes commonly used by male and female : " tee," usually single ; " tiptee," repeated ; " tip " or " chip," repeated. All three may be uttered in the order given. The male has a nuptial song : a rapid " tee, titi, titi, titi." [1] The note of the nestlings is " a curious low humming noise, rather like that emitted by a swarm of bees." [2]

[1] *British Birds* (Mag.), xxvi. 263. See *id*. xxi. 7 (W. M. Marsden).
[2] *Wild Life,* September 1914 (E. Eykyn).

PLATE 88.—KINGFISHER FEEDING ITS YOUNG: A. W. Seaby.

PLATE 89.—CUCKOO

Cuculus canorus canorus Linnæus

I. Description.—Length, 14 in.   Recognized by blue grey upper parts, throat, and upper breast ; tail long, graduated, dark bluish, spotted white ; under parts white, barred with black ; iris and feet yellow, two toes directed forward and two backward. Note characteristic.   Female with rufous tinge on forebreast, slightly smaller.   Young have upper surface and tail rufous brown, barred dusky bluish ; white spot on head and nape.   A redder phase also occurs in the adult female.

II. Range and Habitat.—Summer resident in the British Isles, widely distributed, but scarce in the Shetlands.   It is found not only in the fertile lowlands and wooded country, but also on moorlands to a considerable height.   Abroad it ranges over Europe to lat. 71 ° N., and south to the Pyrenees, Italy and the Mediterranean, as well as Western Asia ; but is replaced in the Iberian Peninsula, North-West Africa, and perhaps some of the Mediterranean islands, as well as in Southern and Eastern Asia to Japan, by allied races.

III. Nest and Eggs.—Unlike all our other breeding birds, the Cuckoo is parasitic in its breeding habits and makes no nest, depositing its eggs in the nests of other birds.   As a rule one egg is laid in a nest, and one of the host's eggs removed at the same time.   Generally it will be found that when two or three Cuckoos' eggs are found in one nest, that they are from different hens, though occasionally at the end of the season a hen may lay two eggs in one nest.   The eggs are laid on alternate days as a rule, and probably the normal number does not exceed 12 or 15, and no doubt is frequently less, but it has been proved by E. Chance that under exceptional circumstances a single Cuckoo may lay up to 25 eggs in a season.   There has been much controversy as to whether the eggs are laid in the nest or introduced by the bill, but it is now known that laying is the normal process, and there is no proof of introduction by the bill.   Eggs : small for the size of the bird, thick-shelled, blunt in shape, and variable in colour and markings.   British eggs show comparatively little variation, but on the Continent and in Asia extraordinarily close mimicry of the eggs of the host is not uncommon.   British eggs are sometimes reddish, but more often greyish, greenish, or bluish, spotted, marbled, and freckled with various shades of grey and brown, and generally, a few blackish fine spots.   Abroad pure blue eggs occur, and great variation in colour.   Average size of 626 eggs (by Rey), 22.4 × 16.5 mm. (.88 × .65 in.).   Laying begins usually about mid-May, but exceptionally at the end of April or early in May.   Incubation period, 12–13 days.   (Plate 184.)

IV. Food.—Chiefly insects, many injurious and not touched by other birds, including larvæ of butterflies and moths (as well as imagines), larvæ of sawflies, larvæ of diptera (flies), beetles, and dragon flies ; also spiders and, exceptionally, worms.   Eggs removed from fosterers' nests are also eaten.

V. Usual Notes.—The well-known " cuckoo " is uttered by the male Cuckoo only ;[1] it is heard from first half of April to end of June, and sometimes later.[2]   That the bird " changes tune " in June presumably refers to the rapid, excited " cuck-cuck-oo," but this may be heard frequently in May, and may be regarded simply as a more emphatic form of the " cuckoo."   Another note sounds like a rapid, hoarse coughing, " whuff, whuff, whuff, whuff ; " it often precedes the " cuckoo," and is uttered by itself.   The writer has heard it coming from a bird when flying alone, when flying with two others, one a female, and when pursued by small birds.   A third note, a clear, liquid, bubbling sound, is peculiar to the female, and often uttered by her after laying an egg.   She utters, besides, a mewing note when she is watching her destined dupes.[1]   The " cuckoo " may be uttered with beak part open or closed.

[1] Edgar Chance, *The Cuckoo's Secret*, 217.
[2] Exceptionally there may be arrivals end of March.

PLATE 89.—CUCKOO UTTERING ITS NOTE: A. W. Seaby.

Order: Charadriiformes. Family: Columbidæ (Pigeons)

Plate 90.—WOOD-PIGEON OR RING-DOVE

Columba palumbus palumbus Linnæus

I. Description.—Length, 16–17 in. Distinguished from the other British Pigeons by the white patch on the outer wing coverts, conspicuous in flight, and by white patch on each side of neck. Head, neck, lower back, rump, and tail coverts bluish grey, with purple and green reflections on the nape and neck ; mantle and wing coverts brown ; tail dusky, with dark bar. Under parts vinous purple on breast, bluish grey on flanks and belly. Young birds lack the white patch on the neck.

II. Range and Habitat.—Resident in the British Isles, but also winter visitor from the Continent. Widely distributed wherever there are trees, but is absent from moorlands, and is a scarce breeder in the Orkneys and Outer Hebrides, and does not nest in the Shetlands. Abroad its range extends over the Continent of Europe, except in the north of Scandinavia and Russia, also in the Mediterranean islands and parts of South-West Asia to Persia ; but in North-West Africa, Madeira, the Azores, and parts of Asia it is replaced by other races.

III. Nest and Eggs.—The normal site for the nest is in a tree or tall straggling hedge, in woods often among ivy, and exceptionally quite low down in small bush or among heath. In large towns where it is semi-domesticated it will breed on houses, and will sometimes nest on bush-grown rocks. The nest is of a flimsy character, composed of thin twigs, so that the eggs are often visible from below. Eggs : normally 2, exceptionally 3 ; smooth glossy white, more elongated than those of the other Pigeons. Average of 100 British eggs, 41.1 × 29.8 mm. (1.61 × 1.17 in.). Laying begins normally about the end of March, but has been recorded in all the months between January and November. Incubation period, 17–18 days ; shared by both sexes. Two or more broods.

IV. Food.—Devours large quantities of grain in the fields (barley, oats, wheat, and rye), also potatoes, beans, peas, clover and turnip leaves, roots, seeds of many species of weeds, fruits and berries of beech, holly, hazel, hawthorn, oak, ivy, gooseberry, cherry, and strawberry. Besides vegetable matter, animal food is taken to a small extent ; earthworms, snails and slugs, as well as beetles and caterpillars.

V. Usual Notes.—The Ring-Dove's song, so compact with promise of sempiternal devotion, may be variously rendered. One form is " coo-cóo-coo-coo-coo " ; another " coo-coo-cóo-coo-coo." Between the strains a set of lower notes may be heard (Naumann). After a few repetitions of the phrase, the bird ends up with a single " coo ! " by way of Amen ! Witchell says that the species has a " grunt of alarm."[1] The writer has heard it clap its wings over its back when startled into sudden flight. It has been heard to do this also while pursuing another Pigeon in the air or while being pursued, and during the nuptial flight.[2] The clapping seems to do duty for utterance.[3] Song period, more or less all the year.[4]

[1] *Cries and Call-notes of Wild Birds*, 57.   [2] E. Selous, *Bird-watching*, 51, 52.
[3] It has been denied that the " clap " is due to collision of the wings.
[4] *British Birds* (Mag.), iv. 276 (Alexander).

PLATE 90.—RING-DOVE COURTING : A. W. Seaby.

PLATE 91.—ROCK-DOVE

Columba livia livia Gmelin

I. Description.—Length, 13–13½ in. Distinguished from the other two Pigeons by the white rump, conspicuous in flight. Head, neck, and tail dark slaty blue ; tail with black terminal bar and white on outermost feathers ; metallic green patch on neck ; mantle and under parts blue grey ; axillaries white.

II. Range and Habitat.—Resident in the British Isles, but pure wild birds are only to be found on the rocky parts of our coasts, chiefly in the west of England and Wales, and in Scotland and Ireland and their islands. Generally most numerous on the side exposed to the Atlantic, where caves are numerous. Abroad it occurs in the Faeroes, but not in Norway ; along the Mediterranean coasts and islands and in the Crimea. In Egypt, Palestine, Iraq, and from Transcaspia to India, Nubia, and also in the Sahara it is replaced by allied races.

III. Nest and Eggs.—The usual site of really wild bird's nest is in a crevice or hollow in the roof of a sea cave, but any niche or hollow may be used, preferably a deep one. The nest is often made of roots, but bents and even seaweed are used. Eggs : normally 2 ; glossy white, smaller than those of Wood-Pigeon. Average size of 100 British eggs, 40.3 × 29.3 mm. (1.58 × 1.15 in.). Laying begins in most cases in April, but occasionally even in February. Incubation period, 17–19 days ; chiefly by hen. More than one brood.

IV. Food.—Where cultivation is within reach it takes grain (barley, oats, rye, etc.), also peas, beans, potatoes, etc., as well as seeds of many species of plants ; but, as a rule, grain forms only a small proportion of the food, which consists mainly of seeds, mollusca (snails, eggs of whelks, etc.), and annelids.

V. Usual Notes.—Renderings of the Rock-Dove's song vary. That of Naumann (anglicized) runs : " Ma-roo-coo " or " murr-coo-coo," or " murr-coo-roo." By the same authority the bird is credited with a note like " hoo " or " hoo-oo " or " ha-ou-a," which serves either as a pairing or alarm note.[1] Song period, not recorded.

[1] *Vögel Mitteleuropas,* vi. 10–11.

PLATE 91.—ROCK-DOVE ALIGHTING ON ITS NEST: Winifred Austen.

Plate 92.—STOCK-DOVE

Columba œnas œnas Linnæus

I. Description.—Length, 13–13½ in. Distinguished from Wood-Pigeon by its smaller size and absence of white on wings ; from Rock-Dove by absence of white on rump. Upper parts bluish or slaty grey, with green and purplish reflections on sides of neck ; patches of black on wing form broken bars ; throat and breast vinous purple, rest of under parts greyish ; axillaries grey. Young birds lack metallic green on sides of neck.

II. Range and Habitat.—Resident in the British Isles, but local, though spreading. Its favourite haunts are parks with old timber, but sand-hills and rocky country as well as sea cliffs are also favoured. In England and Wales it is now very widespread, but has only recently colonized Scotland, chiefly on the east side north of the Clyde area, and is not recorded as breeding in any of the islands. In Ireland, too, it has spread widely since about 1875, when it first appeared. Abroad it is found from South Sweden and Finland to the Mediterranean, east to Asia Minor and Transcaspia, while local races have been described from various districts in Central Asia.

III. Nest and Eggs.—Generally breeds in a good-sized hollow in some old tree, but also nests in rabbit holes, hollows in face of cliffs, in ruins or old buildings, and at times under thick bushes. The nest is of a perfunctory character, often only a few stalks. Eggs : normally 2, but 3 recorded many times ; more rounded than Wood-Pigeon's, with a faint creamy tinge, and smaller. Average size of 100 British eggs, 37.9 × 29 mm. (1.49 × 1.14 in.). Laying begins about the end of March, sometimes early in the month. Incubation period, 17–18 days ; both sexes taking part. Double brooded.

IV. Food.—Very like that of the Wood-Pigeon, but less destructive ; mainly vegetable, grain of all kinds, clover, turnip, and swede leaves, peas, beans, and seeds of many plants. Small snails also recorded.

V. Usual Notes.—Little has been recorded of the utterances of the Stock-Dove. The song heard by the writer reduced itself to a musical " oo-oof," as in " roof," repeated. Jourdain describes the note as more monotonous and less musical than that of the Wood-Pigeon, in fact, more of a grunt than a coo.[1] Like the Wood-Pigeon, it claps its wings above its back.[2] Song period, same as the Wood-Pigeon's.[3]

[1] W. H. Hudson, on the other hand, found the song very attractive. **See** *Birds and Man*, chap. iv.
[2] E. Selous, *Bird-watching*, 38. See footnote 3, page 90.
[3] *British Birds* (Mag.), iv. 276 (C. J. and H. G. Alexander).

PLATE 92.—STOCK-DOVE DRINKING : G. E. Collins.

Plate 93.—TURTLE-DOVE

Streptopelia turtur turtur (Linnæus)

I. Description.—Length, $11\frac{1}{4}$–$11\frac{1}{2}$ in. Markedly different from the other Pigeons in shape, size, and colour, being smaller, more slender, with long graduated tail, and has wing coverts and scapulars rich reddish brown with black centres ; black side feathers of tail broadly tipped with white ; head, nape, rump, and outer wing coverts bluish ash ; on sides of neck conspicuous patch of alternating bands of black and white ; under parts vinous purple, passing to white on belly. Young birds lack the neck patch.

II. Range and Habitat.—Summer resident to England and Wales, breeding more sparsely in the north, but as far as Durham and Cumberland ; only on passage in Scotland, and a scarce summer visitor to South Ireland, where it is said to have bred on a few occasions. Haunts cultivated ground, preferring lowlands and valleys. On the Continent it ranges from Southern Sweden and Finland south to the Mediterranean and West Asia, but is replaced by allied races in North-West Africa, the Sahara, North-East Africa, and in Asia from Palestine east to Turkestan and Afghanistan.

III. Nest and Eggs.—Breeds in hedges, thickets, young plantations, orchards, etc., making a slight nest of fine twigs, through which the eggs can readily be seen. Exceptionally the nest has been met with actually on the ground. Eggs : normally 2, though 3 has been recorded ; much smaller than those of other Pigeons, white and glossy. Average size of 100 British eggs, 30.7×22.9 mm. ($1.20 \times .90$ in.). Laying begins about the middle of May. Incubation period, 13–$14\frac{1}{2}$ days ; shared by both sexes. A second brood often reared.

IV. Food.—Chiefly seeds of various species of weed, especially common fumitory, though occasionally corn and leaves of seedlings are also taken.

V. Usual Notes. — The Turtle-Dove's song is a musical inward crooning, and is fairly adequately figured by the bird's specific Latin name, "Turtur," thus : " woo-tur-r-r, tur-r-r," repeated with individual variations. It may be heard from the bird's arrival, end of April, to late August.[1]

---

[1] *British Birds* (Mag.), iv. 276 (C. J. and H. G. Alexander). S. Morris records a late date : Sept. 18, 1900, in *Bird Song*, 119.

PLATE 93.—TURTLE-DOVES : A. W. Seaby.

PLATE 94.—PALLAS'S SANDGROUSE

Syrrhaptes paradoxus (Pallas)

I. Description.—Length, $16\frac{1}{2}$–20 in. Distinguished from all other British birds by its peculiar feet, which are feathered to the claws, together with the absence of a hind toe. The three toes are joined together and form a flat sole which extends to the claws. The male has a band on breast feathers edged with black ; head grey, golden yellow on cheeks and nape ; back, scapulars, and rump warm buff, barred black ; wings and tail blue grey, two central tail feathers $3\frac{1}{2}$ in. longer than the rest ; breast grey buff ; belly buff, with black band, and white towards vent. The female is duller, with shorter tail, more black on upper parts, and black band on throat. Young much like female.

II. Range and Habitat.—An irregular visitor to the British Isles, arriving at long intervals in considerable numbers, and occasionally breeding in sandy wastes and bare wolds. After the invasion of 1888 it bred in Elgin and Yorkshire, but failed to establish itself and disappeared. Abroad its range extends from South-East Russia (Khirgiz steppes) east to Mongolia, and it has appeared in numbers in China (Pechili).

III. Nest and Eggs.—Only a few cases are on record of breeding in Great Britain, and only two clutches exist, both taken on the wolds of Yorkshire, but breeding also took place among the Culbin sands. We have little detail as to its nesting in Asia, but apparently no nesting material is used, the eggs being laid on the bare ground. Eggs : 2–3, rarely 4 ; elongated and elliptical in shape, the ground colour varying from light stone colour or almost white to light brown, blotched and spotted with yellowish brown and ashy shellmarks. Average of 100 eggs, 42.1×29.6 mm. (1.65×1.16 in.). Laying in Asia begins very early, from the end of March onward, but the English eggs were laid in mid-June and early July. Incubation period, 22–28 days in incubator. Probably single brooded. (Plate 185, f. 3.)

IV. Food.—The stomach contents of birds killed in England have contained only vegetable matter (seeds of many species of weeds and grasses, leaves of clover, and grains of corn picked up on the stubbles). In Asia said to feed on young shoots of salt plants (*Salicornia*) and seeds of *Salsola*.

V. Usual Notes.—The male Sandgrouse " often utters a peculiar note in flight, something like the words ' truck, turuck, truck, turuck ' " Whether this represents the song of the species is not clear. It is frequently uttered in the spring and summer.[1]

[1] *British Bird Book*, ii. 530, 537 (Jourdain).

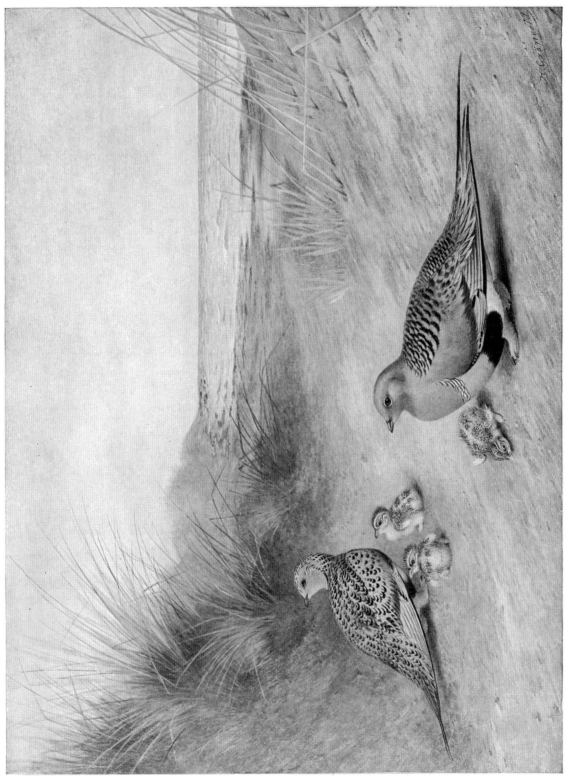

PLATE 94.—SANDGROUSE AND YOUNG (*the cock is the nearer bird, on the right*) : H. Grönvold.

Family : Alcidæ (Auks)

Plate 95.—SOUTHERN-GUILLEMOT

Uria aalge albionis Witherby

NORTHERN-GUILLEMOT

Uria aalge aalge (Pontoppidan)

I. Description.—Length, 18 in. Distinguished at once from Razorbill by slender pointed beak and slimmer neck. In the southern race the head, neck, and upper parts are mouse grey in winter, becoming chocolate brown in the breeding season ; under parts white, and narrow white bar on wing. In the northern race the brown is considerably darker and more blackish ; also more streaked on flanks. Some individuals of both races have a narrow white ring round the eye with a line passing backward. Sexes alike. In winter the throat and part of the sides of the head and neck become white.

II. Range and Habitat.—Resident in the British Isles, breeding on sea cliffs and spending the rest of the year at sea. The Southern form breeds north as far as the Yorkshire cliffs on the east side, and at least to Ailsa on the west, but in the Shetlands and Outer Hebrides is replaced by the Northern race, which also breeds in some of the Inner Hebrides. Birds from the east of Scotland are somewhat intermediate, but closer to the Northern form. Abroad the Northern race breeds on both sides of the Atlantic from Newfoundland northward to South Greenland, Iceland, the Faeroes, Bear Island, Norway, and the Murman coast, while the Southern form ranges south to Brittany and possibly the islands off the coast of Portugal.

III. Nest and Eggs.—Usually breeds in colonies, often of vast extent, on open ledges or horizontal recesses in the face of perpendicular cliffs and on isolated stacks ; also on the flat summits, as at the Farne Islands. Frequently the same range of cliffs is also inhabited by other species, such as Razorbill, Puffin, Kittiwake, etc., but generally each species associates together. No nesting material is used, the single egg being laid on the bare rock, and not infrequently falling into the sea. Egg : single, strongly pyriform in shape, very variable in colour and markings, the ground ranging from white to creamy, yellowish, ochreous, blue, or deep blue green, with the most extraordinary variety of markings, interlacing lines, spots, blotches, or uniform masses of colour ranging from bright red or brown to deep black and greenish black ; at times also quite devoid of markings. Average of 90 British eggs, 83.03 × 50.4 mm. (3.26 × 1.98 in.). Those of the Northern-Guillemot go through the same variations as the Southern form. Laying begins after mid-May, often not till late in May. Incubation period, variously estimated at from 28–33 days ; shared by both sexes. Single brooded. (Plate 186.)

IV. Food.—Mainly small fish, especially sand eels (*Ammodytes*), but crustacea are also taken, as well as small marine mollusca.

V. Usual Notes.—The long crooning note, listened to repeatedly by the writer, resolved itself into two distinguishable sounds which seemed at times to merge into each other : a drawled-out " ur " and a short, hollow barking " hoo." These are combined in varying pitch and sequence : " ur-hoo-hoo-hoo," or " ur-ur-hoo-hoo-hoo," or they may be uttered separately : " ur-ur-ur," " hoo-hoo-hoo-hoo." The note is frequently heard when the pairs are billing ; it also expresses anger, and may be heard uttered as such by birds when another is pushing its way through them back to its nest, or when two are sparring. The species seems to have no alarm note.

95

A.W.SEABY.

PLATE 95.—GUILLEMOTS ON A CORNER OF THE PINNACLES, FARNE ISLES: A. W. Seaby.

PLATE 96.—BRITISH RAZORBILL, *Alca torda britannica* Ticehurst

NORTHERN RAZORBILL, *Alca torda torda* Linnæus

I. Description.—Length, 17 in. Distinguished from the Guillemots by its deep curved and grooved beak with its conspicuous narrow white band, blackish upper parts, and stouter neck. In summer black on upper parts, with greenish gloss; white bar on wing; throat and foreneck dark brown, rest of under parts white. Sexes alike. In winter green gloss is absent; chin, throat, and sides of head white. Young birds are dark brown on upper surface and have smooth bills without white groove, much like winter plumage.

II. Range and Habitat.—Resident, breeding where cliffs are available in Great Britain and Ireland, and spending the rest of the year at sea. Absent from low-lying east coast of England and local on south-eastern coasts. Abroad the smaller northern race breeds on both sides of the Atlantic, from the Bay of Fundy north on the American side to Greenland and Iceland, and on the European side from Brittany and the Channel Isles north to the Faeroes, Scandinavia, and the Murman coast and White Sea, but not proved to breed on Spitsbergen, though it has occurred there and in Novaya Zemlva.

III. Nest and Eggs.—Generally breeds in colonies, sometimes of enormous size, in company with Guillemots, Puffins, etc., in sea cliffs and rocky slopes; but, as a rule, lays its egg well inside a crevice or hole, and not on an exposed ledge like the Guillemot. In default of cliffs it will sometimes lay under a big boulder on the beach. No nesting material is used. Egg: 1 only, less pyriform and more ovate than that of the Guillemot, and showing less variation. Ground colour, white or creamy to light red brown, exceptionally greenish, with spots, blotches of varying size, sometimes uniform cap of blackish to rich chocolate brown. Average size of 100 British eggs, 73.0 × 46.8 mm. (2.87 × 1.84 in.). Laying begins, as a rule, about May 10 (exceptionally earlier). Incubation period, estimated at 25–30 days; shared by both sexes. Single brooded. (Plate 185, f. 5.)

IV. Food.—Mainly small fish, especially sand eels, but also fry of herring, smelt, sprat, etc., as well as crustacea (Amphipoda).

V. Usual Notes.—A harsh continuous croaking, used as a pairing cry and probably to express anger.

GREAT-AUK, *Alca impennis* Linnæus

(No Plate)

I. Description.—Length, 32 in. Now extinct, the last British specimen being taken in 1834. Distinguished from the other British Auks by its great size and inability to fly. Upper parts black, with a white spot in front of the eye; under parts white, the throat and foreneck becoming white in autumn. Wing very short, only about 6½–7 in. from the carpal joint. Bill something like that of Razorbill.

II. Range and Habitat.—Formerly bred in numbers on Funk Island, Newfoundland; also on islets near Iceland and in the Faroes and British Isles. Remains also found in North Norway, Denmark, England, Scotland, Ireland, as well as on the east coast of North America south to Florida from Labrador. In the British Isles the only known breeding places within historic times were on St. Kilda and the Orkneys.

III. Nest and Eggs.—Little on record as to the breeding of this species, but it is known that it only resorted to shelving rocks and low ledges on cliffs or skerries for breeding purposes, and made no nest, laying its single egg on the bare rock. On Funk Island it apparently bred in great numbers, but the British colonies were apparently of no great size. Average size of 29 eggs, 124.2 × 76.4 mm. (4.88 × 3.0 in.); according to Rey, slightly pyriform in shape, white, creamy, and probably blue green, streaked, blotched, and spotted with dark brown or blackish. No reliable information on other points.

IV. Food.—Very little on record, but chiefly fish: *Cottus scorpio* and lumpfish (*Cyclopterus lumpus*) recorded, and according to Naumann *Clupea*; while crustacea are also said to have been taken.

V. Usual Notes.—"The only sound we know this bird to have made is a low croak."[1] Dr. Fleming says that when fed in confinement it expressed anxiety by shaking its head and neck and uttering a gurgling noise.[2]

[1] *British Bird Book*, iii. 36 (Jourdain). *Of. Ibis* 1861, p. 393.
[2] *History of British Animals* (1828).

PLATE 96.—RAZORBILLS WITH CHICK: A. W. Seaby.

PLATE 97.—BLACK-GUILLEMOT, *Uria grylle grylle* (Linnæus)

I. Description.—Length, 11–14 in. Distinguished by large white patch on wings, contrasting with black plumage and vermilion red feet. In summer there is a greenish gloss on the black ; in winter the head and nape are white, mottled with black ; rest of upper surface black, barred with white, except rump and under surface, which are white; wings and tail black. Inside of mouth vermilion. Sexes alike.

II. Range and Habitat.—Resident in the Isle of Man, Scotland, and Ireland, but is absent from the east coast of Scotland south of Sutherland, but common in the Orkneys, Shetlands, and Hebrides, becoming scarce in the south-west of Scotland. In Ireland it is also scarce on the east side, though not uncommon on the west. Abroad it is found on both sides of the Atlantic, from Maine to South Greenland, Iceland and the Faeroes to the Scandinavian and Baltic coasts to the White Sea, but is replaced by an allied form farther north in America, Greenland, Spitsbergen, and Franz Josef Land.

III. Nest and Eggs.—Breeds under large boulders on beaches, in crannies in cliffs, and exceptionally even in holes in walls, but owing to the need of finding suitable sites is less gregarious than the other British Auks. No nest is made, but small fragments of rock appear to be added at times to make a bed for the eggs. Eggs : 2 normally, but clutches of 3 also occur at times. Ground colour, white to pale bluish, rarely with a faint coffee-coloured tinge, usually boldly spotted and blotched with blackish brown and ashy shellmarks ; occasionally white, or only marked with a few fine spots. Average size of 75 British eggs, 57.0 × 39.4 mm. (2.24 × 1.55 in.). Laying begins in second half of May. Incubation period, variably estimated at 21–28 days; shared by both sexes. Single brooded. (Plate 185, f. 6.)

IV. Food.—Small fish (*Gunnellus*), crustacea (small crabs, prawns, shrimps, etc.), mollusca (mussels, etc.). Drowned crane flies and seaweed also recorded.

V. Usual Notes.—" The cry is, for the most part, a weak, twittering sound, but occasionally rises into a very feeble little wail or scream."[1] This latter has also been described as a " low plaintive whine "[2] and a " shrill plaintive cry."[3] On uttering the note the bird opens its beak wide, thus displaying the " wonderful carmine tinged vermilion of the mouth."[3]

PLATE 97.—LITTLE-AUK, *Alle alle* (Linnæus)

I. Description.—Length, 7½–8½ in. Recognized by its small size and black and white plumage. In summer the head, throat, and foreneck, as well as the upper surface, are black, with narrow white edges on secondaries and scapulars ; small white spot over eye ; rest of under parts white. In winter the chin, throat, and foreneck become white. Young birds resemble adults in winter.

II. Range and Habitat.—Only an irregular winter visitor to the coasts of the British Isles, and storm-driven inland, sometimes in numbers. Its breeding range includes Eastern Arctic North America south to Baffin Bay, Greenland, Grimsey, Jan Mayen, Bear Island, Spitsbergen, Franz Josef Land, and Novaya Zemlya. It breeds in cliffs by or near the sea, and spends the rest of the year at sea.

III. Nest and Eggs.—Does not breed in the British Isles. In the Arctic regions there are colonies of enormous extent breeding about arm's length inside crevices among disintegrated rocks, usually in cliffs facing the sea, but also in valleys some distance inland, and among screes of loose boulders on hillsides. No nesting material is used, the egg being laid on bare rock. Egg : 1 only, though 2 have been found in one hole, probably belonging to different birds. Ground colour, pale bluish, often unmarked or with faint yellowish brown spots, but at times with distinct streaks and spots of yellowish brown, chiefly at the big end. Average of 140 eggs, 48.1 × 33.7 mm. (1.89 × 1.32 in.). Laying begins in June. Incubation period, 24 days (Faber); shared by both sexes. Only one brood is reared.

IV. Food.—In its breeding haunts lives almost entirely on small crustacea and other plankton organisms, but in winter has been known to take small fish and even animal offal, according to Saunders.

V. Usual Notes.—Figured variously as " rett-tet-tet-tet " or " trrr, trrr, tet, tet, trrr."[4] These notes, uttered by many hundreds of birds at the breeding place, may be heard from a considerable distance. A high pitched " yip " has been heard from birds at sea.[5]

---

[1] E. Selous, *Bird Watcher in the Shetlands*, 128. [2] Dresser, *Birds of Europe*, viii.
[3] *Wild Life*, 1913, June, 356 (A. M. Stewart). [4] *British Bird Book*, iii. 43.
[5] *Field*, 1930, 782.

PLATE 97.—(*Upper*) BLACK-GUILLEMOTS AND YOUNG; (*Lower*) LITTLE-AUKS IN
WINTER PLUMAGE: A. W. Seaby.

PLATE 98.—PUFFIN

Fratercula arctica grabæ (Brehm)

I. Description.—Length, 12–13 in. Recognized by its extraordinary beak, higher in summer than its length, grooved and strikingly coloured, and bright orange feet. Fore part of beak red, hind part slate blue, divided by yellow line ; but in winter the yellow line and slate blue horny plate are shed, with the creamy fillet at the base of the bill and the slaty appendages above and below the eyes. Upper parts black ; sides of head greyish ; under parts white, except black band round throat. Sexes alike. Young birds have shallower beaks and space in front of eye is black.

II. Range and Habitat.—The British or southern race of the Puffin is resident in the British Isles, also on the coasts of Brittany, formerly on Heligoland, and still in Southern Norway and Sweden. Farther north it is replaced in Novaya Zemlya, Northern Norway, Iceland, South Greenland, and Eastern North America by an allied form, while a larger race is found in Spitsbergen and North Greenland. After the breeding season is over it spends the rest of the year at sea.

III. Nest and Eggs.—As a rule breeds in colonies, often in close association with other species. When on cliffs it prefers the ground near the top, burrowing into the soil, but on low-lying islets may be found nesting in close proximity, so that the ground is honeycombed in all directions, and many burrows communicate with one another. Though rabbit holes are used, the bird is quite capable of excavating its own hole, and generally does so, but holes may be used year after year. Nest material scanty, straw, stalks of weeds, feathers, etc., carelessly arranged. Egg : 1 only ; pointed oval, white, often unmarked or nearly so, but at times with deeply sunk spots of brown and ashy, often tending to form a zone, and more apparent when held up to the light. Average size of 100 British eggs, 60.8 × 42.3 mm. (2.39 × 1.66 in.). Laying begins in early May, often rather later. Incubation period, 36–42 days ; shared by both sexes. Single brooded. (Plate 185, f. 4.)

IV. Food.—The staple food appears to consist of small fish, such as sand eels and fry of *Clupea* ; crustacea are also taken to some extent, chiefly shrimps or prawns.

V. Usual Notes.—A comparatively silent species. It is often content to open its vividly hued beak without utterance. The usual notes have been figured as a long-drawn, very grating " owk " or " ow," and a long-drawn " oooo." The latter is rendered by Naumann " aaaah " or " aahaah," by Selous " awe," presumably the snoring sound one hears at dusk coming from the Puffins' nesting holes. The first note, the " owk," is uttered when the bird is startled ; what other meanings it or the second note has is not yet clear. R. M. Lockley admits only one note : " a low growling ' arr.' " [1]

[1] *British Birds* (Mag.), xxvii. 218.

PLATE 98.—PUFFINS: A. W. Seaby.

Family : Laridæ (Terns, Gulls, Skuas)

PLATE 99.—BLACK-TERN, *Chlidonias niger niger* (Linnæus)

I. Description.—Length, 9½–10 in. About the same size as the Lesser-Tern, but readily recognized by its darker plumage and slender black bill. In summer has the head, neck, breast, and belly black, rest of upper parts sooty grey, except wing coverts, tail coverts, and tail, which are paler grey. Feet reddish brown. Hen in summer generally paler ; under parts grey instead of blackish ; sides of head and nape dark slate. After autumn moult the head and neck is white, except the hinder crown and nape, which have black mixed with the white ; under parts white, mixed with grey. Young have brown markings on upper parts.

II. Range and Habitat.—A marsh-haunting species which formerly bred in the Fens, but has long ceased to do so. It now visits the British Isles irregularly on passage, but is only a rare straggler to Scotland. On the Continent it ranges north to South Sweden and Lake Ladoga in Russia, south to the western Mediterranean, and the Danube valley in the east ; also in the Balearic Isles, and in West Asia from Transcaspia to 85° long. Winters in Africa, and is replaced in America by an allied race.

III. Nest and Eggs.—Has not bred in England since 1858, when it nested in Norfolk. Usually breeds in shallow water, with growth of rushes and water plants, but also at times on ground in neighbourhood of water, and generally in colonies. The nest is merely a heap of rushes, water weeds, etc., lined with finer grasses, and only just above the water level. Eggs : usually 3, sometimes 2 only, while 4 have been recorded. Ground colour, pale yellowish brown, occasionally light greenish, very heavily blotched with blackish brown, sometimes a distinct zone round the large end, with some ashy shellmarks. Average size of 100 eggs, 34.8 × 25.1 mm. (1.37 × .98 in.). Laying begins towards the end of May in Central Europe, earlier in the south. Incubation period, 14–17 days ; shared by both sexes. Single brooded. (Plate 187, f. 6.)

IV. Food.—Chiefly insects taken on the wing in marshes, such as flies (crane flies, gnats, etc.), orthoptera (crickets and grasshoppers), dragon flies, water boatman, mayflies, ants, and water beetles ; also small fish, such as stickleback and minnow, small frogs and tadpoles, leeches.

V. Usual Notes.—A shrill " creek-crick " or " crick-crick," frequently uttered on the wing as it hawks up and down.

PLATE 99.—LITTLE-TERN, *Sterna albifrons albifrons* Pallas

I. Description.—Length, 8½–9½ in. Can be at once distinguished from any of the other British Terns by its small size and the white patch on the forehead. Rest of crown black ; bill yellow, tipped blackish ; feet bright orange ; rump and tail white. Wing beats more rapid than in the other Terns ; notes, sharp, excited " kweeks " and " tiks."

II. Range and Habitat.—Summer resident in British Isles, scattered colonies nesting round the English and Welsh coasts, not very large in extent. In Scotland it is absent from the west and north coasts, but a few breed in the Inner and Outer Hebrides, and it is said to breed in the Orkneys and on the east coast from the Moray Firth southward. On the Continent it breeds from South Sweden to the North African coast, as well as in the Canaries and Madeira ; also in the Black and Caspian Seas and West Siberia, but is replaced by allied forms in Iraq and North-West India, Eastern Asia from Korea to Haman and Ceylon, as well as on the American coasts.

III. Nest and Eggs.—Breeds in colonies, but generally of small extent, usually where sand and shingle are mixed on low shores, sometimes on sand. Nest a mere hollow in the sand. Eggs : 2–3, but 4 on record. Ground colour, whitish or bluish (exceptionally) or stone colour to light brownish (normal), usually spotted and smeared with blackish brown and violet shellmarks ; occasionally with large blotches, rarely quite unmarked. Average of 100 British eggs, 32.9 × 23.8 mm. (1.29 × .93 in.). Laying begins at end of May. Incubation period, 20–22 days ; shared by both sexes. Single brooded. (Plate 187, f. 3.)

IV. Food.—All records refer to small fish (sand eels chiefly), but stickleback and smelt also recorded.

V. Usual Notes.—The usual note uttered by the bird when its breeding-place is invaded is a sharp excited " kweek," accompanied often by a sound like " tik " in rapid varying sequence—*e.g.* " kweek-tik-tik-tik " or " kweek-kweek-kweek-tik." Both notes may be uttered separately. A familiar note heard as the birds fly over the beach is an excited, quick " tiri-wiri-tiri-wiri-tiri-wiri," possibly the " kweeks " and " tiks " modified and softened by distance. The writer has heard no other notes. The call note is figured by Naumann, " kriēh " and kleeēh " (anglicized). Voigt, quoted in Naumann, states that this note is not often heard.

PLATE 99.—(*Upper*) BLACK-TERN IN SUMMER PLUMAGE; (*Lower*) LITTLE-TERN,
SHOWING ERECT ATTITUDE OF THE MALE WHEN FEEDING THE HEN:
A. W. Seaby.

PLATE 100.—COMMON-TERN

Sterna hirundo hirundo Linnæus

I. Description.—Length, 14–14¼ in. Closely resembles the Arctic-Tern, both having crown and nape black, but the under surface of the Common-Tern is white and not pearly grey as in the Arctic-. Mantle and wings silvery grey; rump and tail white; bill coral red, with blackish tip; feet red; broad dark band on inner web of primaries; tarsus longer than in Arctic-Tern. In autumn white feathers in black of crown.

II. Range and Habitat.—Summer resident in the British Isles. Breeding in colonies locally along the coasts of England and Wales, and more commonly in Scotland and East Ireland; scarce in Orkneys, and first recorded breeding in the Shetlands in 1901. On west coast of Ireland outnumbered by Arctic-Tern. On the Continent ranges from the North Cape and White Sea south to the Mediterranean, Black, and Caspian Seas; also to the Azores, Canaries, and Madeira, and east to Iraq and the Yenisei and Mongolia in Asia; also in North America, but replaced by an allied race in Asia from Turkestan to Tibet.

III. Nest and Eggs.—Breeds in colonies, but sites vary considerably, some being on shingly beaches, others among sand-hills or on turf in salt marshes, and at times on bare rocks. Nests also vary a good deal; some birds are content with a hollow scratched out in sand, but generally a few stalks, weeds, bits of grass, or feathers are added as lining. Eggs: normally 3, but at times only 2, while 4 occurs at times, though 5 is probably due to two hens laying together; variable, the ground ranging from bright blue, bluish white, or pink (rare) to grey, stone colour, or brown (more commonly). The markings (which are sometimes altogether absent) consist of spots and blotches of dark brown, with ashy shellmarks, and sometimes tend to form a zone or cap. A rare erythristic type also occurs. Average of 100 British eggs, 40.9 × 30.3 mm. (1.61 × 1.19 in.). Laying begins towards end of May as a rule. Incubation period, 21–22½ days, sometimes longer; both sexes taking part. Single brooded. (Plate 187, f. 2.)

IV. Food.—Chiefly small fish, especially sand eels, but 15-spined stickleback, herring fry, whiting, and very small plaice also recorded; crustacea (sandhopper, shrimps) and insects (beetles, dragon flies, crane flies, etc.).

V. Usual Notes.—The ordinary call of the Common-Tern is a long-drawn disyllabic " keee-yerrr," which can be distinguished from the shorter note of the Arctic-Tern : " kerr " or " kerr-err." Both utter a note like " ptip " repeated, of which the meaning is uncertain. The Common-Tern utters a rapid " kik-kik-kik," followed or preceded by " kerrs " or " kwerrs," uttered singly or repeated, and sometimes independently of the " kiks." Whether used together or apart these notes are heard when the birds are fighting or attacking intruders. The corresponding note of the Arctic-Tern is rendered in the writer's notebooks sometimes by the " kiks " and " kerrs," sometimes by " titiwerr, titiwerr, titiwerr." According to Naumann there is a difference between all the utterances of the two species, but it is not easily defined.

PLATE 100.—COMMON-TERN RISING WITH FISH : A. W. Seaby.

PLATE 101.—ARCTIC-TERN

Sterna macrura Naumann

I. Description.—Length, 15 in. Not easily distinguished from the Common-Tern, but has the breast grey and not white, the bill blood-red to the tip, a narrow dark band on inner web of primaries, and shorter tarsus. Crown and nape black; mantle dark grey; rump whitish; tail white; feet coral red. In winter some white on forehead, and soft parts duller. Young have bill and feet reddish yellow, black in winter; crown and nape streaked dark brown; mantle barred ashy.

II. Range and Habitat.—Summer resident in the British Isles, but not known to breed on the east side south of the Farnes, or on the south except on the Scillies, and is very local on the west side of England and Wales, but common in Scotland and Ireland. Abroad it breeds in the Faroes, Iceland, Spitsbergen, and Franz Josef Land, and on the European coast from the shores of the Arctic south to Holland, and a great part of the Baltic, also in Greenland, northern North America, and from

Common-Tern's primary.

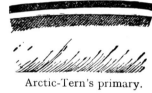

Arctic-Tern's primary.

the Commander Isles west along the Siberian coast, wintering south to the Antarctic Ocean.

III. Nest and Eggs.—Frequently on rocky islets, where hardly a trace of a nest is made, but also on shingle and occasionally inland on shores of lakes. Nest very slight; often no material whatever, but at times a few stalks. Eggs: normally 2, 3 occasionally met with, but not normal, and 1 in some places common; as a rule slightly smaller than those of Common-Tern, more heavily marked, elongated specimen rarer. Ground colour, ranges from pale blue, pinkish, greyish white, brown, but the two former types are rare. Some eggs are quite unmarked with blue or bluish white ground; the rare erythristic type has rich red brown markings on a pinkish ground, while normal eggs have blackish brown spots and blotches and ashy shellmarks. Average of 74 British eggs, 40.8 × 29.3 mm. (1.60 × 1.15 in.). Laying begins in early June. Incubation period, 21–22 days, apparently sometimes longer; shared by both sexes. Single brooded. (Plate 187, f. 4.)

IV. Food.—Chiefly small fish, such as stickleback, fry of herring, etc., but also largely crustacea (sandhopper, *Clio*, *Hippolyte*, etc.); insects (large beetles, moths and caterpillars, crane flies, etc.), also small mollusca and worms.

V. Usual Notes.—See COMMON-TERN, p. 100.

PLATE 101.—ARCTIC-TERN CHASED BY ARCTIC-SKUA : G. E. Lodge.

PLATE 102.—ROSEATE-TERN

Sterna dougallii dougallii Montagu

I. Description.—Length, 15–17 in. A longer, slender-looking bird, distinguished by black beak, red at base, long white streamers to tail, rosy flush on breast, and very different note. Crown and nape black ; mantle rather paler than in Common- and Arctic-Terns ; feet red ; inner webs of primaries altogether white. In winter much white on forehead.

II. Range and Habitat.—A local summer resident in the British Isles, and rather capricious ; in a few places forming large colonies in company with other Terns, in others only a few scattered pairs nesting. The main colony in Wales was long deserted, but there are small colonies at the Farnes and Skerries, and large numbers nest now off the Irish coast. Other known breeding places abroad are Brittany, the Tunisian coast, some of the Atlantic island groups, the east coast of North and South America. Other allied races breed in the Indian and Pacific Oceans and the Australian seas.

III. Nest and Eggs.—Prefers to make its nest on rocky ground in natural hollow, sometimes in recess on face of outcrop, exceptionally like Common-Tern. Nest material very scanty indeed or altogether absent. Eggs : normally 2, but in some colonies 1 very common, very rarely 3 ; more elongated and pointed than the other Terns. Ground colour, buff or creamy, spotted with brown frequently in a zone round the large end, with ashy shellmarks. Average size of 100 British eggs, 44.0 × 29.9 mm. (1.73 × 1.17 in.). Laying begins early in June. Incubation period, 24–26 days ; shared by both sexes. Only one brood is reared. (Plate 187, f. 1.)

IV. Food.—Hardly any definite records, but all refer to small fish taken from the sea.

V. Usual Notes.—The most characteristic utterance of the Roseate-Tern is " a long piping note, ' kēē-ēē-ēē,' almost like a whistle, readily distinguishable among the babel of cries raised by the accompanying throng of Common-Terns and Arctic-Terns." [1] A note, classed as a call, is variously rendered " krr-ēēē " and " che-wick " ; another, classed as an alarm note, is rendered " craak " or " crrark," and described as a sound harsher than the first note of the Common-Tern and not disyllabic. The species utters a " kik-kik-kik " similar to that of the Common- and Arctic-Terns.

---

[1] *British Bird Book*, iii. 97, where the evidence from Oswin Lee, Cummings and Oldham, Bickerton and Jourdain is given.

PLATE 102 —ROSEATE-TERN BRINGING A FISH TO ITS YOUNG : A. W. Seaby.

PLATE 103.—SANDWICH-TERN

Sterna sandvicensis sandvicensis Latham

I. Description.—Length, 15–16½ in. The largest of the British Terns described here, recognizable by its black mane-shaped crest and crown, with relatively long black bill, tipped with yellow, and black feet, with white tail and rump; mantle and wings pearl grey. Young show black or dusky markings on the upper surface. Note, a sharp " kirr-whit," and stouter build also distinctive.

II. Range and Habitat.—Local on the British coasts, but now breeds in considerable numbers in Norfolk, as well as at the Farnes; till recently there was a fine colony in Cumberland, now much reduced; it breeds at Walney and in Anglesey, and a few pairs elsewhere. In Scotland its most northerly station is in the Orkneys, and there are other colonies, chiefly on the west side. The Irish colonies are chiefly in Ulster. It is a summer resident, and on the Continent breeds on the Baltic and North Sea coasts as well as by the Mediterranean, Black and Caspian Seas, wintering on African and South Asiatic coasts. An allied race breeds in North America.

III. Nest and Eggs.—Breeds in close-packed colonies usually on sandy shores of islands, sometimes on sandhills among marram grass. Nest often merely a hollow scratched in the sand, grass stalks, however, sometimes used. Eggs : normally 2, but often 1 only; 3 very scarce in the British Isles. Ground colour varies from white (sometimes quite unmarked) to creamy or pinkish brown, spotted, blotched, and smeared with brownish black or red brown and violet shellmarks. Average size of 100 British eggs, 51.7 × 36.1 mm. (2.03 × 1.42 in.). Laying begins early May, exceptionally at end of April. Incubation period, 20–21 days ; shared by both sexes. Only one brood. (Plate 187, f. 5.)

IV. Food.—Almost entirely small fish, chiefly sand eels; but sprat, weaver, young herring, young whiting, and garfish also recorded.

V. Usual Notes.—The usual call is, as above stated, a sharp " kirr-whit." The note uttered when intruders are near the nest appears in the writer's note-books as " kwuk " (from a distance), and " keek " or " kweek " or " kwrreek " (near to). Another note is a " kwerr " or " kwarr," not unlike a corresponding utterance of the Common and Arctic forms.

103

PLATE 103.—SANDWICH-TERNS: (*foreground*) COCK ABOUT TO FEED HEN, (*left*) A PAIR DISPLAYING, (*right*) SITTING BIRDS. A. W. Seaby.

PLATE 104.—BLACKHEADED-GULL

Larus ridibundus ridibundus Linnæus

I. Description.—Length, 15–16 in. Distinguished from Common-Gull by red feet and bill, and in breeding season by coffee-brown head, except for greyish white feathers behind the eye. Back and wings pearl grey; primaries show a good deal of white, especially the three outermost, but with black tips. Rest of plumage white. Sexes alike; male larger. Immature birds have broad penultimate blackish brown band on tail, and have more or less brown on the wing coverts.

II. Range and Habitat.—A local resident in the British Isles, colonies being found in many counties of Great Britain and Ireland, as well as in the Shetlands and Outer Hebrides, etc. Abroad it is found in the Faeroes and on the Continent from Southern Scandinavia, Finland, and Archangel in Russia, south to the Mediterranean, and also across Asia to Kamtschatka; but East Siberian birds have been separated as an allied race. Winters in North Africa, South Asia, and the Philippines.

III. Nest and Eggs.—Nests in colonies of varying size, some being of enormous extent. Sites very variable: among sand-hills by the sea, or shingle beds, on islets in lakes, or in marshes by water inland or on moors at a considerable elevation. Nests sometimes very bulky, while others are slight, built of materials to hand : marram grass, reeds, rushes, grass, bracken, etc. Has been recorded on buildings and trees, often in shallow water. Eggs : normally 3 or 2 at times, but 4 occur seldom. Although normally there is little variation, ground varying from greenish olive to brown with blotches or spots of dark umber and ashy shellmarks, varieties of pale blue, unmarked or slightly marked, erythristic or with large cap of umber, etc., have occurred from time to time. Average of 100 British eggs, 51.9 × 37.2 mm. (2.40 × 1.46 in.). Laying begins towards the end of April. Incubation period, 22–25 days as a rule ; by both sexes. The eggs are hatched at intervals of about 24 hours. Single brooded. (Plate 188, f. 1.)

IV. Food.—Collinge has shown that insects form a large proportion of the food of this species even in winter, chiefly beetles, while moths and flies were also well represented. Earthworms are taken largely ; also sand eels. Other food recorded includes snails and slugs, crustacea, millipedes, centipedes, dead moles, mice, small birds (Pipit and Willow-Wren), and vegetable matter (grain, potatoes, seeds of various plants, etc.).

V. Usual Notes.—Repeated observation from season to season has not enabled the writer to distinguish more than four notes, at least at the breeding place. The commonest sounds like "kwurp," and sometimes "kwowp" without any *r* sound ; it signifies rising or falling anger, food-hunger, sex-hunger, and is a call to the mate. In moments of increased excitement the "kwurp" becomes a wide-beaked "kwarr," often repeated without closing of the mandibles ; it expresses maximum anger, and is also a call. The alarm note is a short, abrupt "kwup," the beak being quickly opened and shut. The fourth note is a crooning "kwo-oo-oo" ; usually uttered beak to ground, the beak closed or slightly open ; it is the food call to the chicks, but has other meanings, and at times sounds like a muttered "kwurp." The usual scream of attacking Blackheads, heard when one passes through a gullery, is either "kwarr" or a stuttered form of the same that sounds like a frenzied screech. When the attacking bird alights to rest, the anger note descends from "kwarr" to "kwurp," and may alter to the "kwup" of alarm according to the movements of the intruder.

LITTLE-GULL, *Larus minutus* Pallas

(No Plate)

I. Description.—Length, 10–11 in. In breeding plumage, like a Blackheaded-Gull, but smaller, with a *black* hood, and also distinguished by dark under surface of wing and absence of black on primaries. Mantle and wings bluish grey, neck and tail as well as under parts white, bill red brown, feet red. In winter the head is white, with ashy nape. Young have black and grey marks on head, brown band on tail, bill blackish, feet pinkish.

II. Range and Habitat.—Irregular winter visitor to the British Isles, breeding on the Continent from North Russia and Finland to Gotland, Öland, Denmark, Esthonia, and Prussia. Also in Asia east to the Sea of Okhotsk. Winters in the Mediterranean, Black and Caspian Seas, and in the North Pacific.

III. Nest and Eggs.—Does not breed in the British Isles. Nests in scattered colonies, sometimes in shallow water or on low-lying sandbanks, frequently in company with Terns and other Gulls. Nest built of water plants, sedges, rushes, reeds, etc. Eggs : usually 2–3, but 4 and 5 exceptionally recorded ; much resembling those of the Common-Tern. Ground colour buffish to olive brown, with dark brown spots and blotches and ashy shellmarks. Average size of 119 eggs, 41.5 × 30.1 mm. (1.63 × 1.18 in.). Laying begins late in May as a rule. Incubation period not known. Single brooded.

IV. Food.—Chiefly insects (beetles, flies, and neuroptera) and small fish, during the breeding season ; but also crustacea (shrimps), sandworms, and earthworms. Grain (barley) has also been recorded.

V. Usual Notes.—A characteristic note is a penetrating "kayéé" rapidly repeated, often as many as twenty to forty times, as the birds fly overhead. Other notes are a low "tok, tok, tok" and a soft "kie, kie." [1]

---

[1] *British Bird Book*, iii. 152. The renderings are by Henrici (*Ornith. Monatsschrift.*, 1903, p. 201).

PLATE 104.—BLACKHEADED-GULLS FOLLOWING THE PLOUGH : A. W. Seaby.

PLATE 105.—COMMON-GULL

Larus canus canus Linnæus

I. Description.—Length, 17–18 in. A miniature Herring-Gull; in size comes close to the Blackheaded-Gull and Kittiwake; but is distinguished from the Blackheaded-Gull by its yellowish green feet and bill, and from the Kittiwake in flight by the presence of white spots near tips of black primaries. Head, tail, and under parts white; back and wings pearl grey except primaries. Sexes much alike. Immature birds have broad brown tail band, and in winter adults have a good deal of ashy brown on head and neck. Young birds also have much ashy brown in plumage.

II. Range and Habitat.—Resident in Scotland and Ireland, breeding generally near the coast in Scotland and on the adjacent islands, and in Ireland chiefly in the northern counties, and on the west coast to co. Kerry. In England it has bred on the Solway and also on the Farnes, and at Dungeness (Kent), but is mainly a winter visitor when adult. On the Continent its range extends from North Russia and Finland, through Scandinavia and the Baltic to Denmark; locally Holland and North Germany, and apparently to South-East Russia, wintering as far south as North Africa. Also from Transcaucasia and Transcaspia to Siberia, but from the Yenisei to the Pacific and in Western North America it is replaced by allied races.

III. Nest and Eggs.—Not a cliff breeder, but breeds in colonies on islets off the coast or in lakes, and also on moorlands and grassy hills both inland and near the coast. Nest rather variable in size, but at times bulky, built of materials at hand, heather, grass, bracken, seaweed, etc. Eggs: usually 3, not infrequently 2, only rarely 4. Ground colour varying from pale blue (scarce) to olive and brown; occasionally unmarked, but generally spotted and blotched with dark umber and some shellmarks. Average size of 100 eggs, 58.4 × 41.3 mm. (2.29 × 1.62 in.). Laying begins latter part of May or early June. Incubation by both sexes; period, 28 days. One brood. (Plate 188, f. 2.)

IV. Food.—Almost omnivorous; has been seen to swallow an eel a foot long! Will take carrion, also field voles, small birds, and eggs of any kind of bird within reach up to Redthroated-Divers; fish, mollusca (slugs, cockles, etc.), earthworms, insects (beetles, flies, caterpillars, etc.), crustacea, millipedes, etc., as well as vegetable matter, potatoes, turnips, grain, grass, seeds, seaweed, and refuse of all kinds.

V. Usual Notes.—Its usual note sounds to the writer like a high-pitched " kweee-ah "—almost a clear whistle; it is heard when the birds are circling overhead or pursuing each other, and may be repeated several times to form a prolonged cachinnation. By others it is figured as " skeeah," " kleeah," " kaeeeeow," and finally " gnyee-eh " (anglicized). The alarm note is " kak," also rendered " skak " or " yak."

105

PLATE 105.—COMMON-GULLS IN WINTER: Winifred Austen.

PLATE 106.—HERRING-GULL, *Larus argentatus argentatus* Pontoppidan

YELLOW-LEGGED HERRING-GULL, *Larus argentatus cachinnans* Pall

I. Description.—Length, 22–24 in. Much larger than any of our Gulls here described except Lesser Blackbacked (slightly smaller), Iceland (the same), Great Blackbacked, and Glaucous (much larger). Distinguished from the Blackbacked Gulls by its pearl grey mantle, and from the Iceland and Glaucous by its black primaries with white spots near tip ; head, tail, and under parts white ; mantle and wings (except primaries) pearl grey ; feet flesh-coloured ; bill yellow with red spot. Female smaller. In winter head and neck streaked with grey. Young freely mottled with brown, tail barred brown, under parts white.

II. Range and Habitat.—Resident, breeding on the coasts (except where very low-lying) of Great Britain, Ireland, and the adjacent island groups. On the Continent it breeds on the north coasts of Russia and Finland, Scandinavia and the Baltic (except in the Gulf of Finland), Denmark, Holland, and France ; also in Greenland and North America (sometimes regarded as a subspecies), while the yellow-legged forms replace it on the White Sea, Lake Onega, Gulf of Finland, and on the Black, Caspian, and Mediterranean seas, as well as on the coast of Portugal and Spain, and in the Canaries, Azores, and Madeira. One obtained in England and others seen. Other races also occur in Eastern Asia and Arctic America.

III. Nest and Eggs.—Breeds usually on broken, grassy cliffs or on small islands in the British Isles, but abroad nests on open moors and among sand dunes. Nest bulky, built of varied materials : heather, seaweed, grasses, etc., and neatly lined with fine grasses, etc. Eggs : normally 3, occasionally only 2, and 4 recorded. Ground colour, olive to brown, spots of dark umber, usually rather small, with ashy shellmarks. A type with blue ground, sometimes unmarked, also occurs. Erythristic type only recorded from the Continent. Average of 50 British eggs, 69.8 × 48.3 mm. (2.74 × 1.90 in.). Laying begins latter part of April. Incubation period, about 26 days ; shared by both sexes. One brood. (Plate 188, f. 3.)

IV. Food.—Also omnivorous : dead mammals up to size of sheep, also young rabbits, moles, etc. ; wounded and small birds (young Kittiwake, Corncrake, Dunlin, and smaller species) ; eggs of large and small birds (Guillemot, Razorbill, Cormorant, Gannet, etc.) ; stranded fish of all kinds, marine mollusca, crustacea (crabs, shrimps, etc.), earthworms and marine worms, insects and larvæ (beetles, flies, earwigs, etc.). Also much vegetable matter : turnips, potatoes, grain, and many seeds and berries as well as refuse.

V. Usual Notes.—A common call is the somewhat plaintive mewing " kwee-ow " or " kyow," which in moments of excitement becomes " klee-ow." It is heard at all seasons. The chief alarm note sounds like a laugh : " ha-ha-ha," or " ga-ga-ga-ga " as rapidly uttered as possible. Listened to attentively it becomes " ow " or " kwow." A note heard uttered by a few birds when sailing, while their fellows uttered the " ow," sounded like " kwee-orr," and possibly corresponds to the " kiiauw " of Portielje, described by him as a minor alarm note and as an anger cry.[1] The same authority renders thus the loud, wild cachinnation that the bird utters while it goes through the curious display of lowering its head in a regurgitative manner to toss it, wide-beaked, towards the heavens :

Head down.	*Head up.*
aow ! aow ! aow ! kyeee.	owky owky owky ow.

The outburst sounds differently to the writer, who has been able to distinguish only two parts, and no great difference between them : *Head down,* " ée-er, ée-er, ée-er " ; *Head up,*" eow ! eow ! eow ! ow !" or " eee-áh . . ." or " a-er . . ." Among other notes ascribed to the species by Portielje are a cooing " hoo-oh," and a cackling pairing note, " how, how, how." All renderings from the German are here anglicized.

[1] *Ardea*, xviii. 112–149.

PLATE 106.—BRITISH LESSER BLACKBACKED-GULL

Larus fuscus graellsii Brehm

SCANDINAVIAN LESSER BLACKBACKED-GULL

Larus fuscus fuscus Linnæus

I. Description.—Length, 21–23 in. The dark back and wings distinguish it from all the other Gulls described except the Great Blackbacked, which is larger, and has flesh-coloured instead of yellow feet. Head, neck, and under parts white; mantle and wings in the British race dark slate grey; primaries black, with white "mirrors"; beak yellow with red patch. Female smaller. Scandinavian birds have the mantle much darker. In winter the head and neck are streaked with grey. Young are mottled with brown, and are darker than young Herring-Gulls.

II. Range and Habitat.—The British race breeds locally on the cliffs of the coasts of Great Britain, becoming more numerous in the north, and is found on all the island groups; also locally on the coast and inland in Ireland. Its range includes the Faeroes; it is found in small numbers in Holland, and from the Channel Isles to North-West France. The Scandinavian form breeds along the coasts of Northern Europe south to the Baltic, and in Siberia east to the Dwina. In Wales, Scotland, and Ireland there are colonies on moors inland as well as on the coasts.

III. Nest and Eggs.—Usually breeds in colonies on small islands or grassy cliffs, but also on wet moorlands often many miles from the sea. Nest large, built of heather, grasses, seaweed, or dead stalks, lined with finer grasses. Eggs: usually 3, sometimes only 2, and 4 recorded; slightly smaller on the average than Herring-Gull's. Ground colour, ranging from olive brown to very dark brown, with bold blotches and spots of dark sepia and shellmarks. A light blue type also occurs, sometimes unmarked; also pale greenish grey eggs, sparsely marked. Average of 100 eggs, 67.9×47.2 mm. (2.67×1.85 in.). Laying begins early in May. Incubation period, 26 days; said to be shared by the sexes. One brood. (Plate 188, f. 4.)

IV. Food.—Another omnivorous species; carrion; kills Puffins, Shearwaters, young Lapwings, etc., and is destructive to eggs of Cormorant, Ducks, Grouse, Terns, and small birds; fish (stranded and caught alive up to size of eel), marine mollusca, worms, insects, chiefly beetles and flies and their larvæ. Also takes grain, seaweed, etc.

V. Usual Notes.—Its utterances have not been as closely studied as those of the Herring-Gull. It utters much the same alarm note: "ha! ha! ha!" or "ow-ow-ow"; also the mewing call note. The cachinnation heard by the writer from birds in captivity ran usually thus: "ooo," or "or," repeated (head down); "er," or "ar," or "eow," repeated (head thrown up). It may end with an "ow" or two.

PLATE 106.—ICELAND-GULL

Larus leucopterus Vieillot

I. Description.—Length, 22 in. A miniature Glaucous-Gull in colouring, but about the size of the Lesser Blackback, and has extremely long wings in proportion to its size; mantle and wings pearl grey, rest of plumage white in adults. Young similar in colouring to young Glaucous.

II. Range and Habitat.—Winter visitor to the British Isles. Apparently breeds on Jan Mayen (but not on Iceland), Greenland, and Eastern Arctic Canada. (Also said to breed on Novaya Zemlya, but probably in error.)

III. Nest and Eggs.—Does not nest in the British Isles. Breeds sometimes in colonies on ledges of cliffs, and also on low islets. Nest built of mosses, seaweed, and grass, and somewhat bulky. Eggs: 2–3, decidedly smaller than those of Glaucous-Gull. Ground colour, stone buff or yellowish clay, with dark brown spots and blotches and ashy shellmarks. Average size of 61 eggs, 68.6 × 48.2 mm. (2.70 × 1.89 in.). Laying begins about end of May. No details of incubation period or share of sexes. Single brooded.

IV. Food.—Carrion when available; also stranded fish and young fish of several Arctic species taken alive, crustacea and mollusca; also vegetable matter (barley, oats, etc.) and refuse of all kinds. Young said to be fed on berries of crowberry.

V. Usual Notes.—Not much is known. The species has the usual alarm note, figured variously as repetitions of " gag " or " gog " or " gi."

For the Herring-Gull and Lesser Blackbacked-Gull shown on Plate 106,
see pages 106 and 106-A.

PLATE 106.—LESSER BLACKBACKED-GULLS AND HERRING-GULLS (*right hand*) AND ICELAND-GULL (*left*):
A. W. Seaby.

PLATE 107.—GREAT BLACKBACKED-GULL

Larus marinus Linnæus

I. Description.—Length, 26–33 in. In colour pattern closely resembles the Lesser Blackbacked, but is decidedly larger, with a deeper note, and has flesh-coloured and not yellow feet. The mantle is also black rather than slaty. Bill yellow, red spot at angle. Young are paler than corresponding stage in Lesser Blackbacked- and Herring-Gulls.

II. Range and Habitat.—Resident on the coasts of Great Britain and Ireland. Scarce on south English coast except in Scillies, and absent from east coast, but breeds locally on west and more commonly in Scotland and the islands, but not on the south-east coast of Scotland. In Ireland chiefly on west side. Breeds on islets and stacks at sea ; also on islands in lakes inland. Abroad it breeds in Iceland, Faeroes, Bear Island (1921), and on the Continent from North Russia and Finland, Scandinavia and the Baltic east coasts and islands, Brittany ; also in Greenland and Eastern Canada.

III. Nest and Eggs.—Although single pairs may often be found nesting on islets, where numerous this species is decidedly sociable in the breeding season, and some of the colonies are of considerable size even in the British Isles. It is not a cliff builder, the nest being usually placed on low ground. Nest bulky, built of heather stalks, seaweed, grasses, stalks, and a few feathers. Eggs : usually 3, sometimes 2, 5 once recorded. Ground occasionally blue, sometimes unmarked, but as a rule stone colour to olive brown, spotted or blotched with dark umber and ashy shell-marks. A beautiful erythristic type occurs in Norway. Average of 100 British eggs, 77.3 × 53.9 mm. (3.04 × 2.12 in.). Laying begins from early May onward. Incubation period, 26–28 days ; shared by both sexes. Only one brood is reared. (Plate 189, f. 2.)

IV. Food.—Varied, ranging from carrion, especially dead sheep, and also at times injured or helpless ewes, lambs, small mammals (rabbit, rat, mole, field mice, etc.), birds of many species and their young, wounded Ducks, Puffins, Manx-Shear-waters, Petrels, Little-Auk, Oyster-Catcher, and smaller birds, and young of Cormorant, Merganser, Eider, Curlew, etc., as well as eggs of Ducks, Guillemots, etc., fish, mollusca (whelk, etc.), crabs, starfish, worms, beetles, and some vegetable matter.

V. Usual Notes.—Utters a sound like " ow," either harsh or deep or liquid. It passes into " eow," or " meow." Is used in driving off other birds. As an alarm it is uttered quickly : " Ow ! ow ! ow ! " Has no doubt other meanings. It is sometimes mixed with " or," or combined to form " ow-or." A loud, wild cachinnation is uttered with an accompanying display, the beak being usually held between the feet and then tossed forward or upward. The utterances composing the cachinnation were heard at close quarters by the writer from birds in captivity. The note uttered with the head down varied from " oooo ! " to " oo-or " or " or," the mandibles being either closed or slightly open. The up-note varied from " arh " to " a-er " or " er," repeated with the mandibles open, the sound being finished before they were closed. The cachinnation usually, but not always, ended with one or more " ows." It was at times uttered with little or no display, and even when the bird was sitting on the ground. A soft low " cok-cok-cok " is uttered by both sexes as a kind of love note.[1]

[1] B. Lloyd, *in litt.*

107

PLATE 107.—GREAT BLACKBACKED-GULLS : A. W. Seaby.

Plate 108.—GLAUCOUS-GULL

Larus hyperboreus Gunnerus

I. Description.—Length, 26–33 in. About the same size as the preceding species, but distinguished at once by the entire absence of the black on mantle and wings, which are pearly grey ; while the rest of the plumage is white. In winter the head and neck are striped with ashy. The only species with which it can be confused is the rare Iceland Gull, which is smaller. Most of the birds which visit us are immature ; white mottled with pale brown, with greyish white primaries. There is a brief stage when the whole plumage is white.

II. Range and Habitat.—Winter visitor to the British Isles, chiefly in the north and east. Breeds in small numbers in Iceland, commonly Bear Island and Spitsbergen, islands and coast of North Russia and Siberia ; also Greenland and East Canada south to Newfoundland. In the Arctic it is generally parasitic on the colonies of sea birds, and breeds close to them.

III. Nest and Eggs.—Does not nest in the British Isles. Breeds in colonies where numerous, always close to breeding places of rock birds ; sometimes on low sandy islets, but more usually on grassy slopes at top of cliff. Nest built chiefly of mosses torn up from close at hand, but Arctic plants also used, and occasionally seaweed or marram grass. Eggs : usually 2–3, but 4 on record. Ground colour stone buff to reddish brown, occasionally bluish green, spotted and blotched with dark umber brown, and the usual shellmarks. Average of 115 eggs from Spitsbergen, 76.8 × 53.9 mm. (3.02 × 2.12 in.). Laying begins late in May. Incubation period, 27–28 days. Single brooded.

IV. Food.—Carrion (remains of whales, blubber, walrus, polar bear, etc.), birds (including Kittiwake, Little-Auk, Puffin, Guillemot, young Ivory-Gull, Ducks, and Coot, probably in most cases injured in some way), great numbers of eggs and young of rock-breeding birds, droppings of large Arctic mammals, fish, crustacea, starfish, sea urchins, mollusca, refuse of all kinds, etc. Also some vegetable matter ; berries of crowberry and seaweed.

V. Usual Notes.—Its notes are usually more high-pitched than those of the preceding species. The bird utters a plaintive mewing " ee-ow " or " mee-ow." A form of this, heard from a bird in captivity, is rendered in the writer's note-book as " mèèèè-ee-owww," long-drawn, with the mandibles open all the time. The same bird or its mate, when trying to escape from a breeding Great Blackbacked-Gull, uttered a high-pitched " uck-ee " several times. The pair had a cachinnation not unlike that of other Gulls, but the full details were not recorded. A shrill laughing note is uttered when the breeding place is invaded ; this has been figured as " gaga-gak," " gogogok," [1] which clearly corresponds to the " ah ! ah ! ah ! " or " ow ! ow ! ow ! " or " ga-ga-ga " of the Blackbacks and Herring-Gull.

---

[1] Naumann, *Vögel Mitteleuropas*, xi. 271.

PLATE 108.—GLAUCOUS-GULLS: Winifred Austen.

PLATE 109.—KITTIWAKE

Rissa tridactyla tridactyla (Linnæus)

I. Description.—Length, 15–16 in. About the same size as the Blackheaded-Gull, and only slightly smaller than the Common-Gull. In the hand the vestigial hind toe—absent, or a warty excrescence with a small claw—is a certain distinction from both. In summer the head is pure white, beak greenish yellow, feet almost black. In flight the wings show a triangular black tip ; note (kitti-a-way) also characteristic. Mantle and wings chiefly bluish grey, rest of plumage white. Young have bill black, black band at end of tail, dark ring round neck, but lack the brown markings of the other juvenile Gulls.

II. Range and Habitat.—Resident in the British Isles. Absent from the south and east coasts of England north to Yorkshire, where it has greatly increased in numbers, but still breeds in Cornwall and locally in west of England and Wales. As it requires precipitous cliffs, and breeds in colonies, it is necessarily a localized species, and in Scotland is more numerous on west than on east side. Abroad it breeds in Brittany and from Scandinavia to the West Siberian coast, and on all the Arctic islands ; also in Greenland, Jan Mayen south to the St. Lawrence River in Canada. In Europe winters south to the Mediterranean. In Alaska and Berings Sea it is replaced by an allied race.

III. Nest and Eggs.—In the British Isles this species always nests in colonies, often in company with other rock-breeding species, on precipitous cliffs or caves overhanging the sea, but in the Arctic colonies exist on cliffs inland. As a rule there is a tendency to place the nests as low as can be done with safety from the waves in stormy weather. Nest neatly built of mosses, grasses, or seaweed on ledge of rock, and firmly attached to site. Eggs : in most colonies, 2, but in the south many sets of 3, while in the far north 1 and 2 form the normal set. Colour variable, ground ranging from pale blue, sometimes unmarked, to bluish grey, stone colour, reddish brown, deep brown, etc., blotched or spotted with brown and ashy shellmarks. Average size of 100 British eggs, 55.9 × 40.8 mm. (2.20 × 1.60 in.). Laying begins at end of May. Incubation period, 26 days ; by both sexes. Single brooded. (Plate 189, f. 1.)

IV. Food.—Much more marine in its feeding habits than the other Gulls : chief item of diet fish and fish refuse, but also takes crustacea and mollusca, sea urchins, etc. Also occasionally earthworms, insects (beetles and larvæ, flies, etc.), once a pygmy-shrew, and vegetable matter (grain, seeds, aquatic plants, etc.).

V. Usual Notes.—The commonest utterance is that which gives the species its name ; it can be fairly well imitated by pronouncing " kitti-way-ék " as a parrot would. The bird may repeat the note rapidly, the outburst ending with an excited high-pitched " k'wake," like the squeak of a pencil on a slate. It is the usual call of mated birds one to the other on the return of one of them to the nest. The writer heard it twice used by fighting birds, on the second occasion the note being reduced to " kit." Another common note is " ur " or " kur " or " urkur." It may frequently be heard on the return of a bird to the nest, usually after the " kitti-way-ék." Its significance is obscure. A curious note is a " kik-kik," uttered with a jerk of the beak as if to toss something away. Occasionally, on the return to the nest, a rapid " powp " may be uttered. There is finally a mewing cry, rare in the writer's experience.

PLATE 109.—KITTIWAKES : A. W. Seaby.

PLATE 110.—GREAT-SKUA,[1] *Stercorarius skua skua* (Brünnich)

I. Description.—Length, 24–25 in. Recognized by hooked bill and bluish cere, general dark umber brown of upper plumage and lighter under surface, and white patch at base of primaries, which is noticeable in flight. Bill and feet black ; paler buff streaks on both upper and under surface ; middle tail feathers only slightly longer than the rest.

II. Range and Habitat.—In the British Isles it only bred at certain localities in the Shetlands till comparatively recently, but has now spread to the Orkneys, and has several large colonies in the Shetlands besides the old ones at Foula and Hermaness. Otherwise it is a scarce winter visitor. Abroad it breeds in the Faeroes, Iceland, and possibly in Arctic Canada, but record unsatisfactory. Winters as far south as the Mediterranean.

III. Nest and Eggs.—Breeds in colonies, but the nests are some distance apart from one another, on moorlands, sometimes low down, but at times at considerable elevation and generally not far from the sea. Nest slight ; a hollow among heather or grass, lined with heather twigs and grasses. Eggs : normally 2, but sometimes 1 only, and 3 several times recorded. Ground colour, usually olive grey to reddish brown, sometimes very pale greyish or almost white or pale blue, occasionally without markings, but usually with dark brown spots or blotches. Average size of 80 British eggs, 70.3 × 49.3 mm. (2.76 × 1.94 in.). Laying begins in latter part of May. Incubation period, 28–30 days ; shared by both sexes. Single brooded. (Plate 189, f. 4.)

IV. Food.—Parasitic on Terns and Gulls, forcing them to disgorge their food, and then catching it on the wing and devouring it. Remains of Kittiwake (perhaps wounded) near nest, but usually herrings, often in numbers. Has been known to kill Herring-Gull, Ducks, and Coot. Also takes carrion.

V. Usual Notes.—The note uttered during the display, when the pair stand with head up and wings raised, is " skirrr " or " skeerrr " ; and during the nuptial flights, " a-er " repeated.[2] A croaking " ag-ag " or " ak-ak " is heard before or after the attacks upon intruders into the breeding place.

PLATE 101.—ARCTIC-SKUA,[3] *Stercorarius parasiticus* (Linnæus)

I. Description.—Length, 20 in. Distinguished from the Great-Skua by smaller size and shape of tail, which has the two middle feathers elongated and pointed, not twisted as in the Pomatorhine, and not nearly so long as in Buffon's-Skua. In the hand distinguished from Buffon's by having the shafts of all the primaries white, instead of only the two outer on each side. There are two forms : the dark, in which the adult is uniform sooty brown, and the light, with upper parts brown, crown blackish, sides of rich creamy or yellowish ; under parts white ; feet black. Young are brown, paler below ; middle tail feathers slightly longer than the rest.

II. Range and Habitat.—Very local summer resident in the extreme north of Scotland, and in some of the island groups to the west and north, but otherwise only a passage migrant. A few still breed in Sutherland and Caithness, also in the Inner and Outer Hebrides, and commonly at some places in the Orkneys and Shetlands. Abroad it breeds in the Faeroes, Iceland, Scandinavia, Finland, North Russia and its islands ; across Siberia, Alaska, Arctic America, Greenland, Jan Mayen. In winter : Cape, Australia, South America.

III. Nest and Eggs.—Breeds on moors and tundra, usually in colonies, with the nests not very close together, and sometimes far inland, though generally near the sea. In the high north also breeds on shingly coasts. Nest very slight : a neatly rounded hollow with a scanty lining of lichens, heather twigs or roots. Eggs : normally 2, but 3 recorded ; pointed ovals, usually olive brown to umber brown, but occasionally light greenish or even pale blue, quite unmarked, but normally with blotches and streaks of dark umber. Average size of 55 British eggs, 57.3 × 40.5 mm. (2.25 × 1.59 in.). Laying begins towards the end of May in Scotland. Incubation period, probably 28 days ; shared by both sexes. Single brooded. (Plate 189, f. 3.)

IV. Food.—Parasitic on Terns and Gulls, but also lives independently at times ; has been known to kill lambs exceptionally ; will attack wounded birds, and has been seen to kill Purple-Sandpiper and Lapland-Bunting. Destructive to eggs and young of other birds (Ducks, Plovers, and Gulls, as well as Grouse). Other food includes fish, worms, crustacea, sea-anemones, insects (beetles, flies, dragon-flies, etc.), mollusca, etc. Crowberries also taken.

V. Usual Notes.—When its territory is invaded the bird utters sometimes a sound like " sku-arr," and sometimes a mew.[4] When in company with other birds of the same species on the wing, it gives forth a ringing cry that has been figured as " yah," or " ia," or " io " ; or, according to Jourdain, a loud ringing " yeouw, yeouw."

---

[1] Local names : Bonxie, Skooi (Shetlands).

[2] E. Selous, *Bird Watching*, 101.

[3] Also known as Richardson's Skua.

[4] *British Birds* (Mag.), xvi. 198–202 (F. Pitt).

PLATE 110.—GREAT-SKUA CHARGING UPON AN INTRUDER: A. W. Seaby.

Plate 111.—POMATORHINE-SKUA

Stercorarius pomarinus (Temminck)

I. Description.—Length, 21 in. Distinguished from the other Skuas by the middle tail feathers, which are about 4 in. longer than the rest and are twisted round, giving the appearance of a lump in flight. Looks larger than the Arctic or Buffon's but smaller than Great-Skua. Dark brown above; one form also dark brown below; the light form has white on throat, tinged with yellow, and has under surface white, barred with brown on flanks. In the young the two middle tail feathers are only slightly longer and the feathers have buff margins.

II. Range and Habitat.—Winter visitor to the British Isles, sometimes in numbers, but very irregularly. Its breeding range is circumpolar, but actual nesting records are surprisingly few; it undoubtedly breeds on the Yenisei and the Siberian coast, Novaya Zemlya, almost certainly Greenland and Alaska. Winter range as Arctic-Skua. A tundra-haunting species.

III. Nest and Eggs.—Does not breed in the British Isles. Apparently breeds separately, each nest well apart from any others on tundra. Nest, depression in the moss or heath with scanty lining. Eggs: 2, generally rather dark brown, inclined to reddish or olive, with rather scanty markings of dark brown. Average of 19 well-authenticated eggs, 64.0 × 44.8 mm. (2.51 × 1.76 in.). Laying begins in June. No data as to incubation period or share of sexes. Single brooded.

IV. Food.—Parasitic to some extent on Gulls and Terns, but can live independently of them. On nesting ground feeds largely on lemmings, and will also take fish (up to the size of garfish, 11 in. long!), carrion, and is destructive to small birds and eggs of other species.

V. Usual Notes.—The note uttered during intrusion into its breeding ground has been compared by Naumann to the yelping of a small dog.[1] When in pursuit of the birds on which it is parasitic, it has a cry not unlike that of the Arctic-Skua, figured also by Naumann " iäh " (the *ä* = *a* in *care*).

Plate 111.—BUFFON'S-SKUA or LONGTAILED-SKUA

Stercorarius longicaudus Vieillot

I. Description.—Length, 22½ in. A smaller bird than the other Skuas, and is also distinguished by having the two middle tail feathers about 9 inches longer than the rest. Crown black, sides of neck white, tinged yellow; upper parts brownish; under parts white; feet slaty. Young are brown, with buff edges and feathers of flanks and tail; middle tail feathers rather longer than the rest. In the hand the two first primaries have white shafts.

II. Range and Habitat.—Irregular passage migrant to the British Isles. Breeds in Northern Scandinavia, Finland, North Russia, Novaya Zemlya, Siberia, Greenland, and parts of Arctic Canada; but has not been found nesting in Iceland or Spitsbergen.

III. Nest and Eggs.—Does not breed in the British Isles. Nests on the tundra often far inland, not in colonies, but each pair within reach of others. Some pairs breed at considerable elevations. Nest slight, a rounded hollow in the tundra with scanty lining. Eggs: 2 normally, occasionally 1 only. Ground colour varies from olive greenish to dark brown, with blotches and streaks of dark umber. Elongated and pointed oval in shape. Average of 73 eggs, 55.4 × 38.4 mm. (2.18 × 1.51 in.). Laying begins in June. Incubation period, 23 days, shared by both sexes. Single brooded.

IV. Food.—Less parasitic in its habits than the other Skuas, and on its breeding ground frequently lives independently, hunting for lemmings, field mice, and small birds. Also takes fish, earthworms, insects (beetles, larvæ of crane flies, Mayflies, earwigs, etc.), carrion, crustacea, eggs of other birds, and vegetable matter (crowberries, leaves and tops of willow and heather, etc.).

V. Usual Notes.—The cry which accompanies the attack upon intruders has been figured " i-i-i-ah, je-ah, je-oh, jē-oh." [2]

[1] *Vögel Mitteleuropas*, xi. 315.　　　　[2] *British Bird Book*, iii. 228 (Jourdain)

PLATE 111.—POMATORHINE-SKUA: A. W. Seaby.

LONGTAILED-SKUA: A. W. Seaby.

Family : Burhinidæ (Stone-Curlews)

PLATE 112.—STONE-CURLEW [1]

Burhinus œdicnemus œdicnemus (Linnæus)

I. Description.—Length, 16 in. Distinguished by its large eye with yellow iris, long yellow legs, and general buff-brown and white colouring. Upper parts mostly buff, streaked with dark brown ; two white bars on wing ; breast streaked brownish ; chin and throat white ; under parts whitish, streaked pale brown on flanks ; wing quills dusky, with white patches near tips of outermost. Tail graduated ; bill yellow with black tip.

II. Range and Habitat.—In England a summer resident, occasionally wintering in the south-west, now local and confined to the east coast counties from Yorkshire southward, the south coast counties west to Dorset, and locally in Surrey, Wilts, Berks, Bucks, Herts, and Cambridge. To the rest of the British Isles it is only a vagrant. On the Continent breeds in Central and Southern Europe from the Baltic to the Mediterranean, and replaced by allied races in the Canaries, North Africa, perhaps some Mediterranean islands, and Southern Asia. In the British Islands it is a bird of downlands, breck country, and open heaths.

III. Nest and Eggs.—Breeds, as a rule, in quite open country, allowing a view from a considerable distance when approached, but will continue to breed even when trees have grown up round. No nesting material, a mere scratching in the soil with often rabbit droppings in it, on plough land, bare pasture, or downland, heath, etc. Eggs : 2 normally, but 3 on record ; 4 probably due to two hens laying together ; shape rather elongated. Ground, yellowish buff or light brownish, occasionally almost greyish white, with sepia brown streaks and spots which sometimes form a zone, and a few shellmarks. Average size of 100 British eggs, 53.8 × 38.4 mm. (2.12 × 1.51 in.). Laying begins in mid-April, but usually early May. Incubation period, 25–27 days ; shared by both sexes. Sometimes double brooded. (Plate 190, f. 4.)

IV. Food.—Chiefly worms, snails and slugs, and insects, especially beetles, caterpillars, flies, grasshoppers, and earwigs. Also takes frogs and field mice ; a few cases of game chicks (Partridge and Pheasant) being killed. Only vegetable matter recorded, heather tips.

V. Usual Notes.—The usual note uttered by the bird during the daytime, and when on the ground, has been figured by Farren " dhu-le-eep," the first syllables very short, the last drawn out into a shrill squeal. At night, long, weird, wailing variants of " cour-lee-vee " or " courlis," sometimes by single birds, sometimes by many together, are heard coming from the air. The species has also " a cry of remarkable carrying power which may be described as a monotonous whistle on one note " (Farren), uttered frequently throughout the breeding season.

[1] Also Norfolk Plover, Thick-knee.

PLATE 112.—STONE-CURLEW ALARMED, LEAVING CHICKS: A. W. Seaby.

Family : Charadriidæ (Plovers)

PLATE 113.—REDNECKED-PHALAROPE

Phalaropus lobatus (Linnæus)

I Description.—Length, 7 in. Distinguished from the Grey-Phalarope by the thin, tapering bill. In autumn, plumage resembles Grey-Phalarope ; forehead white, crown and eye stripe sooty brown, feathers of back with white edges, cheeks and under parts white. In spring, chin and throat white, head, nape, and shoulders lead grey, bright rufous patch on each side of neck, almost meeting in front ; upper breast leaden grey, under parts white, white bar on wing ; feet greenish. Young have buffish white edges to feathers on mantle in autumn. Female larger than male.

II. Range and Habitat.—Local summer resident in Scotland and Ireland ; otherwise scarce winter visitor. In Scotland it breeds in the Shetlands, Orkneys, Outer Hebrides, on Tiree in the Inner Hebrides, and a few pairs have also nested on the mainland. In Ireland there is one large colony on the west side, and a few pairs also breed at other locations on the west side. Abroad it breeds in Iceland, the Faeroes, Norway, Finland, North Russia, and east through Siberia to Alaska, while thence it ranges across Canada to Greenland. Breeds near marshy pools on tundra or moorland, always close to water.

III. Nest and Eggs.—Breeds in marshy ground with pools, overgrown with rushes and coarse grass. Nest built chiefly of dead grasses, concealed in tussock near water. Eggs : 4, but sometimes only 3, and 6–7 on record ; pyriform, smaller on the average than those of Grey-Phalarope, but similar. Ground, stone colour to light greenish or olive, blotched and spotted brownish black all over. Average of 90 British eggs, 30.0 × 21.0 mm. (1.18 × .82 in.). Laying begins end of May or early June. Incubation period, 18–20 days ; by male alone. Probably single brooded. (Plate 192, f. 1.)

IV. Food.—Mainly insects picked up off the surface of water (small beetles, flies, Mayflies, etc.). Also small mollusca and worms.

V. Usual Notes.—The notes that appear to be most usually heard are one rendered as " plip-plip " or " pleep-pleep," and another, a short, sharp, and repeated " quit," or " wit," or " tweet."

PLATE 113.—GREY-PHALAROPE

Phalaropus fulicarius (Linnæus)

I. Description.—Length, 8 in. In autumn plumage, when it visits us, the forehead and under parts are white, back pearly grey, white wing-bar ; irregular black markings round eye and back of head. The Phalaropes are distinguished from all other British birds by their lobed feet and small size : the bill of this species is much broader than that of the Rednecked species. The breeding plumage is strikingly different : crown black, cheeks white, throat and under parts reddish chestnut ; mantle black, with pale buff margins ; wing coverts leaden, tipped white ; feet yellow. Young have some pale chestnut on breast, otherwise like adults in autumn. Female larger than male.

II. Range and Habitat.—Passage migrant or casual in the British Isles. The numbers occurring are very variable, chiefly in autumn, after storms. The Eastern race breeds in Iceland (very sparsely), Spitsbergen, Novaya Zemlya, and East Greenland ; probably also it is this form which is found in Siberia. The Western form breeds in West Greenland and Arctic Canada to Alaska. A marine species, breeding on the coast and adjacent tundra, but always near water.

III. Nest and Eggs.—Does not breed in the British Isles. Breeds on islands on the coast, and also in marshy ground in valleys at some distance from the coast. Nest varies ; sometimes a mere depression in wet moss or on rocky ground, but where there is grass, a neat nest is built of dead bents. Eggs : 4, occasionally only 3, pyriform in shape. Ground, stone colour or olive, with large blotches of blackish brown and a few shellmarks. Average of 124 eggs from Spitsbergen, 30.2 × 21.8 mm. (1.18 × .85 in.). Laying begins latter part of June. Incubation period, probably about 20 days ; by male only. Single brooded.

IV. Food.—In the Arctic regions, crustacea (sandhoppers, etc.), small mollusca, insects (flies and beetles), sandworms, leeches, acaridæ, etc. Also seaweed.

V. Usual Notes.—A noisy species. Although none of their notes are loud, they keep up a continual twittering when in flocks. The alarm note has been rendered as a quick " vik-a " (Naumann) and a chirruping " zhit, zhit " (M. Haviland).[1] This note evidently corresponds to the " wit " of the Rednecked species.

[1] *British Birds* (Mag.), ix. 11.

PLATE 113.—(*Upper*) REDNECKED-PHALAROPES; FEMALE CHASING MALE.
(*Lower*) GREY PHALAROPE, WINTER PLUMAGE: A. W. Seaby.

PLATE 114.—WOODCOCK

Scolopax rusticola rusticola Linnæus

I. Description.—Length, 13–14¼ in. Distinguished from the Snipe by larger size, broad dark bands crossing the back of the head and nape from side to side, breast pale buff or whitish, with much narrower and more defined dusky bars. Back and wings have intricate pattern of chestnut and black, varied with silver grey; tail feathers 12, tips grey above, silvery beneath; primaries dark grey, with chestnut patches and white tips.

II. Range and Habitat.—Resident in well-wooded districts of Great Britain and Ireland; also passage migrant. In England local, preferring larger and moister woodlands, such as the Lakeland district. Also numerous in wooded parts of Scotland and Ireland. Abroad it breeds throughout Europe from Scandinavia and North Russia to the Pyrenees, Alps, and Northern Balkan Peninsula; also in Madeira, the Canaries, and Azores, and in Asia south to the Himalayas, and east to Japan. Replaced by an allied race on the Riu Kiu Isles. Winters south to North Africa and Southern Asia.

III. Nest and Eggs.—Breeds in moist woodlands. Nest a hollow in moss often at foot of tree in wood. Eggs: normally 4, occasionally 5, or 3 only, but 6 and 8 on record; slightly pyriform at times; creamy white to warm reddish buff, spotted or blotched with shades of brown, and ashy shellmarks; white and rich brown varieties also occur. Average of 100 British eggs, 44.1 × 33.5 mm. (1.73 × 1.32 in.). Laying begins mid-March. Incubation period, 21–23 days; by female alone. Two broods often reared. (Plate 190, f. 1.)

IV. Food.—Chiefly earthworms; also insects (beetles and their larvæ, earwigs, caterpillars, etc.), small mollusca, etc.; exceptionally small crustacea. Maize found in stomach.

V. Usual Notes.—When the birds are " roding " or " roading," that is, following time after time, in a kind of song-flight, certain well-marked air-roads—*e.g.* along a glade, over a plantation—which they do at dusk or dawn, they utter a deep, repeated croak: " croho, croho, croho," varied at intervals by a shrill screech " chizzic " (C. B. Moffat). The former of these evidently corresponds to that figured by Ziemer as " kworr-kworr-kworrorr . . .", with second intervals. This he ascribes to the male only; the female utters, according to him, the note given by Naumann as " psiep." He states that these notes serve also and mainly as calls, and that when the pair are together they utter, not the calls, but a note rendered as " slit " or " pip." [1] The alarm note is a muffled " katch." Other notes appear to be uttered by the male when displaying on the ground with puffed-out feathers and fanned tail. These notes have been figured " whe-e-esp " and " lvee." [2]

[1] Naumann, *Vögel Mitteleuropas*, ix. 212–14. For the view that the croak is **made** by the wing, see *Scottish Naturalist*, 1936. 165–72.
[2] De Visme Shaw, *Snipe and Woodcock*, 132.

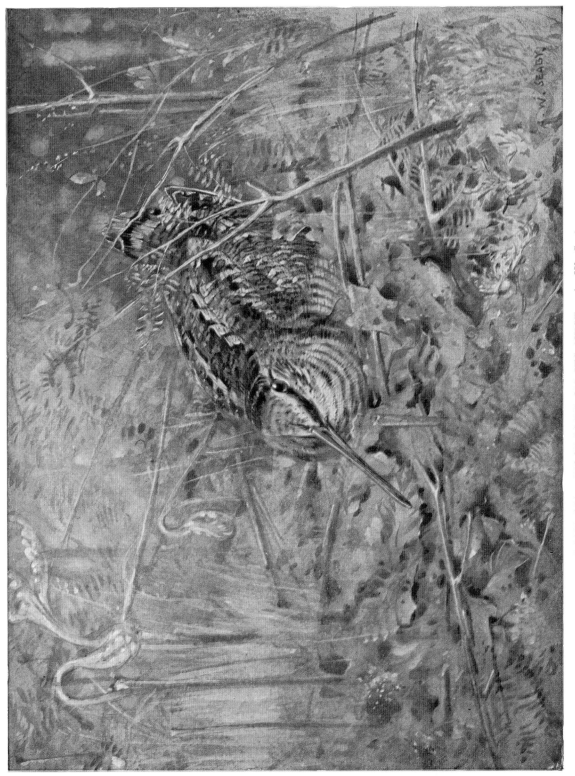

PLATE 114.—WOODCOCK ON ITS NEST : A. W. Seaby.

PLATE 115.—COMMON-SNIPE, *Capella gallinago gallinago* (Linnæus)

FAEROE SNIPE, *Capella gallinago faerosensis* (Brehm)

AMERICAN SNIPE, *Capella gallinago delicata* (Ord)

I. Description.—Length, 10–10½ in. Distinguished from Woodcock and Great-Snipe by smaller size, but larger than Jack-Snipe; buff lines on crown run lengthways; tail feathers 14; three buff stripes on head and four parallel ones on back. Colour of upper parts chiefly black, and shades of buff with grey on wings. Black tail banded with yellow and white terminal edge; under parts whitish, vaguely barred with dusky grey; axillaries white barred, dark grey.

II. Range and Habitat.—Resident in the British Isles, but also partial migrant and passage migrant. In Great Britain it breeds in most counties, but is least numerous in the south, and absent from some of them. Localized by need of marshy ground, wet moors, etc., and prefers lowlands. Abroad it breeds from Scandinavia, Finland, and North Russia to the Pyrenees, Alps, and Balkans, wintering south to North Africa; but is replaced by allied races in Iceland and the Faeroes (probably regular winter visitor), Eastern Asia, and North America, a rare straggler.

III. Nest and Eggs.—Breeds in marshy ground, wet heaths, and moors. Nest a hollow made in a grass tussock, lined with dead bents. Eggs: 4, but 3 in second layings, and 5 occasionally met with; pyriform. Ground colour, varying from pale blue or greenish to buff, stone colour, olive, or deepish brown. Some eggs almost unmarked, but most have spots of dark sepia and ashy shellmarks. Rotary smears at times. Average of 100 British eggs, 39.4 × 28.7 mm. (1.55 × 1.13 in.). Laying begins usually in early April, sometimes in March. Incubation period, 19–19½ days; probably by female. Apparently second brood in some cases. (Plate 190, f. 2.)

IV. Food.—Chiefly the smaller species of earthworms, obtained by boring in mud; also insects (beetles, crane flies and their larvæ, moths, larvæ of Mayflies, etc.), snails and water mollusca, as well as eggs, wood lice, etc.; some grain and seeds of weeds also taken.

V. Usual Notes.—The most characteristic sound produced by this bird is known as "drumming" or "bleating." It is made by either sex, both in the daytime and at night, when circling high in the air. The circles are broken at intervals by oblique descents, followed by rises to the former level. It is during the descent that the "drumming" or humming sound is heard; it is now known to be produced by the play of the wind in the outer feathers of the wide-spread tail, the quaver of the sound being determined (according to J. Rohweder) by the increase or decrease in the force of the wind current effected by the rapidly moving wings.[1] On the ascent the bird may utter a few notes, figured in the note-book of the present writer as "yuk, yuk, yuk." It has been heard to utter a note "chick chack" at the same time as it drummed.[2] Both these notes are evidently the same as that uttered by the bird when perched; this is variously rendered by "chack," "chuk," "tchup," "chip," "chip-it," "zip," "dsipp," etc. The note heard when the bird is startled into its famous zigzag flight sounds like "scape" or "scaap."

[1] Full accounts are given in the *Proceedings Zool. Soc.*, 1907, 12 (P. Bahr), and in Naumann's *Vögel Mitteleuropas*, ix. 184–7 (J. Rohweder).
[2] *British Birds* (Mag.), xx. 70 (E. Peake).

PLATE 115.—COMMON-SNIPE CROUCHING: A. W. Seaby.

PLATE 116.—JACK-SNIPE

Lymnocryptes minimus (Brünnich)

I. Description.—Length, 7½ in. Distinguished by its size (smallest of described snipes), and has a distinct median black stripe on crown, and 12 tail feathers, middle pair longest ; axillaries white. Has four longitudinal buff stripes on back, and metallic purple gloss on rump, and green on scapulars. Under parts mostly dull white, streaked with dark brown.

II. Range and Habitat.—Passage migrant to the British Isles. Breeds on the Continent in Lapland, Finland, Esthonia, and apparently south to North Germany and Bavaria, Poland, North Russia, and Siberia, east to the Kolyma valley. This is also a tundra-haunting species. Winters in North Africa and Southern Asia.

III. Nest and Eggs.—Does not breed in the British Isles. Breeds in the marshes and tundra of Arctic Europe and Asia. Nest a hollow in a dry spot, lined with grass, mare's tail, or dwarf birch leaves. Eggs : 4 normally, 3 at times, rather pyriform ; variable, but generally smaller, with browner ground, sometimes very dark, and as a rule rather smaller markings than Common-Snipe's. Average of 136 eggs, 38.6 × 27.4 mm. (1.52 × 1.07 in.). Laying begins in early June. Incubation period, not less than 24 days. One brood.

IV. Food.—Earthworms, insects (smaller beetles and their larvæ, flies, etc.), small mollusca (snails and aquatic mollusca) ; also some vegetable matter, including grasses and seeds.

V. Usual Notes.—When put up the bird may utter a low husky " ehtch " (Naumann) ; usually it is silent. In its Continental breeding haunts it has been heard producing a rapidly repeated note as it circles in the air. The sound has been likened to the distant canter of a horse on a hard hollow road (Wolley), and to the rattling of a damaged cartwheel (Russow). Whether this strange music is produced by the bird's voice organ or its feathers is not known.

GREAT-SNIPE

Capella media (Latham)

(No Plate)

I. Description.—Length, 11½ in. Distinguished from Common-Snipe by larger size, bolder barring on under side to the vent ; and 16 tail feathers (exceptionally 18 during moult) as against 14. The outer ends of the four outer pairs of tail feathers are also white, but mottled in the Common-Snipe. In young birds these feathers are barred with brown. Sexes alike.

II. Range and Habitat.—A scarce passage-migrant in the British Isles. On the Continent it has disappeared from districts where it formerly bred, but nests in Scandinavia, formerly in Denmark and Slesvig, also in Russia and Siberia, apparently south to Bessarabia. It is a moorland and tundra bird, and not a forest dweller like the Woodcock.

III. Nest and Eggs.—Does not breed in the British Isles. Nests on heaths and marshy ground, sometimes near birch trees. Nest a mere depression hollowed out in the moss. Eggs : 4, occasionally 3 only, pyriform. Ground, stone buff to greyish, handsomely blotched and spotted with rich brown and ashy shellmarks. Average of 100 eggs, 45.3 × 31.8 mm. (1.78 × 1.25 in.). Laying begins latter half May in Central Europe. Incubation said to be by hen ; period, 22–24 days. One brood.

IV. Food.—Chiefly earthworms, but also insects (larvæ of crane flies and Mayflies, as well as various water insects), small snails and slugs.

V. Usual Notes.—Notes on passage not recorded. In its breeding haunts the male birds assemble at regular meeting-places, where they indulge in remarkable displays, accompanied by special utterances, and also by a peculiar snapping sound caused by striking the mandibles rapidly together. As many as a hundred birds may take part in this performance. A full description is given in Naumann's *Vögel Mitteleuropas*, ix. 172–4.

PLATE 116.—JACK-SNIPE MISSED BY A MERLIN : G. E. Lodge.

PLATE 117.—DOTTEREL

Charadrius morinellus Linnæus

I. Description.—Length, 9 in. Distinguished from the other British Plovers by the white band across the upper breast, with chestnut patch below it shading into black on the belly ; crown blackish, with white stripe passing over the eye backward round the nape ; upper surface ashy brown, with paler edges ; chin and throat whitish ; tail coverts and vent white. Young birds lack the white gorget, and have under parts dull white. Female rather larger than male.

II. Range and Habitat.—Summer resident in the northern parts of Great Britain, but necessarily local, as it nowhere breeds with us under 3,000 ft. In England breeds in small numbers in the Cumbrian Mountains : in Scotland locally from Tay area north to the Cairngorms and Grampians (Moray and Dee areas). Formerly bred also in West Ross and Solway area, as well as Roxburgh. Otherwise only scarce passage migrant. On the Continent it breeds in Scandinavia, Finland, North Russia, and adjacent islands ; also in some mountain ranges of Central Europe, Riesengebirge, Transylvania, Styria, etc., and across Asia. Winters in North Africa and parts of Southern Asia.

III. Nest and Eggs.—Its haunts in the British Isles are the plateaux and slopes from about 3,200 to 4,000 ft., where vegetation is scanty, and consists chiefly of mosses and lichens with some heath. The nest is a little hollow in the moss. Eggs : normally 3, but sometimes 2 only, but 4 have been recorded ; shape oval. Ground, yellowish stone thickly blotched with brown black, with few shellmarks, sometimes approaching heavily marked eggs of Common-Tern in appearance. Average of 100 British eggs, 41.1 × 28.8 mm. (1.62 × 1.13 in.). Laying begins late in May, often in June. Incubation by male ; period, 21–22 days (D. Nethersole Thompson). One brood. (Plate 191, f. 1.)

IV. Food.—On its breeding ground chiefly insects, especially the smaller beetles and their larvæ, and flies and earthworms. Small mollusca and berries of crowberry also recorded.

V. Usual Notes.—The usual note uttered by the bird when disturbed has been described variously as a soft twittering whistle : " wit-e-wee " (Aplin) ; [1] a " tinkle of notes very soft and liquid " (Haviland) ; [2] a low, windy whistle (E. Blezard) ; [3] a monotonous metallic whistle : " peek-peek-peek " (Buxton).[4] During approach to the nest a harsh " wer-r-r-r " has also been heard (Meares).[5]

---

[1] *Field*, lxxix. 665. [2] *British Birds* (Mag.), xi. 6. [3] *Ibid.* xx. 17–19.
[4] *Field*, cviii. 2. [5] *British Birds* (Mag.), xi. 12.

PLATE 117.—DOTTEREL AND CHICKS: A. W. Seaby.

PLATE 118.--RINGED-PLOVER, *Charadrius hiaticula hiaticula* Linnæus

ARCTIC RINGED-PLOVER, *Charadrius hiaticula tundræ* Lowe

I. Description.—Length, 7–8 in. Recognized by white forehead and stripe behind eye, black lores, and stripe across forecrown ; nape brown ; white throat and collar ; bill yellow, black at tip ; feet orange ; upper parts brown, under parts white, with broad black gorget across breast. Young birds lack the black band on forehead ; beak blackish ; feet pale yellow.

II. Range and Habitat.—Resident on the coasts of the British Isles, but also winter visitor, and on passage. Widely distributed wherever there is any extent of sand and shingle everywhere on the coasts and islands, also summer resident at some inland localities, in some cases far from the sea. Abroad it breeds in Iceland, the Faeroes, Bear Island, Spitsbergen, and along the northern coasts of Europe and the Baltic, but scarce in the Mediterranean, and chiefly in the north-west. Winters south to Cape. Also ranges north to Greenland and Cumberland Sound in America. The race inhabiting the Siberian coast has been separated, and there is little doubt that other races exist in Europe ; but owing to the scarcity of breeding specimens in museums little has been definitely decided.

III. Nest and Eggs.—Normally breeds on sandy shores or in fine shingle, sometimes in the open, but at other times under shelter of plants, and exceptionally in cornfields, grass-lands, etc. The nest is a hollow in the sand, often lined with bits of shell or white stones ; sometimes vegetable matter such as dead grass or stalks, and even growing plants have been used. Eggs : normally 4, sometimes only 3, and occasionally 5, pyriform in shape. Ground colour, stone buff, sometimes nearly white, and occasionally warm reddish buff, finely spotted with black, and some underlying ashy spots. Exceptionally unmarked sets are found ; some have a distinct greenish zone, others have bold blotches. Average of 100 British eggs, 35.9 × 25.9 mm. (1.41 × 1.02 in.). Laying begins sometimes in March, usually in April. Incubation period, variously estimated at 22 to 25 days, both sexes taking part. Double brooded. (Plate 190, f. 5.)

IV. Food.—Includes insects (chiefly beetles and larvæ of diptera), crustacea (sand-hoppers, amphipods, etc.), worms, small univalve molluscs, as well as seeds of grasses and other vegetable matter.

V. Usual Notes.—The note usually uttered as a reaction to intrusion is a melodious flute-like " tooli." This, or variants of it, repeated quickly, are said to serve as " love " notes. A call note, uttered by a sitting bird just before the return of its mate to the nest, has been rendered, " ko-eel, ko-eel, ko-eel," rapidly repeated, and very different from the alarm note.[1] The species appears to have a wide range of notes, but a complete record has yet to be made.

PLATE 118.—KENTISH-PLOVER

Charadrius alexandrinus alexandrinus Linnæus

I. Description.—Length, 6½ in. Distinguished from the far commoner Ringed-Plover by black bill and feet, and two patches of black, one on each side of upper breast, instead of continuous black gorget ; the top of the head and nape are also reddish brown. Female has brown throat patches instead of black. Young much like the female.

II. Range and Habitat.—Formerly summer resident on the coasts of Kent, breeding on the vast expanses of shingle near Dungeness, and otherwise rare casual. Abroad its range is far more southern than that of the Ringed-Plover ; except in South Sweden, it does not extend north of the Baltic, while southward it ranges to the Azores, Canaries, Madeira, Cape Verde Isles, and across the Sahara to Iraq, Central Asia, and Corea, but is replaced in China, Japan, Somaliland, Ceylon, and North America by allied races. Abroad it breeds in sandy districts by river banks, and far inland as well as on the coast.

III. Nest and Eggs.—Although the Kentish birds bred among shingle, as a rule this species prefers to make its nest in sand, in which the eggs are often found half buried. Nest material either altogether absent or very scanty, and perhaps accidental. Eggs : normally 3, though sets of 4 have occurred, and 5 are said to have been found ; shape ovate. Ground colour, dull yellowish stone with numerous small streaks and spots of black, occasionally with dark brownish or greenish ground, and in Hungary erythristic type recorded. In some sets the streaks form a zone at the big end. Average of 100 British eggs, 32.9 × 23.5 mm. (1.29 × .92 in.). Laying begins about end of April or early May. Incubation shared by both sexes ; period uncertain. Possibly double brooded, but not actually proved. (Plate 190, f. 3.)

IV. Food.—Insects, chiefly beetles and flies, spiders, small snails, worms, and sand-hoppers.

V. Usual Notes.—A noisy species. Its usual note is a flute-like " piu," repeated at intervals, and sometimes with the addition of a soft " pit-pit." A repetition of these notes, or variants of them, is said to constitute the song.

[1] *British Birds* (Mag.), xv. 28 (T. Leslie Smith).

PLATE 118.—RINGED-PLOVER : A. W. Seaby.

KENTISH-PLOVER : A. W. Seaby.

PLATE 119.—SOUTHERN GOLDEN-PLOVER

Charadrius apricarius apricarius Linnæus

NORTHERN GOLDEN-PLOVER

Charadrius apricarius altifrons Brehm

I. Description.—Length, 9–11 in. Recognized by black or dusky crown and upper parts spangled with bright yellow, white line above eye, bordering black face and throat, and black under parts, bordered on sides with white. The southern race has much less black on under surface than the northern. Under wing and axillaries white. Females show less black than males on breast. After the autumn moult under parts are white, yellowish brown on breast. Young much like winter adults, but are yellower. No hind toe ; bill and feet black.

II. Range and Habitat.—The southern race is resident in the British Isles ; in small numbers also in Holland, Denmark, and probably North Germany as well as South Sweden. In the British Isles it is found upon the higher moors of the Devonian peninsula, also in Wales and on the spurs of the Pennine and Cumbrian Mountains, while in Scotland and Ireland it is more widely distributed, and is common on the northern islands. It is replaced by the northern race in the Faeroes, Iceland, probably Bear Island, Scandinavia, Finland, North Russia, etc., and in Siberia ranges eastward to the Yenisei ; it winters in Northern Africa and Western Asia.

III. Nest and Eggs.—Often breeds on patches of moorland where heather has been burnt, leaving little cover. Nest a hollow in peaty soil or grass, with a scanty lining of heather twigs, lichens, etc. Eggs : normally 4, sometimes only 3, and rarely 5 ; an instance of 7 eggs in a nest probably due to two hens ; pyriform and very handsome. Ground colour, ranging from yellowish stone to rich warm buff or pale greenish, blotched and spotted with brownish black. Average size of 100 British eggs, 51.8 × 35.8 mm. (2.04 × 1.41 in.). Laying begins latter part April or early May. Incubation period, about 27 days (incubator) ; both sexes apparently take part. Single brooded. (Plate 191, f. 3.)

IV. Food.—Varied, including earthworms, small molluscs (snails, slugs, and marine species), insects, chiefly beetles and their larvæ, earwigs and larvæ, caterpillars, larvæ of flies, ants, etc. ; spiders, small crustacea, etc. ; also seeds of grasses and weeds, berries, grass, and seaweed.

V. Usual Notes.—The bird has a whistling double call-note, and a song uttered in flight, described by Abel Chapman as " a peculiar rippling song or warble." [1] The alarm note has been figured as " tu," " tiu," or " tui."

[1] *Bird Life of the Borders*, 28.

PLATE **119.**—GOLDEN-PLOVERS: A. W. Seaby.

PLATE 120.—GREY-PLOVER

Squatarola squatarola (Linnæus)

I. Description.—Length, 10–12 in. Somewhat resembles Golden-Plover, but is distinguished by black and white barred upper parts in summer, while at all seasons and ages the axillaries are black, conspicuous against the light under surface of the wing, and upper tail coverts white. In summer the forehead is white, face and under parts are black edged at the side by white as in the Golden-Plover ; short hind toe. Beak and feet black. After the autumn moult the under parts are mostly white ; forebreast ashy brown, with dusky mottling ; upper parts mostly ashy, marked with whitish. Young have dark brown axillaries, not black ; otherwise much like young Golden-Plover.

II. Range and Habitat.—Winter visitor to the British Isles, breeding in North Russia, Kolguev, Dolgoi, South Novaya Zemlya, and Northern Siberia to Kamtschatka, but the East Siberian race and that inhabiting Western Arctic America have been separated, though apparently on insufficient grounds. Winters in Africa, while American birds range south to Brazil. A tundra-haunting species.

III. Nest and Eggs.—Does not nest in the British Isles. Breeds on the Siberian tundra. Nest a depression in mossy peat, lined carelessly with bits of mosses and lichens. Eggs : normally 4, sometimes 3 only ; pyriform. Ground, stone buff to greyish olive with black spots and blotches, and a few shellmarks, larger than Lapwings' eggs, and less rich in colour than Golden-Plovers'. Average size of 50 eggs, 51.6 × 35.9 mm. (2.03 × 1.41 in.). Laying begins in June in Siberia. Incubation period unknown ; both sexes take part. Single brooded.

IV. Food.—Insects in various stages, spiders, worms, snails, slugs ; and in winter small shore animals, molluscs, crustaceans, worms. Appears to be no certain record of its vegetable diet.

V. Usual Notes.—The note usually uttered by the species when the nest is approached sounds like a loud-ringing " pee-u-wee " (W. Rowan).[1] Identical, no doubt, with it is a sound described by Droste-Hülshoff as " tly-e-ih," but taken by him to be a call note. The species has other utterances not yet clearly defined.

For the Whimbrel shown on Plate 120 see page 131.

[1] *British Birds* (Mag.), xx. 42.

PLATE 120.—(*Right hand*) GREY-PLOVER, ADULT AND IMMATURE ; (*Left*) WHIMBREL : A. W. Seaby.

PLATE 121.—LAPWING [1]

Vanellus vanellus (Linnæus)

I. Description.—Length, 12½–13 in. Recognized by long, curved, glossy green-black crest and crown ; mantle coppery green, glossed purple ; upper and under tail coverts warm chestnut ; tail white, with subterminal black band except on two outside feathers ; under parts white, with metallic black throat and upper breast. In flight broad rounded wings with white axillaries are characteristic. Throat white after autumn moult. Male has longer crest and more rounded wing. Young have short crest and greyish buff edges to feathers of mantle.

II. Range and Habitat.—Resident in the British Isles, but also partial migrant and winter visitor. Generally distributed in open country and edges of moorlands ; but does not range very high in the mountains, and avoids the heath-grown moors, preferring rough pastures. On the Continent ranges from the Arctic Circle south to the Mediterranean, possibly breeding in Marocco, but not in the south of the Balkan Peninsula or Southern Italy and the Mediterranean islands. In North-Central Asia it ranges east to Ussuria, wintering in Southern Asia and the Mediterranean region.

III. Nest and Eggs.—Breeds on rough pastures, meadows, and arable land. Nest a hollow made by the breast of the bird, and muddy, with stalks and grasses, varying in amount, but at times substantial, on slightly raised ground. Eggs : normally 4, at times only 3, rarely 5 ; generally with stone-coloured ground and spots of black. Not as a rule variable, but in large series some have very large black blotches, others have ground almost hidden by streaks ; bluish green ground and erythristic types also occur, as well as sage greenish or bluish eggs almost unmarked. Average of 100 British eggs, 47.0 × 33.7 mm. (1.85 × 1.32 in.). Laying begins at end of March, usually in April. Incubation period, 24–26 days ; chiefly by female, but male also takes some part at times. Only one brood, but lays several times when disturbed. (Plate 191, f. 5.)

IV. Food.—Earthworms, mollusca (snails, slugs, and small marine as well as land species), insects (beetles and their larvæ, especially wireworms, larvæ of crane flies and moths, orthoptera, etc.). Also vegetable matter : seeds of various weeds and grasses, grass, moss, leaves of plants and seaweed.

V. Usual Notes.—When its breeding place is invaded the bird utters the familiar " pee-wit " or variants of it : " peet " or " pee-ee." These seem also to serve as call notes and love notes. The full song uttered during the rushing, whirling, tossing, tumbling nuptial flight has been given various renderings, one being as good as another to those who have witnessed the performance. The following are a selection : " pēēs-weep-weep-weep, pēēs-weep " (R. H. Brown), and " co-u, whee-whee-whee, co-u-whee " (Boraston), " willuch-ooee-willuch-willuch-coo-ee " (Brock), and " coo-oo-oo, hook-a-coo-ee, coo-ee " (Selous). Period : January–June.[2]

---

[1] Also Peewit, Green-Plover.
[2] *British Birds* (Mag.), xxix. 198 (H. G. Alexander).

PLATE 121.—LAPWINGS: A. W. Seaby.

PLATE 122.—BRITISH OYSTER-CATCHER

Hæmatopus ostralegus occidentalis Neumann

I. Description.—Length, 16–17 in. Easily recognized by long, straight orange red bill, black and white plumage, and pink feet. Head, neck and throat, mantle and wings black (with white bar on wings) ; breast, belly, lower back and rump white ; tail white at base, rest black. From autumn onward front and sides of neck are white. Young have feathers of upper parts edged with brown.

II. Range and Habitat.—Resident (and also passage migrant) in the British Isles, breeding only locally along the south and east coasts of England, but commonly from the Welsh coast northward, and plentiful in Scotland, on the islands as well as the mainland, penetrating up the rivers far inland. Also numerous on the Irish coasts. Abroad it breeds in Iceland and the Faeroes (said to be a local race) ; on the coasts of Northern Europe, the Baltic, and south to North Spain, the Camargue, Venice, and Macedonia. Also in Asia Minor and the Black and Caspian Seas. Recently the European races have been divided, but require confirmation ; East and West Asiatic and Australian forms are better defined. With us haunts chiefly coasts, shores of lakes, and river valleys.

III. Nest and Eggs.—Most numerous on low-lying coasts, with sandhills and extensive mud flats, but also breeds on rocky islets. Nest may be a hollow in sand or shingle, or a depression in turf or among rocks ; sometimes lined with fragments of shell, and occasionally with bits of drift and dead stalks of grass. Eggs : usually 3, sometimes 2 only ; 4 not rare, and 5 and 6 on record. Ground colour, yellowish stone, occasionally whitish or greenish, spotted and streaked, occasionally blotched with black and ashy shellmarks. Average of 101 British eggs, 57.0 × 40.0 mm. (2.24 × 1.57 in.). Laying begins late in April or early in May. Incubation period, 21–24 days, both sexes taking part. Only one brood. (Plate 190, f. 6.)

IV. Food.—Principally marine molluscs, limpets, mussels, cockles, and periwinkles ; also small whelks, shrimps, earthworms, sandworms, holothurians, and insects (beetles, larvæ of crane flies and moths, etc.). Also some vegetable matter, seeds, etc.

V. Usual Notes.—The usual call of the Sea-Pie is a loud, shrill, oft-repeated " kwick." The note enters largely into the piping that accompanies what is known as the " piping performance." In this one or more birds may take part. The performer holds the head and beak downward and the neck forward ; it may stand still or move about with quick steps. The piping sequence is rendered by Farren thus : " kewick, kewick, kwick, kwick, kwick kwick, kwirrr." [1] It has a shrill beginning, and sinks to a drawn-out quavering. It may be uttered in flight, and is heard both in and out of the breeding season. It expresses sex emotion, hostility, and is probably also a manifestation of surplus energy.[2] The alarm note has been figured " heep-a." [1]

---

[1] *British Bird Book*, iii. 396–400.
[2] The most complete account of the piping performance is that by J. S. Huxley and F. A. Montague in the *Ibis*, 1925, 868 -97.

PLATE 122.—OYSTER-CATCHERS: A. W. Seaby.

PLATE 123.—TURNSTONE

Arenaria interpres interpres (Linnæus)

I. Description.—Length, 8–9½ in. Recognized in summer by stout black bill, orange red feet, and plumage of black, white, and chestnut; crown and nape white, with dark streaks, white also forming a band on each side of neck; white patch at root of bill, succeeded by black; broad black gorget on breast, belly white; mantle marked with black and chestnut; white of lower back and upper tail coverts divided by black of rump; tail mostly dark grey, with white base and tip. After autumn moult chestnut disappears from the back; throat white, sides of head ash brown mixed with white; sides of breast brown black, tipped white; upper breast ash brown, rest white; feet pale red.

II. Range and Habitat.—Common winter visitor and passage migrant, which may possibly have nested in the Shetlands. Abroad breeds in Greenland, Iceland, Spitsbergen, and the coasts of Northern Europe and the Baltic south to Danish and Swedish isles, wintering farther south in Europe and Africa; also breeds in North Asia to Alaska, but replaced in Arctic Canada by an allied form. Usually found breeding on islets off the coast or near the sea.

III. Nest and Eggs.—No proof of breeding in the British Isles. In Northern Europe generally nests in small islands off the coast, or close to the shore on the mainland, and takes advantage of cover, under shelter of stone or low bush, in Puffin's hole, grass tussocks, etc. In the Arctic the nest is often quite exposed, and nest material absent. Eggs: usually 4, sometimes 3 only; broad ovate. Greyish to greenish ground, spotted and blotched with brown and ashy shellmarks. Average size of 100 eggs, 40.5 × 29.2 mm. (1.59 × 1.15 in.). Laying begins early in June in North Europe. Incubation period unknown, but male takes some part. One brood.

IV. Food.—Small marine molluscs, sandhoppers; insects, including beetles, crane flies and larvæ, bees, caterpillars, etc., spiders, acarids, and fish thrown up on strand. Also vegetable matter (seeds, seaweed, etc.).

V. Usual Notes.—The alarm note is a metallic " tche," " repeated once or twice with a two-second interval." The same, with an added " wick," forms the challenge or attack note: " tche-wick . . . tche-wick, tche-wi-i-i-i-ck." The succession of *i's* stands for a rippling note difficult to reproduce.[1] Also a loud mellow call, " dwee, dwee, dwee." [2]

PLATE 123.—AVOCET

Recurvirostra avosetta Linnæus

I. Description.—Length, 18 in. Recognized at once by its slender up-curved black bill, leaden blue feet, and black and white plumage. Crown to below the eye, nape, primaries, some of inner secondaries, and wing coverts black, rest of plumage white. In autumn some parts of the white plumage are tinged with grey. In the young the crown and nape are sepia, tipped buff.

II. Range and Habitat.—Formerly bred in East Anglia, now extinct as breeder, but irregular migrant. Breeds in South Spain, the Camargue, Holland, the German coasts and islets, Jutland; formerly in Algeria; locally in the Mediterranean, Black, Caspian, and Aral seas, and across Asia to China; also breeds locally in Africa to the Cape. Other forms are found in North America and Australia.

III. Nest and Eggs.—Does not now breed in the British Isles. Breeds in colonies on low-lying flats near water; on grass in central Europe, or on bare mud or sand. Nest a depression in turf or sand, carelessly lined with bits of stalks or dead vegetation. Eggs: usually 4, sometimes 3 or 5, 7 on record, probably by two birds. Ground, clay colour, spotted with black; shape pyriform. Average of 100 eggs, 50.5 × 35 mm. (1.98 × 1.38 in.). Laying begins in late April in Spain, but not till May in Central Europe. Incubation period, 24–25 days; shared by both sexes. Only one brood. (Plate 191, f. 6.)

IV. Food.—Crustacea (shrimps, *Corophium*, and sandhoppers); also insects, including small beetles, flies and larvæ, etc.; worms and fish spawn are also said to be taken.

V. Usual Notes.—The Dutch name for the species describes its usual call: " kluit." The same note, rendered in greater detail by Jourdain, runs thus, " tweet-tweet-tweet," varied by ' tu (or ' twer ') tu, tu, tweet." [3] The species utters, as warning note, " a reedy ' koek,' " and also " a curious moaning sound akin to that of the Eider-Drake." [4]

[1] *Breeding Habits of the Turnstone in Spitsbergen*, by A. H. Paget Wilkes in *British Birds* (Mag.), **xv.** 172.
[2] C Oldham and B. Lloyd (*in litt.*).   [3] *British Bird Book*, iii. 418.
[4] *British Birds* (Mag.), xiv. 194–202 (E. L. Turner).

PLATE 123.—TURNSTONES: A. W. Seaby.

AVOCETS: G. E. Collins.

PLATE 124.—DUNLIN, *Calidris alpina schinzii* (Brehm)

LAPLAND-DUNLIN, *Calidris alpina alpina* (Linnæus)

I. Description.—Length, 7½–8 in. Recognized in summer plumage by the black patch on lower breast. Crown rufous brown, marked black ; mantle chestnut, with black markings ; throat greyish white, streaked darker ; lower breast black, belly white ; rest of plumage ashy grey. Bill and feet black ; bill slightly decurved. In winter ash grey above, with white bar on wing ; under parts white. Generally in flocks which manœuvre simultaneously.

II. Range and Habitat.—The barely distinguishable southern race breeds in Great Britain from mid-Wales (sparingly) to the Pennines, becoming more numerous in the north, and common in Scotland and on the island groups. In Ireland it is absent from Munster, but occurs locally in the other provinces. This form also breeds on the Continent from Holland to Denmark on both sides of the Baltic, but the Lapland race, which visits us in winter and on passage, inhabits North Scandinavia, North Finland, and Russia with its islands, and also Spitsbergen, Iceland, etc., but is replaced by other forms in Greenland, Arctic America, and Siberia. A bird of the wet moorlands and marshes, where coarse grasses and heaths intermingle.

III. Nest and Eggs.—Nests generally in grass tussocks in rough pasture ; also at times among heath. Nest of dead bents when in grass, or with scanty lining of *Vaccinium* leaves among heath. Eggs : usually 4, but 3, 5, and even 6 on record ; pyriform. Ground colour, ranging from light blue green to buff or ochraceous ; boldly spotted or finely speckled with chocolate brown and ashy shellmarks and sometimes smears. Average of 100 British eggs, 34.7 × 24.7 mm. (1.36 × .97 in.). Laying begins from mid-May. Incubation period, 21–22 days ; shared by both sexes. Probably only one brood. (Plate 192, f. 2.)

IV. Food.—Molluscs, including slugs, snails, and small marine univalves, crustacea (shrimps, sandhoppers, *Corophium*), earthworms, and marine annelids, insects (small beetles, flies and larvæ, etc.), spiders. Also, in small quantities, seeds and grass.

V. Usual Notes.—When the nest is approached the Dunlin utters a " purring " note of alarm : " purre." The quite distinct call has been variously figured as a whistled " trui," or " dwee," or " wheeze." Repetitions of this note, or something like it, appear to compose the song uttered by the male during its nuptial flights ; the song has been described by different observers as a trilling, " a bleating, buzzing whistle," and a string of notes : " whiz-whiz-whiz-whiz, whiz," on a descending pitch.

PLATE 124.—PURPLE-SANDPIPER, *Calidris maritima maritima* (Brünnich)

I. Description.—Length, 8–8½ in. Distinguished by rather short yellowish feet, rather " dumpy " appearance, and general dark colouring, showing white on the secondaries during flight. General colour of upper parts dark grey, nearly black on mantle, with spots of rufous and buff edges ; throat and breast greyish, streaked brown ; belly whitish, with dark streaks and spots on flanks. Purplish gloss on some of the feathers of back and tail. In winter the breast is dark ashy brown. Young birds have white edges to feathers of mantle and breast.

II. Range and Habitat.—A winter visitor and passage migrant to our coasts, especially where rocky and broken. Breeds in the Faeroes, Iceland, Greenland, and Arctic Canada, Spitsbergen, Bear Island, Finmark, North Finland and North Russia, Novaya Zemlya, etc., and in Siberia. Replaced by allied races in the island groups of the North Pacific and Berings Straits. A tundra-breeding species, but usually close to the sea.

III. Nest and Eggs.—Does not breed in the British Isles. Breeds on the tundra at high levels in the southern part of its range, and at times far inland, but in the Arctic generally near the coast. Nest a small circular hollow, partly filled with dead leaves of dwarf willow. Eggs : normally 4, but sometimes only 3 ; pyriform. Ground colour, ranging from bluish green to buff, handsomely spotted and blotched with brown, and at times black, with ashy shellmarks. Average of 100 eggs, 37.3 × 26.5 mm. (1.46 × 1.04 in.). Laying begins in latter part of May, but in the Arctic not till June. Incubation period not less than 20 days ; mainly by male, but hen takes some part. Single brooded.

IV. Food.—Crustacea (sandhoppers and many small pelagic species), molluscs (mussel, periwinkle, etc.), insects (beetles, larvæ of flies, etc.), spiders, *Thysanura*, etc., and worms. Also considerable quantities of vegetable matter (seaweeds, grasses, moss, buds, and seeds) ; and remains of fish, probably stranded.

V. Usual Notes.—Not much recorded. The usual note has been described as a " squeaky, harsh, and low ' chēē-you-chĭ-chĭ ' or ' ăh-chēē-chēē,' slightly reminiscent of the note of the Turnstone." [1]

[1] *British Birds* (Mag.), xxxi. 268 (F. L. Blathwayt).

PLATE 124.—MALE DUNLIN DISPLAYING; FEMALE SITTING: A. W. Seaby.

PURPLE SAND-PIPERS IN WINTER PLUMAGE: A. W. Seaby

Plate 125.—LITTLE-STINT

Calidris minuta (Leisler)

I. Description.—Length, 6 in. Not unlike Dunlin, but distinguished by straight bill and no black on belly. Upper parts rufous and black, chin white, throat and upper breast pinky cinnamon, rest of under parts white ; bill and feet black. Outer tail feathers ashy brown. In autumn the reddish on throat disappears, and back is less rufous, though always more so than in Temminck's-Stint. Young have light edges to feathers on back.

II. Range and Habitat.—A passage migrant to our coasts, chiefly in autumn. Breeds locally in North Norway, islands and coast of Finland and North Russia, including Kolguev, Novaya Zemlya and Waigatz, as well as North Siberian tundra ; but limits in Far East uncertain. Migrates to Africa and India. A tundra-haunting species.

III. Nest and Eggs.—Does not breed in the British Isles. Breeds on tundra with stunted growth of dwarf willow, grass, etc. Nest a depression in the ground, lined with leaves of willow, but not with bents. Eggs : usually 4 ; a case of 7 due to two hens ; pyriform and glossy. Ground colour, ranging from stone colour to light greenish, usually more boldly marked than in Temminck's-Stint, with red brown spots and blotches and some ashy shellmarks ; occasionally finely spotted. Average of 100 eggs, 28.8 × 20.7 mm. (1.13 × .81 in.). Laying begins late in June. Incubation period unknown ; both sexes share in task. Single brooded.

IV. Food.—Insects (beetles, crane flies, and larvæ of mosquito, caddis flies, etc.), also worms, small crustacea (shrimps, sandhoppers, etc.), small marine mollusca, and also various kinds of seeds.

V. Usual Notes.—The usual note is a soft, high-pitched twitter : " twicky-twick, twicky-twick." [1] This evidently corresponds to the soft, high-pitched, humming " dürr, dürrü " or " dirrr, dirrrit-it-it " given by Naumann, who adds that when uttered by several together it sounds like the chirping of crickets. He states further that, after repeated observations, he failed to hear any other note from the species. [2]

Plate 125.—CURLEW-SANDPIPER

Calidris testacea (Pallas)

I. Description.—Length, 7–8 in. Recognized by decurved bill, and in summer by the chestnut red of the head, neck, and mantle, but in winter plumage when it visits us the red is lost, and the general colouring is greyish above and white below ; upper tail coverts are white and conspicuous in flight ; bill blackish ; feet olivaceous brown. Young birds show the characteristic white tail coverts, but have feathers on back edged with buff ; bill shorter and straighter than in adult.

II. Range and Habitat.—A passage migrant, chiefly to east and south coasts of Great Britain. Breeds in Arctic Siberia ; definitely recorded as nesting on the Yenisei mouth, the Taimyr Peninsula, and the New Siberian Isles, but probably much more widely distributed. In winter almost cosmopolitan, recorded from South Africa, Australia and New Zealand, and South America. A bird of the high Arctic tundra.

III. Nest and Eggs.—Does not breed in the British Isles. Breeds on the Siberian tundra. Nest a mere hollow among moss, rather deep, and usually on a dry ridge. Eggs : usually 4, sometimes 3. Ground colour, greenish grey, boldly blotched with rich red brown and ashy shellmarks. Average size of 20 eggs, 36.2 × 25.6 mm. (1.42 × 1.00 in.). Laying begins about the end of June. Incubation period not known ; both sexes take part. Single brooded.

IV. Food.—Little recorded : small crustacea (sandhoppers and shrimps), worms, insects (beetles, flies and larvæ, etc.), small molluscs, and seeds.

V. Usual Notes.—When the birds are put up they utter a short note, variously rendered as " twee," " tweet," " tweety." The species has another note, described by Naumann as a " humming," short, high-pitched, and trill-like. [3]

[1] C. J. Patten, *Aquatic Birds*, 297. [2] *Vögel Mitteleuropas*, viii. 201 (col. 2).
[3] *Vögel Mitteleuropas*, viii. 228.

For the Sanderling shown on Plate 125, see page 127.

PLATE 125.—(*Left hand, four birds*) SANDERLINGS IN SUMMER AND WINTER PLUMAGE ; (*Right, one bird*) CURLEW-SANDPIPER IN SUMMER PLUMAGE ; (*Foreground, two*) LITTLE-STINTS IN SUMMER AND WINTER PLUMAGE : A. W. Seaby.

PLATE 126.—KNOT

Calidris canutus canutus (Linnæus)

I. Description.—Length, 10 in. In summer plumage recognized at once by the red brown of head, neck, and under parts (larger than Curlew-Sandpiper, or Grey-Phalarope), with straight black bill and olive green feet ; rump and tail coverts whitish, barred blackish ; crown and hind neck streaked with black ; back black with bay margins. In winter the upper parts become ashy grey, while the red is lost and the under surface becomes white with greyish streaks. The young birds have a buff tinge on under parts, and feathers on mantle have white tips.

II. Range and Habitat.—A winter visitor and passage migrant to our coasts, especially the east and south sides. Breeds in the high north, North-East Greenland, and Grinnell Land ; but these records may belong to the American race. Icelandic records unreliable. Rare in Spitsbergen. In Siberia known to breed on the Taimyr Peninsula and New Siberian Isles. Allied forms have been separated from East Siberia and from Arctic America. Breeds on stony plateau beyond the limit of the tundra. Winters south to South Africa, India, Australia and New Zealand.

III. Nest and Eggs.—Does not breed in the British Isles. The few nests which have been found have occurred on bare, stony ground, with hardly any vegetation, and the nest is described as a mere hollow in stony ground, with a few lichens as lining. Eggs : normally 4, ovate. Ground colour, greenish grey, spotted, streaked, and blotched with dark brown, generally rather finely with ashy shellmarks. Average size of 14 eggs, 43 × 30 mm. (1.69 × 1.18 in.). Laying begins late in June or early July. Incubation period not known, but estimated at 20–25 days ; both sexes take part. One brood.

IV. Food.—Molluscs, including slugs, marine univalves, etc., earthworms, crustacea (sandhoppers, etc.), insects (flies, caterpillars, hymenoptera, etc.), spiders ; and in summer buds of Arctic plants and seaweed.

V. Usual Notes.—The male has a song flight seen in his northern breeding haunts. He mounts to a great height, uttering " the most beautiful flute-like notes." [1] The song has been rendered as " tullawee-tullawee-whee-whee." [2] The flocks seen on our shores in the winter keep up a continual warbling like the " twittering of a flock of linnets " (J. Cordeaux). The characteristic note is a clear " knot " or " knut," hence probably the name of the species.

---

[1] A. L. V. Manniche, *Terrestrial Mammals and Birds of N.E. Greenland*, 132.
[2] *Ibis*, 1877, 407 (Feilden).

Plate 126.—BARTAILED-GODWIT

Limosa lapponica lapponica (Linnæus)

I. Description.—Length, 15–16 in. The Godwits are distinguished by their large size, very long, slightly upturned bills, and in spring by the bright bay of the head, neck, and breast. The Bartailed-Godwit has the rump white, streaked dark brown ; tail barred with black, bay extends from breast to belly ; mantle variegated brown and black. After autumn moult the bay colour disappears ; under parts mainly white, breast and flank grey with dark streaks ; tail ash grey, marbled at the base, but long tail coverts barred ; upper parts ash grey. Young have bars on tail and buff under surface as well as a tinge of buff on upper parts. Females larger than males.

II. Range and Habitat.—Winter visitor and passage migrant to British Isles. It breeds on the tundra of North-East Norway, North Finland, and North Russia east to the Yenisei (lat. 69°–72°), and probably to the Taimyr. In East Siberia it is replaced by an allied race. As a winter visitor it is a bird of the coastal mud flats. Migrates as far as tropical Africa and South-Western Asia.

III. Nest and Eggs.—Does not breed in the British Isles. In Lapland its nesting haunts are hummocky marshes with occasional trees, not on the tundra. Nest, scantily lined depression in the ground, on a hummock with a few bents or leaves. Eggs : usually 4, but occasionally 3 only ; pyriform in shape. Ground colour, olive green varying in depth of shade, blotched or spotted with olive brown of rather darker shade, but not contrasting strongly. Average size of 51 eggs, 53.4 × 37.3 mm. (2.10 × 1.46 in.). Laying begins early in June. Incubation period not known ; but both sexes take part. Only one brood.

IV. Food.—Worms, insects (including larvæ of moths, beetles, flies, etc.), and small mollusca ; also, on coasts, crustacea (shrimps, sandhoppers), marine worms, etc.

V. Usual Notes.—Naumann, who observed this species closely, states that the usual call, uttered in flight, and often by many individuals at the same time, varies in sound from " kjäu, kjäu " (*j* = *y* in *yot*; *äu* = *oi*) to " kew-kew-kew " to " keu-keu-keu " (*eu* = *oi*) to " kei-kei-kei," and that, at a distance, it becomes " vet-vet-vet " (anglicized), or " yeck-yeck-yeck " (anglicized).[1] The courting or spring note is rendered by Droste-Hülshoff [2] as " viy-ou " (anglicized) ; but with regard to this and the song-flight of the species information is lacking.

[1] *Vögel Mitteleuropas*, ix. 126.   [2] *Vogelwelt der Nordseeinsel Borkum*, 204–5.

PLATE 126.—BLACKTAILED-GODWIT

Limosa limosa limosa (Linnæus)

I. Description.—Length, 16–20 in. Resembles previous species, but is larger, and has white bar on wings, belly white instead of warm bay, with blackish bars on lower breast, and upper tail coverts white ; tail white, with broad subterminal black band. After autumn the reddish fawn on head, neck, and breast disappears, and is replaced by ash brown above, greyish below, vent white. Young have rufous tinge on neck, which gradually disappears. Females larger than males.

II. Range and Habitat.—Formerly summer resident in East England, now passage migrant only, chiefly on south-east and south coasts of England. On the Continent breeds south of the Baltic (except in South Sweden), north to about lat. 65°, and south to South Russia, Bessarabia, Hungary, North Germany, and the Low Countries. The birds breeding in Iceland, and sparingly in the Faeroes, have been recently separated. Also breeds in West Siberia, but is replaced by another race in East Siberia. Winters chiefly in the Mediterranean region, South Asia, and North Australia.

III. Nest and Eggs.—Formerly bred in the British Isles. In Holland breeds freely in the meadow grass of the polders, but also on dry heathland and sandhills. Nest, a thick pad of dried grasses, generally in thickly growing grass. Eggs : usually 4, occasionally only 3, while 5 to 7 have been recorded ; pyriform. Ground colour, greenish olive to brownish olive, exceptionally reddish or grey, with blotches or spots of rather faint brown and sometimes a black streak. Average size of 100 eggs, 54.7 × 37.3 mm. (2.15 × 1.47 in.). Laying begins towards end of April. Incubation period, 24 days ; shared by both sexes. Single brooded.

IV. Food.—Insects and their larvæ, including beetles, orthoptera, dragon flies, etc. ; worms, frog spawn and tadpoles, mollusca (snails, slugs, small fresh-water molluscs, etc.), also small crustacea (sandhoppers).

V. Usual Notes.—When the breeding ground is invaded, the birds utter a shrill " tíderit " (female), and a sound variously rendered as " grütto " (hence the Dutch name of the species), " djodjo "[1] (Naumann), " tjäääh "[1] (Droste-Hülshoff), " tu-ee-tooo " (A. C. Chapman). The species appears to have other notes ; these have still to be distinguished. The male has a remarkable song-flight described by several observers. The most complete account is that given by J. S. Huxley and F. A. Montague from observations on the island of Texel.[2] The bird rises on quick-beating wings, uttering a trisyllabic "tur-ee-tur." At the peak of its flight it suddenly changes the note to a disyllabic " ghru-toe " or " grutto," and flies with slow clipping strokes, usually in a circle, rolling from side to side as it goes, these movements being regulated, apparently, by side to side jerks of the full-fanned tail. The descent is usually silent, a steep nose-dive, followed by shooting " side-slips in all directions, " being its chief feature. Occasionally the bird, with its wings about two-thirds open, " swoops down with a loud roaring of wind in the feathers, audible at quite a distance."

[1] *j* = **y** in *yot* ; *ā* = **a** in *care*.   [2] *Ibis*, 1926, 3–5.

PLATE 126.—(*Left hand, one bird*) BLACKTAILED-GODWIT IN SUMMER PLUMAGE ; (*Middle, three birds*) KNOTS IN WINTER AND SUMMER PLUMAGE ; (*Right, two birds*) BARTAILED-GODWITS IN WINTER AND SUMMER PLUMAGE : A. W. Seaby.

PLATE 127.—RUFF

Philomachus pugnax (Linnæus)

I. Description.—Length, 10½–12½ in. In breeding plumage the male has a shield-like erectile " ruff " or frill, " ear " tufts, and yellow warts on the bare face. The coloration of these parts and the back is very variable, and may be any pattern of white, black, chestnut, brown, grey, or buff. The Reeve has no ruff, ear tufts, or warts. After the moult the sexes are much alike, but males larger ; upper parts dark brown, with buff edges and white on each side of tail ; under parts whitish, neck and breast buff. Feet yellow. Young have conspicuous buff margins to feathers of back.

II. Range and Habitat.—Passage migrant to the British Isles, occasional at other seasons. Formerly bred in the fenny districts of England in some numbers, and a few pairs bred in Norfolk till recently. On the Continent it breeds from North Scandinavia, Finland, and Russia south to North France, the Low Countries ; locally in Germany, Hungary, and South Russia, wintering south to Africa. Also breeds in Siberia east to the Kolyma Valley. A marsh-haunting species, several pairs generally breeding not far apart.

III. Nest and Eggs.—Has apparently ceased to nest in the British Isles. The Reeves are, as a rule, found nesting in thick grass or marsh vegetation within reach of a " hill," where the males assemble. The nest is a hollow in a grass tussock neatly lined with dead bents, and well concealed. Eggs : 4 ; pyriform. Ground colour, varying from pale blue-green to greyish or ochreous, boldly blotched with rich dark umber and violet grey shell-marks ; white and bluish types, almost unmarked, have been recorded. Average of 141 eggs, 43.9 × 30.7 mm. (1.72 × 1.21 in.). Laying begins about mid-May in Central Europe. Incubation period, 21 days ; by female only. Single brooded. (Plate 192, f. 3.)

IV. Food.—Chiefly insects, including many species of beetles, flies (crane flies and smaller species), earwigs, and grasshoppers, larvæ of caddis fly and Mayfly, water boatman and water fly (*Limnophilus*) ; also small crustacea, small molluscs and worms, and seeds of many plants. In winter, rice and durra.

V. Usual Notes.—A relatively silent species. The alarm note of the hen when put off the nest is described as " a curious guttural double note something like a quack " (E. L. Turner),[1] and a " low quacking or guttural note " (W. Farren). Naumann mentions what may be the same note, a soft " kack kack, kick kack," heard at night and on migration.[2] The Ruffs, when on the " hill " where they display, are silent.

PLATE 125.—SANDERLING

Crocethia alba (Pallas)

I. Description.—Length, 8 in. Distinguished from other waders of similar size in the hand by absence of hind toe. Bill and feet black. In winter, when it visits us, the light colour of its plumage is very striking : the upper parts are mostly ashy grey with darker striations, neck and under parts white. In spring the head, neck, and forebreast, as well as upper parts, are mostly rufous and black ; lower breast and belly white. Young birds have mantle black and white, with some pale buff on the sides of the neck and breast.

II. Range and Habitat.—Winter visitor and passage migrant to our coasts. Breeds in small numbers in Spitsbergen, and in Siberia (Taimyr Peninsula and New Siberian Isles), also in Greenland and Arctic America. On migration ranges to South Africa, Australia, and Patagonia. A coast-haunting species, breeding on stony plateaux near the sea.

III. Nest and Eggs.—Does not breed in the British Isles. Nests mainly beyond the tundra area on stony ridges, making a hollow for the nest at the side of a clump of some Arctic plant, but no lining except dead willow leaves. Eggs : 4, or only 3. Ground, greenish when first taken, but fading to buff ; freckled over with small brown spots and ashy shellmarks, with occasionally a black streak. Average of 41 eggs, 35.6 × 24.7 mm. (1.40 × .97 in.). Laying begins latter part of June. Incubation period, 23–24 days ; by female alone (Manniche), but others say by both sexes. Only one brood.

IV. Food.—Molluscs (small bivalves and univalves, pteropods, and eggs of whelk), worms, small crustacea (sandhoppers, etc.), insects (small beetles and flies), remains of fish and medusæ cast up on shore and, during summer, buds of Arctic plants, bits of moss and seaweed, as well as seeds.

V. Usual Notes.—The male has a song flight seen in his northern breeding haunts. He is said to rise to a few feet above the ground, and, continuing a horizontal course, to utter a curious harsh note, rendered " trr-trr-trr." He may utter the same when perched.[3] The flight note heard on our shores is a short, sharp " wick, wick," or " swink, swink.' When feeding, the birds make a subdued chirping or twittering.

[1] *Broadland Birds*, 26.　　[2] *Vögel Mitteleuropas*, viii. 263, col. 1.　　[3] *Ibis*, 1904, 230 (Walter).

PLATE 127.—TWO RUFFS DISPLAYING TO A REEVE : H. Grönvold.

PLATE 128.—SANDPIPER

Tringa hypoleucos Linnæus

I. Description.—Length, $7\frac{1}{2}$–8 in. Recognized by clearly marked white bar along the length of the edge of the wing, very conspicuous in flight, and by notes. Upper parts bronze brown, minutely flecked, barred, and striped with umber; under parts white, streaked on neck and forebreast; tail white at end and sides; feet yellowish. After autumn moult the umber brown marks disappear and upper parts become more uniform. Young have feathers of back margined with buff.

II. Range and Habitat.—Summer resident in the British Isles, chiefly confined to the more hilly districts in Great Britain, the Devonian Peninsula, Wales, and on the spurs of the Pennine and Cumbrian chains, as well as Scotland and its islands. Widely distributed in Ireland except in the south-east. On the Continent it breeds from Scandinavia and North Russia to Central Spain, North Italy, Greece, and, it is said, also in the Canaries. In Asia it breeds east to Japan and south to Kashmir. Migrates in winter south to South Africa, India, Australia, etc.

III. Nest and Eggs.—A stream-haunting species, breeding far inland, also by lake sides. Nest, a hollow with scanty lining of grasses and bits of drift, often well concealed among grass under burdocks, exceptionally among corn or even on a stump. Eggs : normally 4, occasionally 5, while 6 and even 7 have been recorded, probably by two hens ; pyriform. Ground colour, creamy white to rich warm buff, with spots (occasionally large blotches) of red brown, chiefly towards big end, and a few shellmarks. Average of 100 British eggs, 36.4 × 25.9 mm. (1.43 × 1.02 in.). Laying begins early in May, usually mid-May. Incubation period, 21–23 days ; by male alone according to Stein, but hen also takes some part. One brood. (Plate 191, f. 2.)

IV. Food.—Principally insects during summer : beetles, Mayflies, caddis flies, ants, and small orthoptera ; also worms, water spiders, small molluscs, and crustacea.

V. Usual Notes.—The male utters a musical trill as it flits with vibrating wings by the side of river or lake. It is almost impossible to figure. One rendering is " twee-te tee-tee twee-te tee-tee repeated rapidly." [1] This trill is described by Dresser as a modification of the ordinary call-notes, which he figures as " dì, dì, dì," and of which popular renderings are " kittie-needie " or " willy-wicket."

[1] *British Bird Book,* iii. 497 (O. R. Owen).

PLATE 128.—COMMON-SANDPIPERS : G. E. Collins.

PLATE 129.—WOOD-SANDPIPER

Tringa glareola Linnæus

I. Description.—Length, 7½–8½ in. Recognized in the hand by white axillaries, flecked with brown. In the field is not easy to distinguish from Green-Sandpiper, but looks smaller, and has less white on outside feathers of tail. Upper parts greenish brown, with buffish white spots on edge of feathers, upper tail coverts white; tail with numerous bars; under parts white; feet yellowish olive. Young have spots on the mantle elongated and well defined.

II. Range and Habitat.—Bred in Northumberland in 1853, but now passage migrant only, and met with chiefly in south-east and east of England. On the Continent breeds from north of Scandinavia, Finland, and Russia, south to Belgium, Holland, and from the Urals to the Pacific and the Commander Isles; it winters in Africa, Southern Asia, and Australia. Haunts heaths and moorlands.

III. Nest and Eggs.—Does not now breed in the British Isles. In Europe generally met with on heather-covered ground, sometimes interspersed with trees; in Siberia also in forest near rivers. Nests usually in hollow on ground among heath, but also in old nests of other species. Eggs: usually 4, occasionally 3 only. Ground, pale clear greenish to creamy buff, handsomely spotted and blotched with deep red brown and the usual shellmarks. Average size of 100 eggs, 38.3 × 26.4 mm. (1.50 × 1.03 in.). Laying begins about end of May or in June. Incubation period not known; both sexes taking part. Only one brood. (Plate 191, f. 4.)

IV. Food.—Principally insects: beetles and their larvæ, flies and larvæ, small rhynchota, etc.; also worms, spiders, small fresh-water mollusca, etc.

V. Usual Notes.—The species has a song flight described by various writers; it utters the song also when perched.[1] The usual cry is a high, clear " tschititit," like the twitter of House-Martins according to a good observer, Droste-Hülshoff.[2]

PLATE 129.—GREEN-SANDPIPER

Tringa ochropus Linnæus

I. Description.—Length, 9½ in. Distinguished from the Common-Sandpiper by larger size and white tail coverts with greenish upper parts: from Wood-Sandpiper by blackish axillaries with narrow white bars, more white on rump and on outer tail feathers. Under parts white; feet dark green. Young show less green on upper parts, and spots less plentiful.

II. Range and Habitat.—Passage migrant and winter visitor chiefly to Great Britain. No proof of breeding in the British Isles, but on the Continent breeds from the White Sea and Scandinavia south to some localities in Germany, Czecho-Slovakia, Roumania, and in Asia in Transcaspia and Turkestan. Migrates south to South Africa, South Asia, and the Malay Archipelago. A bird of the wet forests.

III. Nest and Eggs.—Generally to be found in the neighbourhood of marshes or water in heavily wooded districts. Sometimes builds a scanty nest in hollow on ground, but usually adopts the old nest of some other species or a natural platform of accumulated leaves. Eggs: usually 4, occasionally 3, or even 2 only; an instance of 7 eggs, evidently due to two hens; shape pyriform. Ground colour, creamy to warm buff, rarely greenish, with fine and rather sparing freckles of red brown and grey. Average size of 100 eggs, 39.1 × 28.0 mm. (1.54 × 1.10 in.). Laying begins about mid-April in Central Europe; a month later in Scandinavia. Incubation period not known; females found sitting. One brood.

IV. Food.—Mainly insects: beetles and their larvæ, larvæ of caddis fly and flies; also small worms, wood lice and spiders, as well as fresh-water mollusca. Vegetable matter also recorded, including seaweed and plant buds. In winter also small, thin-shelled crustacea.

V. Usual Notes.—According to Droste-Hülshoff, what distinguishes the utterances of the Green-Sandpiper from those of the Common- and Wood-Sandpipers is their silvery, bell-like tone.[2] Dobbrick, quoted by Voigt, gives the alarm note as a harsh " kit kit," and the usual call as a clear " kick kick," and describes a flute-like song.[3]

---

[1] A summary of the accounts is given in the *British Bird Book*, iii. 506–7 (Farren).
[2] *Vogelwelt der Nordseeinsel Borkum*, 192. [3] *Excursionsbuch z. Studium der Vogelstimmen*, 236.

PLATE 129.—WOOD-SANDPIPERS RESTING ON MIGRATION IN THE "DRAIN" OF A SALT-MARSH, SUMMER PLUMAGE: A. W. Seaby.

GREEN-SANDPIPERS ON MIGRATION, SUMMER PLUMAGE: A. W. Seaby.

PLATE 130.—CONTINENTAL REDSHANK, *Tringa totanus totanus* (Linnæus)
BRITISH REDSHANK, *Tringa totanus britannica* (Mathews)

I. Description.—Length, 10–11 in. Recognized when adult by brilliant red feet, white on wing, inner primaries, and secondaries and upper tail coverts. Upper parts mostly greyish brown, heavily marked with dusky brown, grey, and black ; tail barred black ; under parts white, streaked on upper area, and more or less barred on lower area with dusky grey ; beak red, dusky, blackish towards tip. After autumn moult, upper parts are greyer and under parts more faintly marked. Young birds have yellowish feet ; feathers on mantle edged rufous.

II. Range and Habitat.—Mainly summer resident, but also passage migrant in British Isles, now widely distributed in suitable localities, having increased its inland range. Still scarce interior of Wales and outlying island groups of Scotland, and not found on south coast of Ireland. The Continental race breeds from about lat. 70° in Norway and Russian Lapland throughout Europe, possibly in Marocco and Sardinia ; also from Asia Minor to West Siberia. Migrates in winter to Africa and Southern Asia. Replaced by allied races in Iceland and the Faeroes, also in Central and Eastern Asia. Generally found in marshy districts near the coast and in valleys inland.

III. Nest and Eggs.—Breeds in meadows and marshes as a rule, taking advantage of every bit of cover available. Nests generally in grass tuft, building a neat nest of dead bents and bringing the grasses together overhead ; sometimes, however, in quite exposed sites. Eggs : usually 4, occasionally 5, 6 to 8 probably by two females ; pyriform. Ground colour, buff to ochreous and reddish or rarely greenish, freely spotted and blotched with warm sienna and ashy grey shellmarks ; blue variety has occurred. Average of 100 British eggs, 44.5 × 31.5 mm. (1.75 × 1.24 in.). Laying begins in first half of April. Incubation period, 22½–25 days ; chiefly by male, but evidently both sexes take part. Probably single brooded, but eggs may be found late in the season. (Plate 192, f. 4.)

IV. Food.—During summer largely insects : beetles, crane flies, larvæ of mayflies and caddis flies, etc. ; also earthworms, marine worms, mollusca (small marine univalves, cockles, etc.), small crabs, shrimps, sandhoppers, spiders, and small frogs.

V. Usual Notes.—The male has a song flight and song dance ; the song has been described as a yodelling " dhu-lee, dhu-lee, du-lee, du-le, dle-dle-dle-dle " ; it begins slowly and quickens towards the ending. When the birds are disturbed in their breeding place they utter short, angry notes, figured variously as " tchu " or " düh," and " quit," or " dick," or " tuick." They thus appear to have two alarm notes, and this was the opinion of Droste-Hülshoff,[1] who figured the notes as (1) " djü " with equal stress on *j* (=*y* in *yot*) and *ü* (=*u* in French *du*), and (2) " dick." [2] The first of these is not unlike the ordinary call, which varies much in length and pitch.

PLATE 130.—GREENSHANK, *Tringa nebularia* (Gunnerus)

I. Description.—Length, 13–14 in. Distinguished from Redshank by larger size, olive green feet, slightly upturned bill, which is black, and general dark greyish of upper parts ; rump white, tail white, mottled and barred brown ; under parts white, ashy streaks on breast and flanks. In winter back is greyer and under parts whiter. Young have light brownish margins to feathers of mantle.

II. Range and Habitat.—Resident in Western and Northern Scotland, otherwise passage migrant on the coasts of the British Isles. In Scotland it breeds from the north part of the Tay area northwards, but is absent from most of Dee area ; has occasionally bred in the Inner Hebrides, and regularly in the Outer Hebrides, but not in Orkneys and possibly in Shetlands. On the Continent it ranges from Scandinavia, Finland, and North Russia east to Kamtschatka across Siberia, wintering in Africa, Southern Asia, the Malay Archipelago, and Australia. In summer it haunts moorlands, feeding near water.

III. Nest and Eggs.—Breeds on wild moorlands, but is not averse to the neighbourhood of pine forest, and perches freely on trees. Nest usually a depression in the peat, lined with leaves of *Vaccinium*, etc., and a few lichens, often close to or even actually on, a grey stone, or by a dead fragment of wood. Eggs : usually 4, occasionally 3 only, or 5 ; 8 also on record ; pyriform. Ground stone colour to warm buff, richly marked with purplish or reddish brown blotches and irregular markings, with some ashy shellmarks. Average of 100 British eggs, 51.4 × 34.8 mm. (2.02 × 1.37 in.). Laying begins about May 7. Incubation period, 24–25 days (D. N.-Thompson) ; male sometimes takes part. One brood. (Plate 192, f. 5.)

IV. Food.—In summer insects, including beetles (chiefly aquatic), crane flies, water boatmen, etc. ; also small fresh-water mollusca, tadpoles and young frogs, fish spawn and small fish. In winter months also crustacea (small crabs, sandhoppers, shrimps, etc.), lug worms and smaller marine species of fish.

V. Usual Notes.—The usual call is rendered by Droste-Hulshoff as " tiütüi " (the *u* as in French *tu*), and differs from the Redshank's in being harsher (dürch seine Härte).[3] By the same observer the alarm note is figured as a screeching " krji, krji " (*j*=*y* in *yot*). This appears to correspond to J. Walpole Bond's " tyee-tyee-tyee " or " dear, dear dew." [4] Another distinct cry, of which the precise meaning seems uncertain, is rendered by Walpole Bond as a loud, far-carrying " tchook " or " kewth," or " cheuke," with disyllabic variants. The song, uttered on the wing, is a rich, full-toned, and moderately fast repeated " tew-hoo " (Walpole Bond), or " tlowit " (Droste-Hülshoff), to which is sometimes added " a twanging and very metallic-sounding ' chuk, cork, clock ' or ' tluk ' " (Walpole Bond).

[1] *Vogelwelt der Nordseeinsel Borkum*, 187.
[2] According to Voigt the latter note, which he figures " djip " (=dyip) signifies rising emotional intensity.
[3] *Op. cit.*, 180–1.   [4] *British Birds* (Mag.), xvi. 212 (J. Walpole Bond).

PLATE 130.—MALE REDSHANK DISPLAYING TO FEMALE: A. W. Seaby.

GREENSHANKS ALARMED IN THEIR BREEDING HAUNTS: A. W. Seaby.

PLATE 131.—CURLEW, *Numenius arquata arquata* (Linnæus)

I. Description.—Length, 21–26 in. Recognized at once by its large size, long, de-curved bill (4.7 to 6 in.), general light and dark brown pattern of upper parts and tail, with white rump and upper tail coverts; under parts mostly whitish, streaked brown; crown pale brown, regularly streaked dark brown. In winter under parts almost white. Young have a buff tinge on under parts. Females larger than males.

II. Range and Habitat.—Resident, breeding sparingly on heaths and moorlands of England, commoner in Devon, Wales, and the borders and North England; also widely distributed and common in Scotland (except in the Outer Hebrides) and Ireland. Our breeding birds apparently move westward in winter, migrants also arriving from the Continent. On the Continent it ranges from Scandinavia, North Finland, and North Russia to Brittany, the Low Countries, Switzerland, Roumania, and the Kirghiz Steppes. In Asia it is represented by other forms. Winter quarters, from the Mediterranean region to South Africa. A shore bird outside the breeding season.

III. Nest and Eggs.—Breeds often among heath on open moorland, but also in rough grass on hillsides and mountain pastures. Nest a hollow in the ground, lined with dead grasses. Eggs: usually 4, sometimes only 3, but 5 and even 6 recorded; shape pyriform. Ground colour, generally from light greenish to olive, or even brownish, generally spotted with smallish markings of brown. Exceptionally white and grey eggs have been recorded, and also eggs with bold markings, but only exceptionally. Average of 100 British eggs, 67.6 × 47.9 mm. (2.66 × 1.88 in.). Laying begins latter half of April. Incubation period, 29½–30 days, both sexes taking part. Single brooded. (Plate 193, f. 1.)

IV. Food.—In summer insects and their larvæ (crane flies and larvæ, caterpillars, crickets, water boatmen, beetles, mainly aquatic, etc.), snails and slugs, small frogs, worms, and berries of *Vaccinium* and crowberry; also on coast crustacea (small crabs, etc.), lugworms, shore fishes such as blennies, marine molluscs, chiefly bivalves, and some vegetable matter, such as grass and seeds of weeds.

V. Usual Notes.—The beautiful whistle of the Curlew has given the species its name. The usual rendering is " courlis " or " kour-lie," which must be taken as a general symbol covering many variants. The note mostly uttered when the nest area is invaded has been rendered " whoo-wee, whoo-wee, whoo-wee " (Coward). The male has a song flight yet to be closely described. A note quite different from those just mentioned is a " long, liquid, bubbling call " (Coward), heard both in and out of the breeding season. The various accounts of the notes of this species leave one in doubt as to how far they represent the same or different sounds.[1]

PLATE 120.—WHIMBREL, *Numenius phæopus phæopus* (Linnæus)

I. Description.—Length, 16–18 in. Resembles Curlew in type of bill and general coloration, but is much smaller, and bill is only 3½ in. long, and is also distinguished by having dark brown crown with a broad, pale streak down the middle, and upper parts darker. Young are spotted on back, and barred on wings with buffish white; tail more heavily barred than in adult. Females rather larger than males.

II. Range and Habitat.—Chiefly passage migrant in British Isles, but also summer resident in small numbers in North Scotland, Shetlands, Orkneys, on islets in Outer Hebrides, and occasionally reported as breeding on mainland in extreme north. Also Iceland, the Faeroes, East Greenland, and from North Scandinavia, Finland, and Russia, but does not range far south; West Siberia, but is replaced by another form in East Siberia. Winters on East African coast and island group, also West India. A tundra-haunting species in summer.

III. Nest and Eggs.—Breeds on moorland, nesting in depression in the peaty turf, and very scantily lined with bents, etc. Eggs: usually 4, but 3 or 5 occasionally met with; broad pyriform in shape. Ground colour, ranging from olive green to brownish, exceptionally pale bluish green, blotched and spotted (usually more boldly than Curlew eggs) with brown and ashy shellmarks. Average size of 100 eggs, 58.9 × 41.3 mm. (2.32 × 1.62 in.). Laying begins, as a rule, early in June. Incubation period about 12–25 days (?); shared by both sexes. One brood. (Plate 192, f. 6.)

IV. Food.—Insects, including beetles, earwigs, crickets, larvæ of flies, etc.; earth-worms and shoreworms, crustacea (small crabs, shrimps, sandhoppers, etc.), mollusca (snails, slugs, and marine molluscs); also some vegetable matter, crowberries, bilberries, grass, etc.

V. Usual Notes.—The note heard on passage is " whee, whee, whee . . . whit " (Patten). The following is based on first-hand observation of the species in a breeding place in Iceland.[2] The call note, uttered with almost closed beak and inflated throat, is a repeated soft, long-drawn " kwüi " (may be the " whee "). The alarm cry is a long, repeated, whistling note. The flight song is uttered as the bird mounts into the air on quick wing strokes to descend with spread wings to the ground. It is a " long continuous fluting trill."

[1] A. Voigt in his excellent *Excursionsbuch zum Studium der Vogelstimmen*, and W. Farren in the *British Bird Book*, iii. 532, both give summaries.

[2] By Dr. Riemschneider, quoted in Naumann's *Vögel Mitteleuropas*, ix. 156.

PLATE 131.—CURLEW CHASING A RAVEN FROM ITS BREEDING PLACE : A. W. Seaby.

PLATE 132.—GREAT-BUSTARD

Otis tarda tarda Linnæus

I. Description.—Length, 43–45 in. (male), 36 in. (female). The adult male is recognized by large size, tuft of long white bristly feathers extending backwards from base of bill on each side, and upper parts ochreous buff with black markings; head blue grey. Breast banded with rich chestnut, grey below; belly white; wings white; primaries dark. Female much smaller; no bristles on throat or band on breast. Young much like hen.

II. Range and Habitat.—Now only rare straggler to the British Isles, but formerly bred on open plains of Wilts, East Anglia, Yorkshire, and South-West Scotland. On the Continent it ranges from Germany (formerly Denmark and South Sweden), south to North Marocco, Bulgaria, South Russia, and Western Asia, but is replaced by allied forms in other parts of Asia. A bird of cornlands and open treeless plains.

III. Nest and Eggs.—Does not now breed in the British Isles. Makes no real nest; but a bare spot in a cornfield, where the crop has been trampled on and a few feathers and stalks are lying about, is the usual site. Eggs: usually 2–3, but in Southern Europe 4 occasionally, while 2 is normal in many northern districts. Ground colour varies from pale blue (rare) to greyish; olive green or brown, with usually blotches of brown and some ashy shellmarks; blue eggs occasionally without markings. Average size of 100 eggs, 79.4 × 56.7 mm. (3.12 × 2.23 in.). Laying begins in latter part of May in middle Europe, earlier in the south. Incubation, 25–28 days; by female only. One brood. (Plate 193, f. 2.)

IV. Food.—Both vegetable and animal matter, but chiefly the former; grasses, various kinds of grain, leaves of plants, rape, young wheat, turnip-tops, seeds, etc.; also occasionally field mice, young birds, frogs, lizards, slugs, worms; and frequently insects, including beetles of many species, crickets and grasshoppers, hemiptera and flies; also spiders.

V. Usual Notes.—Relatively silent species. The usual note is a gruff bark, which expresses anger and possibly other emotions. The young, in down, have a peculiar far-sounding and plaintive whistle.[1] The same is occasionally used by the adults, which also hiss in anger. Verner states that when attacked by an eagle an old male uttered a succession of squawking cries.

[1] *British Bird Book,* iii. 551–3 (Jourdain).

PLATE 132.—GREAT-BUSTARDS (*the male in the foreground*) : A. W. Seaby.

PLATE 133.—CORNCRAKE, OR LANDRAIL

Crex crex (Linnæus)

I. Description.—Length, 10½ in. Recognized by its wedge-shaped body, yellowish brown upper parts, each feather with black centre; short bill and chestnut axillaries. Under parts paler, barred with brown on flanks; wings chestnut; grey above eyes, on cheeks, and on breast; throat white. In autumn the grey on head is lost. Females rather smaller and less brightly coloured. Feet brown. Note a rasping crake.

II. Range and Habitat.—Summer resident in most parts of the British Isles, though now scarce in South-East England, and apparently decreasing in many districts, but still numerous in many parts of Ireland and West Scotland. Abroad it breeds in the Faeroes, and on the Continent from the Arctic Circle in Norway and about 60° N. in Russia, south to the Pyrenees, North Italy, and Macedonia. Also in Asia from Asia Minor to the Lena valley. In winter in Africa. Chiefly met with in meadows near rivers and streams.

III. Nest and Eggs.—Breeds in thick mowing grass as a rule, but in the north, where cover is scarce, will nest in clumps of flags, nettles, and rank vegetation of any kind. Nest a pad of dead grasses in a slight depression. Eggs: generally 8–12, but 13, 14, 17, and even 18 recorded. Ground colour varies from greenish grey to buff and light reddish, with spots and blotches of reddish brown and ashy grey; one egg often rather different to the rest. Average size of 100 British eggs, 37.2×26.7 mm. (1.46×1.05 in.). Laying begins in latter half of May. Incubation period estimated at 14, 17, and 19 days; by female alone. Probably only one brood, but eggs found fresh very late in the season. (Plate 193, f. 5.)

IV. Food.—Chiefly insects, including beetles, flies, their larvæ and eggs, grasshoppers and earwigs, etc.; also spiders, horse-leech, millipedes, snails, and slugs; and seeds of weeds and rushes, grains of corn, and green vegetable matter also recorded.

V. Usual Notes.—The most usual note is the familiar crake, which may be syllabled " rerp-rerp," oft repeated. It is uttered chiefly by night, but also any hour of the day. It is heard from the time of the bird's arrival in late April till the end of July, and possibly later. The bird has other notes, one being syllabled by Naumann as a weak, cackling " kjü-kjo-kjä." [1] A male corncrake, infuriated by the sight of a hawk near the young, is recorded as having uttered a piercing cry not unlike that of a hawk.[2] The anger note of combative males is a grunting " urmph " (Jourdain).

---

[1] *j*=*y* in *yot*; *ü* = French *u*; *ä*=*a* in *care*.
[2] *Avicultural Magazine*, ii. 180.

133

PLATE 133.—CORNCRAKE : A. W. Seaby.

PLATE 134.—SPOTTED-CRAKE

Porzana porzana (Linnæus)

I. Description.—Length, 8½–9 in. Rather smaller than Corncrake, and distinguished from it by small white spots on upper parts, thickest on neck and tail coverts ; axillaries barred with white, spotted breast, and green feet. Above olive brown, feathers with black centres ; crown dark brown, rest of head and throat grey, breast brown, belly grey. Young have throat white. Females slightly smaller and duller.

II. Range and Habitat.—Breeds in small numbers in marshy districts in England, Wales, and South Scotland ; also occasionally in Ireland. Summer resident, local, and probably often overlooked. On the Continent its range extends from 65° N. in Norway and 61° in North Russia, south to Spain and Sicily ; but owing to its skulking habits its range is difficult to define, and it may breed in Marocco. In Asia it ranges east to North-West India, wintering mainly in North Africa and India.

III. Nest and Eggs.—Requires dense cover and marshy surroundings, making a neat little nest of coarser sedges, lined with finer grasses in a tussock of sedge, rushes, or marsh grass. Eggs : usually about 8–12, but also 13–15. Ground colour, buff olive, heavily blotched with purplish brown and ashy shellmarks. Average of 100 eggs, 36.6×24.5 mm. (1.44×.96 in.). Laying begins in May. Incubation period, at least 18 days ; probably by both sexes, as male has been found on eggs. Said to be double brooded in Holland. (Plate 193, f. 6.)

IV. Food.—Both vegetable and animal matter, including seeds of many species of plants as well as portions of aquatic plants ; molluscs, chiefly small fresh-water species, snails and slugs, insects (beetles, dragon flies, caterpillars, larvæ of caddis flies, etc.).

V. Usual Notes.—The spring note of the male is a loud sharp " trick, treck " (Ziemer), something like the ticking of a noisy clock. The call to food, by both sexes, is a rumbling " kyeurk " (Ziemer, anglicized).

PLATE 134.—WATER-RAIL

Rallus aquaticus aquaticus Linnæus

I. Description.—Length, 10–11½ in. Recognized from the other Rails by long red bill and conspicuously white and black vertically barred flanks. In summer the male has leaden grey neck and breast ; crown and upper parts olive brown with black streaks ; belly and flanks black, barred white. Feet brownish. Female duller, with white on wing coverts. Young have under parts buffish white, speckled on throat, and barred with brown on flanks.

II. Range and Habitat.—Resident (and also winter visitor) in the British Isles in marshy districts, but local and not known to breed in Shetlands ; rare in North Scotland. Also breeds in Iceland, and on the Continent from Southern Scandinavia and the Gulf of Finland, south to Spain, Marocco, Algeria, and Egypt. Eastward its range extends into Asia, but it is replaced by other races in Persia, Turkestan, and Eastern Asia. Wet marshes with extensive beds of sedge and reeds are its favourite haunt.

III. Nest and Eggs.—Many pairs breed where there are masses of dead reeds, broken down over shallow water, the nest being on the dead reeds, some distance above the water-level. Others are in growing reeds and are easier to see. Nest is built usually of dead reed leaves. Eggs : usually 7–10, also 11 and it is said 16 on record ; like pale eggs of Corncrake, generally sparsely marked with red brown and ashy on a creamy ground, rarely with red blotches. Average size of 100 British eggs, 35.9 × 26.0 mm. (1.41 × 1.02 in.). Laying begins early in April. Incubation period, 19–20 days ; performed by both sexes. Two broods. (Plate 193, f. 8.)

IV. Food.—Very variable : small fish (bullhead), crustacea (fresh-water crayfish), earthworms, molluscs (snails and small fresh-water species), leeches, insects (including beetles, chiefly aquatic species), larvæ of trichoptera (caddis flies, etc.), water boatmen, earwigs, etc., and spangle galls. Also vegetable matter : roots of watercress, seeds of weeds and grasses, occasionally grain, etc.

V. Usual Notes.—Six different notes are ascribed to the species by Ziemer,[1] of which the three usual are (1) a call note something like " gisk," uttered singly ; (2) a " loud buzzing, grunting, squeaking, screeching note," not unlike the voice of the domestic pig, and, on our Norfolk Broads, known as " sharming " ;[2] (3) a loud drawn-out " krouihf " (anglicized), a note uttered when the bird is startled by, for instance, a gunshot. To these many added a " curious purring note " heard by Miss E. L. Turner. It was uttered chiefly by the hen " whether running to the nest or brooding." Occasionally the bird added the " sharming " note as a call to her mate.[3]

---

[1] Quoted in Naumann's *Vögel Mitteleuropas*, vii. 195–6.
[2] Voigt syllables it : " krrooee " (anglicized). *Excursionbuch*, 219.   [3] *British Bird Book*, iii. 584.

PLATE 134.—(*Upper*) SPOTTED-CRAKE AND CHICKS: A. W. Seaby.
(*Lower*) WATER-RAIL: H. Wormald.

PLATE 135.—WATERHEN [1]

Gallinula chloropus chloropus (Linnæus)

I. Description.—Length, 13 in. Recognized at once by general dark colouring, with bright red frontal shield ; bill also red with yellow tip, and under tail coverts (which are frequently jerked) are conspicuously white ; olive brown above, greyish black below ; feet greenish yellow, red band at joint. Young have bill, frontal shield, and feet dull green, throat white, and dull grey under parts.

II. Range and Habitat.—Very generally distributed resident wherever even the smallest pool of water or slow flowing stream exists in the British Isles. Scarce in North Shetlands. On the Continent its breeding range extends from lat. 63° N. in Scandinavia, South Finland, and Esthonia, south to North-West Africa and Egypt ; but possibly the Egyptian birds may belong to one of the allied forms which breed over the greater part of Asia and the islands of the Pacific and Indian Oceans as well as Central and Southern Africa and South America.

III. Nest and Eggs.—Breeds usually among the reeds, sedges, etc., round the margins of ponds or slow streams, but also at times in thorn bushes, and on branches of trees at considerable heights, sometimes using old nests of other species. Nest generally built of leaves of flag, reed, etc. Eggs : usually 5 or 6 to 10, but also at times 11–16, while 19–21 may be from two hens. Ground colour, from whitish grey to pale greenish or warm buff, with spots and occasionally a few blotches or streaks of suffused red brown and some ashy shellmarks. Average of 100 British eggs, 44.4 × 31.4 mm. (1.75 × 1.23 in.). Laying begins in March, but usually in April. Incubation period variable, usually about 20–22 days, but 15, 17, 19, and 28 days recorded ; both sexes take part. Two or three broods. (Plate 193, f. 3.)

IV. Food.—Mainly vegetable : grass, seeds of many species of weed and trees ; fruits of water-lilies and other aquatic plants ; duckweed, grain, berries, and fruit of apple, plum, pear, ivy, blackberry, yew, hawthorn, elder, rowan, sea buckthorn, etc. ; also eggs of other birds, worms, small molluscs, insects (beetles, caterpillars, flies, caddis flies, hymenoptera) ; also aphides and frog-hopper.

V. Usual Notes.—A loud frog-like " kr-rrrrk " or " trrrrek," proceeding from a marsh, pond, or river marks the presence of a Waterhen. The note uttered by the bird during its nocturnal flights has been variously described as " a short squeak," " keck, keck, keck," " pluck, pluck, pluck," and " tit-a-tit." Like the Water-rail, it has a " purring " note, also a clucking food-call to its chicks. A somewhat metallic note " kwon " or " kwon-hon " seems to express various emotions ; the writer has known it used between mated birds, and by one driving away a trespasser. Another note used in resenting trespass sounds like " chk," sometimes uttered with the head bent down. It may be identical with the " keck " above mentioned. A note heard from a hen bird surprised with young is figured by Hesse as " quick, queck, pit, pet," also " quik, quik, quik." [2]

---

[1] Also Moorhen, which dates from a time when *mór* meant morass as well as moor. As it no longer means morass, the name Moorhen is misleading. It should be Merehen or Morhen.

[2] Quoted in Voigt's *Excursionsbuch*, 218

PLATE 135.—WATERHEN : A. W. Seaby.

PLATE 136.—COOT

Fulica atra atra Linnæus

I. Description.—Length, 15–16 in. Distinguished by broad white frontal shield, slaty black general colouring, with white tips to secondaries, forming a white wing-bar, and curious rounded lobes on three front toes ; feet green ; iris crimson. Young birds have white throat, grey under parts, and small frontal shield.

II. Range and Habitat.—More local than the Moorhen in the British Isles, preferring larger pieces of water. Resident and plentiful in many districts, but mainly summer resident in the Shetlands. Abroad it has bred in Iceland, and from Southern Scandinavia and lat. 57° in the Urals it ranges south to North-West Africa and the Mediterranean ; also in Asia east to Korea and Japan, south to India and China. Has also bred in the Azores.

III. Nest and Eggs.—Generally to be found breeding in company with other pairs, though the nests are not very close together ; usually in shallow water with reeds, rushes, etc. Nest built of dead leaves of reed or flags, often very bulky. Eggs : usually 6–9, but 10–13 and 15, and even more, on record, probably in most cases due to two hens. Ground colour, stone colour with fine speckles of very dark brown over whole surface, and rarely showing any variation. Average size of 100 British eggs, 52.0 × 36.1 mm. (2.04 × 1.42 in.). Laying begins in mid-March, but usually later. Incubation period, 21–23 days ; probably by both sexes, but chiefly by hen. Double brooded. (Plate 193, f. 4.)

IV. Food.—Chiefly vegetable : especially young shoots of reeds, and roots of water plants, water weeds, etc. Also at times destructive to eggs of other species, and takes small fish, small fresh-water molluscs, and is recorded as killing but not eating ducklings.

V. Usual Notes.—The familiar call of the Coot is difficult to syllable ; it is something like an explosive single " khon " or " kwon." A variant of this note, if not a different note, is a sharp, high-pitched sound or " squeak " that serves as a challenge to rivals or trespassers. A distinct note " is a sharp clinking, something like that made by striking two pebbles together, and it may be accompanied by what sounds like an explosive expulsion of breath—a kind of phew ! which has to be listened for. This note clearly expresses alarm, and serves as a warning." [1] Anger may be expressed by snapping the mandibles with head bent down ; a sound that was heard by the writer from a Coot irritated by the presence of a lurking Waterhen near its nest. Another mode of expression by sound is smacking the surface of the water with one foot or both ; this marks hostility and sex-emotion. [2] The young utter a persistent piping " kweep " or " kwee-eep," or (at a distance) " kwee-oo " uttered separately, and not in a continuous series like the notes of young Grebes.

[1] *British Bird Book*, iii. 605 (Kirkman).
[2] E. L. Turner, *Broadland Birds*, 44–5.

PLATE 136.—COOT BRINGING NEST MATERIAL TO ITS MATE: A. W. Seaby.

Order : Galliformes. Family : Phasianidæ (Grouse, Pheasants, Partridges)

PLATE 137.—CAPERCAILLIE

Tetrao urogallus urogallus Linnæus

I. Description.—Length, 35–36 in. (male), 25–26 in. (female). Recognized by great size, combined with rounded tail of male, which also has dark grey upper parts of tail nearly black ; wing coverts and scapulars reddish brown and black, throat black, breast dark glossy green, under parts blackish, with white tips to belly feathers. The female is rufous buff on upper parts, marked with black and white, orange buff on throat and breast, barred black and spotted with white. Feet in both sexes covered with hair-like brown feathers ; red wattle round eyes, larger in male. Young more buff than female.

II. Range and Habitat.—Formerly resident in Scotland but became extinct, and was re-introduced in 1837 into Perthshire. Has since spread over all Tay area, most of Clyde (except Ayrshire), Western Forth, Dee, Moray, north to East Ross-shire, and sporadically in the adjacent areas. On the Continent it ranges from Scandinavia and North Finland and Russia to the Alps, Carpathians, and Balkans ; while allied races inhabit the Cantabrian Mountains, Pyrenees, East Russia, and Siberia. A bird of the pine forests.

III. Nest and Eggs.—Generally places its nest at the foot of a pine tree in forest, the female scratching out a hollow among the accumulated pine needles. Eggs : usually 5 or 6 to 9, occasionally 10–12, while 14 and 15 are said to have occurred. Ground colour, yellowish or ochreous, with rather pale and scanty markings of yellowish brown, in the form of spots or blotches. Average size of 100 British eggs, 57.3 × 41.4 mm. (2.25 × 1.63 in.). Laying begins in early May. Incubation period, 26–28 days ; by hen alone. Single brooded. (Plate 194, f. 7.)

IV. Food.—During winter lives almost entirely on young shoots of conifers, and is very injurious to woodlands, chiefly pine and larch ; in spring and autumn takes also insects (beetle larvæ, ants, etc.) ; buds of birch, heather tops, oats, and scattered corn, fruit and berries of juniper, wild raspberry, rose, hawthorn, rowan, blackberry, bilberry, and cranberry ; also bracken shoots, seeds and grasses.

V. Usual Notes.—A curious song is uttered by the male during its " lek " or " spel," a kind of spring display that takes place while it stands on some favourite perch, neck outstretched, tail spread, wings hanging. The song, as described by Fürsterberg,[1] is divisible into three parts :

(1) " Klick-kléck (pause), klick-kléck (pause), klick-kléck," at first like two little sticks knocked together, then quicker and more metallic.
(2) A cork-drawing sound.
(3) A knife-grinding " sch-scht-ssts-pss-sch-scht."

Other accounts agree in describing the performance as intense but unmusical, the excitement of the performer finding relief in wing flaps and wild leaps. The hen's contribution at the " laking " place is usually a note like " back."[2] The species have other notes not yet fully recorded. They include an alarm note figured as " hoch."

[1] *British Bird Book*, iv. 28.
[2] Voigt, *op. cit.* (above, p. 131), 204.

PLATE 137.—CAPERCAILLIE (*male in front*) : G. E. Lodge.

PLATE 138.—BLACK-GROUSE

Lyrurus tetrix britannicus Witherby and Lönnberg

I. Description.—Length, 22–23 in. (male), 15 in. (female). Male is recognized by black, lyre-shaped tail, conspicuous white under tail coverts, and white bar on wing, contrasting with glossy blue-black plumage. In autumn some chestnut or brownish buff in upper parts. The Greyhen is chestnut and buff, barred and freckled with black, much like hen Capercaillie, but much smaller and tail distinctly forked. Young like female, but cocks soon show black in plumage.

II. Range and Habitat.—The British race is confined to Great Britain. It was formerly widely distributed and resident in forested districts of England, now much restricted but still found in the Devonian peninsula, the Border counties, Wales, and from the north Midland counties northward to the mainland of Scotland, and some of the Inner Hebrides, but not on the other island groups. Other races are found on the Continent from Scandinavia, North Finland, and North Russia, south to Switzerland, the Apennines, Balkan Peninsula, South Russia, and Manchuria. Its haunts are heaths and conifer or birch forest.

III. Nest and Eggs.—Breeds on open heaths with dead bracken and scattered trees, also in plantations and coniferous forests. Nest a scrape in grass or heather, generally well sheltered ; exceptionally it has been known to breed in an old nest in a tree. Eggs : usually 6–11 or 12, smaller than those of Capercaillie and generally more strongly marked. Ground colour, yellowish to warm reddish with yellowish brown spots and blotches, occasionally reddish brown. Average size of 100 British eggs, 51.6 × 37.2 mm. (2.03 × 1.46 in.). Laying begins about mid-May. Incubation period, 24–26 days ; by female alone. Single brooded. (Plate 194, f. 8.)

IV. Food.—In winter months buds of birch and shoots of conifers (pine and larch), also catkins ; in spring and autumn insects, especially beetles and gall insects ; shoots of moorland plants (heather, blaeberry, bog myrtle, etc. ; seeds and fruits of rowan, hawthorn, wild strawberry and raspberry, cranberry, crowberry, blackberry, etc. ; seeds of rushes and sedge ; at times potato, turnip, and grain.

V. Usual Notes.—The species is polygamous, and the competing cocks indulge in a great deal of tilting, interspersed with a moderate amount of serious fighting. The challenge they utter is either a warning " hiss," or a weird cry, figured as " gock-au-u-canuel." [1] In these contests a " bubbling " note may be used, but this is primarily the love note, and is " thrilled " forth by all the cocks as soon as a Greyhen appears on the scene. [2] Blackcock may begin " bubbling " and displaying as early as January. A revival of the displays may be witnessed in October and November. The note of the Greyhen is given by Voigt as " bak bak " or " gaggag," and the alarm note of the species as a muffled " kouk." [3]

[1] Or " choc-ke-ra-da " (Selous).
[2] Detailed accounts are given by H. B. Macpherson in *Wild Life*, May 1915 (vi. 131–6), and by E. Selous in *Realities of Bird Life*, 263–82.
[3] *Op. cit.* (above, p. 131), 206.

PLATE 138.—BLACKCOCK (*two challenging*) AND GREYHEN : A. W. Seaby.

PLATE 139.—BRITISH RED-GROUSE

Lagopus scoticus scoticus (Latham)

IRISH RED-GROUSE

Lagopus scoticus hibernicus (Kleinschmidt)

I. Description.—Length, 14–15½ in. Males recognized by chestnut brown colouring with darker breast ; large red wattle above eye. There is much variation in plumage, but three main types, the red, the black, and the white splashed on under side. From June to October males become darker on upper parts, with buff bars. Females are smaller, with smaller wattle and lighter colouring. Primaries dark brown ; only 16 feathers in tail. The Irish race is decidedly paler and yellower as a rule.

II. Range and Habitat.—The British race is confined to Great Britain. It is found in Wales, some border counties, and from the north midland counties north through Scotland to the Inner Hebrides and Orkneys, but not Shetlands. It has also been introduced in Exmoor and also West Germany and Belgium. The Irish race is confined to Ireland and the Outer Hebrides. On the Continent its nearest ally is the Willow-Grouse, which is generally treated as a separate species. The Red-Grouse is a bird of the open moorland and avoids forested country, only leaving the hills when driven off by deep snow.

III. Nest and Eggs.—Breeds among heather or rough pastures on edge of moorland, in hollow on ground, sheltered by tussock or clump of heath, and lined with dead grasses, etc. Eggs : usually 6–10, but 11–16 (and it is said 17) on record. Ground colour, yellowish white, almost concealed by numerous rich chocolate blotches, occasionally bright sienna red ; colour very fugitive when newly laid, and occasionally absent. Average of 100 British eggs, 45.7 × 32.1 mm. (1.80 × 1.26 in.). Laying begins usually in late April, exceptionally in March. Incubation period, 20–24 days ; by hen only. Single brooded. (Plate 194, f. 3.)

IV. Food.—Mainly shoots of heaths, especially *Calluna* and *Erica*, also crowberry, cranberry, rushes, etc. ; also insects, including beetles, flies, small moths, and caterpillars ; fruit and berries of rowan, hawthorn, blackberry, cranberry, crowberry, cloudberry, and blaeberry ; leaves of mountain willow, flowers of buttercup, grain of all kinds, and in winter almost any kind of vegetable matter, turnip tops especially.

V. Usual Notes.—The usual call of the cock-bird as it stands erect on its favourite tussock is " bek, bek, bek." If alarmed it flies off with a " kok, kok, kok," to which it may add " goback, goback, goback."

PLATE 139.—RED-GROUSE; COCK (*upper*) AND HEN: A. W. Seaby.

PLATES 140 AND 151.—BRITISH PTARMIGAN

Lagopus mutus millaisi Hartert

I. Description.—Length, $14\frac{1}{2}$–15 in. Distinguished from Red-Grouse by always showing white on the wings, with dark shafts to the primaries. The male, from April to July, has the upper parts blackish, with mottling of grey brown; tail black, tipped white; under parts white except breast, brown, mottled rufous. In August the upper parts become grey, with black and white markings, under parts chiefly white; and in November all white except black on tail and lores, which is always present. (Plate 151.) Females in April are buff and rufous-grey, with black markings on upper parts, in August darker than the male, and in November white without the black lores. Young are mostly blackish, with rufous markings and brownish black and buff primaries.

II. Range and Habitat.—The Scotch race is resident and confined to high elevations on the mainland of Scotland from Clyde area (Dumbarton) and Forth (East Stirling) northward; also on the Inner and Outer Hebrides, but not in the Orkneys or Shetlands. Formerly its range was more extensive. Prefers the zone of lichens and mosses to the heath-covered slopes at lower altitudes in summer; it descends in winter. Replaced by other forms in Iceland, Spitsbergen, Franz Josef Land, Scandinavia, Finland, North Russia south to the Pyrenees, Alps, Styria, and Carinthia; also in Siberia, Japan, Arctic America, and Greenland.

III. Nest and Eggs.—Breeds on hillsides in alpine zone of mountains, often partly sheltered by outcrop of rock, in hollow in ground, with a few lichens. Eggs: 6–10, but 12, 16, and 17 reported, perhaps due to two hens; smaller and often less red than those of grouse, but similar in type, being covered with blotches and spots of dark chocolate on whitish or yellowish ground. Average size of 100 Scotch eggs, 43.5 × 31.0 mm. (1.71 × 1.22 in.). Laying begins latter part of May. Incubation period said to be nine days longer (!) than that of Red-Grouse (Millais); by hen only. Single brooded. (Plate 194, f. 4.)

IV. Food.—Shoots of mountain plants, especially *Vaccinium*, but also heather, crowberry, mountain willow, and seeds of rushes, etc.; also insects, especially crane flies, a sawfly also reported. In autumn berries of cloudberry, crowberry, cranberry, etc.

V. Usual Notes.—Little is recorded of its utterances beyond the fact stated both by Naumann and Millais that the hen has an alarm note something like a rapidly repeated " ack " or " ee-ack."

PLATE 140.—PTARMIGAN (SUMMER PLUMAGE) HIDING FROM HAWK (*see* Plate 151) : G. E. Lodge.

PLATE 141.—PHEASANT

Phasianus colchicus Linnæus

I. Description.—Length, about 35 in. (male), female shorter tailed. British birds are a mixed race, and show much variation, the characters of various races predominating locally. Males have usually green purple glossed head and neck, often white collar, long reddish buff tail barred black. Females have general sandy brown coloration, with blackish markings and reddish tinge on mantle, flanks, and tail. Young much like hen, but duller.

II. Range and Habitat.—Originally introduced at a remote period from Western Transcaucasia, this bird is now distributed over most parts of the British Isles, but is absent from the Shetlands and Orkneys. The race has been contaminated by importations from almost all Asiatic forms, whose ranges extend from the Caucasus to Japan. Wooded country, well supplied with water and within reach of cultivation, is the most attractive habitat for this species.

III. Nest and Eggs.—Breeds often in hedges or outskirts of woodlands, making a hollow in ground in a sheltered spot and lining with dead leaves and grass with which the eggs are covered during laying. Exceptionally nests in trees. Eggs: 7 or 8 to 12 or 13, and 14, 15, and 21 to 22 recorded, but hens may lay in one another's nests. Ground colour, brownish olive, but pale bluish and even greyish white varieties occur. Average size of 35 eggs, 45.9 × 36.0 mm. (1.80 × 1.41 in.). Laying begins in early April. Incubation, 23–25 days; normally by hen alone. Single brooded. (Plate 194, f. 5.)

IV. Food.—Varied : corn, bulbous roots, nuts, acorns, hawthorn berries, beech-mast, cultivated fruits, berries, and vegetables, berries and fruits of wild strawberry, blackberry, elder, mistletoe, grass, seeds of many species of weed; earthworms, insects (including beetles, caterpillars, ants, flies, and larvæ of crane flies, earwigs, and grasshoppers, etc.); occasionally lizards, slow-worms, and vipers; small slugs and snails also freely taken. A small bird has been found in a crop, and birds have been choked in swallowing field mice.

V. Usual Notes.—The call or crow of the pheasant is a loud, strident " kor-r-rk " or " korrk-kok " and variants of these. Little attention appears to have been paid to its other utterances.

PLATE 141.—PHEASANTS; COCK AND TWO HENS: A. W. Seaby.

PLATE 142.—REDLEGGED-PARTRIDGE

Alectoris rufa rufa (Linnæus)

I. Description.—Length, 13½–14 in.   Recognized from Grey-Partridge when adult by conspicuous black, white, and chestnut barring on lavender grey flanks; upper parts brown, except crown, which is grey; throat white, edged by black band, followed by a broader band of tawny rufous with black tips; breast lavender, belly buff.   Feet red.   Sexes alike, female slightly duller.   Young have head and neck dull buff, and lack black on gorget; flanks unmarked; under parts mostly dull greyish rufous with paler edges to feathers.

II. Range and Habitat.—An introduced species into Britain (*c.* 1770), now established chiefly in eastern and midland counties, occasionally reaching west to North Wales and Somerset.   On the Continent it ranges from North France and Belgium south to the Pyrenees and Switzerland, while it is replaced by allied races in Spain, Corsica, and also in the Canaries, but has been introduced into Madeira and the Azores.   It is most at home on light soils and in dry climate.

III. Nest and Eggs.—Breeds often in hedge bottoms or under cover of bushes or big tussocks, making a scratching on the ground, with a scanty lining of dead leaves, grasses, etc., and often many feathers of the bird herself.   Eggs: 9 or 10 to 15, but 16 to 18, and, it is said, 20 on record.   Ground, yellowish or ochreous, spotted rather finely with dull ochraceous brown or sometimes irregular blotches of reddish ochreous and ashy shellmarks.   Rare variety bluish white.   Average of 100 British eggs, 41.3 × 31.0 mm. (1.62 × 1.22 in.).   Laying begins end of April, often early May. Incubation period, 23–24 days; share of sexes needs investigation.   Portal says that male and female incubate separate clutches.   Other observations state that the hen alone broods.   Single brooded.   (Plate 194, f. 2.)

IV. Food.—Shoots of young corn, grain, leaves of clover and grasses; also small snails, spiders and insects (beetles, grasshoppers, ants and their pupæ, flies, etc.).

V. Usual Notes.—The notes of this species have lent themselves to a confusing number of different renderings, but most agree that one of its most usual notes sounds something like " chuck chucker " or " churk " repeated.   Naumann has figured the usual call or crow as a repetition of " keks " and " kerrecks," and the alarm note as a ringing " rrebbrrebb . . ."

For the Peregrine shown on Plate 142, see page 151.

PLATE 142.—PEREGRINE-FALCON AND REDLEGGED-PARTRIDGE: G. E. Lodge.

PLATE 143.—PARTRIDGE

Perdix perdix perdix (Linnæus)

I. Description.—Length, 12½ in. Males are distinguishable by dark chestnut horseshoe on lower breast, tawny chestnut on head and throat, breast and flanks grey with fine black markings, and chestnut bars on flanks ; upper parts brownish buff with vermiculations of black. In June the neck is brown, streaked buff and black, and throat paler. Females can always be distinguished by buff cross-bars on wing coverts instead of longitudinal stripes as in male. Horseshoe usually wanting in adult hens. Young resemble female, but feet are yellowish instead of bluish white as in adults.

II. Range and Habitat.—Resident in the cultivated districts and light sandy heaths of Great Britain, but local in Scotland, especially in the north, and absent from the Outer Hebrides, Orkneys, and Shetlands. In Ireland it is not numerous, and decreasing. On the Continent it is distributed from South Finland, North Russia, and South Sweden over middle Europe, south to North Spain, Italy, North Greece, etc., but Spanish, Italian, Breton, Dutch, and East European as well as several West Asiatic races have been separated.

III. Nest and Eggs.—Often breeds in hedgerows close to roads and field tracks, but also occasionally in mowing grass, though generally not far from hedge. Nest, a hollow scratched out in ground, lined with dead leaves, grass, etc. ; eggs covered during laying period. Eggs : usually 10–20, but 21 and 22 probably by one bird ; 26–33, and even 40, must be due to two or more hens ; shape slightly pyriform. Colour, olive, but white and bluish varieties recorded. Average of 100 British eggs, 36.8×27.4 mm. (1.45×1.08 in.). Laying begins in late April. Incubation, 23–25 days ; by hen alone. Single brooded. (Plate 194, f. 1.)

IV. Food.—Grasses, leaves of various weeds, clover, etc., form main food ; also turnip tops, heather shoots, corn, and berries of hawthorn, blaeberry, and blackberry. In summer months also beetles, ants and pupæ, crane flies and larvæ, etc. ; also aphides.

V. Usual Notes.—The usual call of the Partridge is a somewhat grinding but still pleasant " krrr-ic." The alarm note, uttered when the bird is put up, has been variously rendered. By Naumann it is given as " ripriprip . . ." beginning rapid and high-pitched. The cry of a pair suddenly put up by the writer sounded like " kwee-hee-hee-hee . . ." which seems to correspond to the " krikrikri . . ." of Voigt. This note may also be heard when the birds are chasing one another.

PLATE 143.—PARTRIDGES : A. W. Seaby.

PLATE 144.—QUAIL

Coturnix coturnix coturnix (Linnæus)

I. Description.—Length, 7 in. Distinguished by its small size and general resemblance to Grey-Partridge. Colour, pale brown with buff stripes, chestnut and pale buff beneath. Male has crown and nape dark brown with buff stripe in middle, blackish patch on throat, and buff stripe over eye, with dark stripe below; back dusky barred pale brown, streaked whitish; breast pale chestnut, striped buff; under parts pale buff; flanks marked black and buff. Female has chin and throat buff, and is slightly larger.

II. Range and Habitat.—Unlike the other game birds, a summer resident only; has decreased in modern times, and fluctuates in numbers. Local and scarce, but breeds occasionally both in Great Britain and Ireland (where it winters at times), north even to the Outer Hebrides, Orkneys, and Shetlands. On the Continent it is found locally from about 65° N. to North Africa and east to Western Asia, but is replaced by allied races in the Azores, Madeira, and Canaries, Cape Verde Islands, Southern Africa, and East Asia to Japan. Haunts cultivated land, corn-fields, and rough pastures.

III. Nest and Eggs.—Often nests in growing corn, also in rough pastures and in other field crops. Nest, a hollow scratched out in the ground and scantily lined. Eggs: usually 7–12, but 13–18 and 26 on record, the last certainly by two hens. Ground colour, yellowish, varying much in markings, some almost covered with big irregular dark chocolate blotches; others boldly spotted or finely specked with brown. Average size of 70 British eggs, 30.3 × 22.8 mm. (1.19 ×.89 in.). Laying begins latter part of May. Incubation, 16–20 days; by female only. Single brooded. (Plate 194, f. 6.)

IV. Food.—Seeds and leaves of many plants, corn, small snails, and insects and their larvæ.

V. Usual Notes.—A good rendering of the treble call or crow is " wit-widwit," with a slight pause after the first syllable, and the rest " a sharply duplicated note accentuated on the first syllable. When heard at close quarters, successive repetitions are connected by a curious metallic inhalation, not distinguishable at a distance." [1] One call is given several times in succession. It may be continued for hours, one bird answering the other. There are many other renderings, more or less adequate, such as the popular " wet-my-lips," " clik-a-lik," " but-for-but." Naumann gives " pickwerwick," and, heard in the distance, " pickenick." [2] This call is apparently confined to the male. The female utters a soft double note. The alarm cry, when the birds are put up, has been figured by Naumann as " trül-reck-reck-reck."

[1] Stanley Morris, *Bird Song*, 121–2. This sound is figured by Voigt as "rauau" (*au*=*ou* in house).
[2] *Vögel Mitteleuropas*, vi. 118.

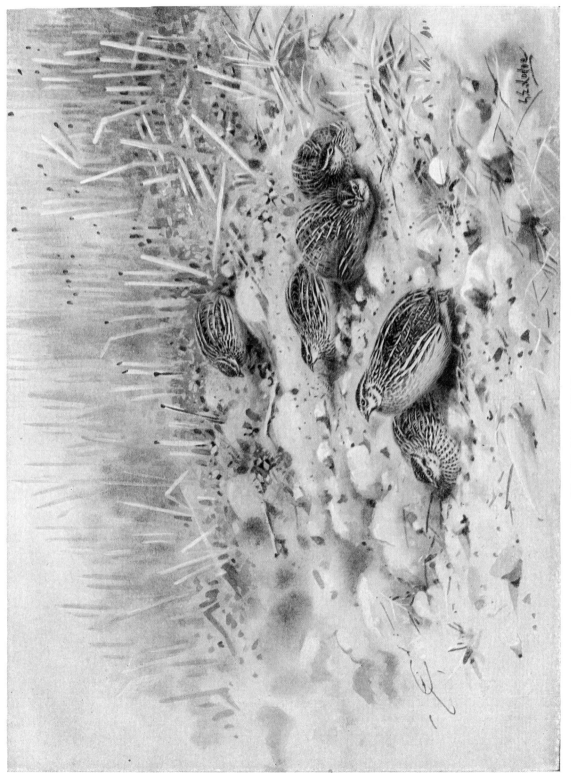

PLATE 144.—QUAIL: G. E. Lodge.

PLATE 145.—GOLDEN-EAGLE, *Aquila chrysaëtus chrysaëtus* (Linnæus)

I. Description.—Length, 32–36 in.   Recognized by its large size, general dark brown coloration with lighter nape, and feet feathered to the toes, which have three large scales only on last joints. In adult the dark tail has a greyish bar on under surface.   Immature birds have a broad terminal band of dark brown, and rest of tail white.   Feet yellow.   Female decidedly larger than male.

II. Range and Habitat.—In the British Isles resident in Scotland only ; till recently a pair or two survived in West Ireland ; in England and Wales it has long been extinct.   In Scotland it is confined to the mountains and moorlands in the areas of Clyde, northern part of Forth, Tay, Moray, Dee, Sutherland, West Ross, Argyll, and Inner and Outer Hebrides, where there are wide stretches of moorland.   On the Continent its range extends from North Russia, Finland, and Scandinavia, south to the Pyrenees, several of the Mediterranean islands, and the Caucasus ; it is found also in Asia Minor, Western Asia, and Siberia, but in Spain, North-West Africa, and the mountains of Central Asia it is replaced by other races, and also in North America.

III. Nest and Eggs.—Most British nests are placed on ledges of cliffs, sometimes readily accessible, but not always ; others are built in trees, usually Scots pines.   The nests are very bulky, generally used again and again in alternate years, built of sticks, heather stems, clumps of grass, etc., usually with some grass and woodrush (*Luzula*) in the lining.   Eggs : normally 2, sometimes 1 only, occasionally but rarely 3, and 4 once recorded.   Ground colour, white or creamy, sometimes quite unmarked, but usually with more or less spotting or blotches of rather purplish brown with ashy grey shellmarks.   Occasionally the egg is almost covered with these markings. Average of 100 British eggs, 76.7 × 59.4 mm. (3.02 × 2.34 in.).   Laying begins towards the end of March or beginning of April.   Incubation period, 33–35 days, or possibly even longer ; apparently by both sexes.   One brood.   (Plate 195, f. 5.)

IV. Food.—Mainly blue hares, but Red-Grouse, and at higher levels Ptarmigan are freely taken ; among less frequently taken game, red deer fawns, lambs, rabbit, rat, mole, squirrel, stoat, and carrion recorded ; and of birds, Hooded-Crow, Lapwing, Curlew, Golden-Plover, Black-Game, Partridge, and Meadow-Pipit.

V. Usual Notes.—The usual cry is an abrupt barking note, repeated again and again, sometimes almost resembling a yelp.   A note that sometimes accompanies the bird's swoops on its prey is a rapid " keck, keck, keck " (Naumann).   The female, when put off her eggs, has been heard to utter " curious, liquid, bubbling notes repeated with great rapidity : ' wow-wow-wow-wow,' while she sat perched on a tree not a hundred yards away." [1]

WHITETAILED-EAGLE, *Haliæetus albicilla albicilla* (Linnæus)

(No Plate)

I. Description.—Length, 33 in. (male), 36 in. (female).   Recognized at all ages by having lower part of tarsus bare ; tarsus and toes are also covered with large scales in front ; adults have bill light yellow and tail white.   General plumage, varying shades of brown, head lighter, less uniform in colour than Golden-Eagle.   Immature birds have beak blackish and tail dark brown.

II. Range and Habitat.—Till recently a rare resident on the rocky coasts of the Shetlands and islands off the West of Scotland ; also extinct in West Ireland, but still occasional passage migrant. On the Continent it breeds in North Russia and Finland, Scandinavia, the Baltic states, locally in Germany, probably Corsica, the Danube valley, Balkan Peninsula, the Black Sea, and Russia ; also in Iceland, and in Asia from Asia Minor and Iraq through North Asia to Kamtschatka and Japan. Is replaced in Greenland by a larger form.   Generally found near the coast or large inland waters.

III. Nest and Eggs.—In the British Isles all nests recorded were on rocks or cliff ledges, generally close to the sea, but on the Continent a large nest is often built in a tree, and, exceptionally, a pair may be found breeding in a marsh or on a sandbank in a lagoon.   Nest built of sticks, heather twigs, grass, seaweed, often with wool and grass in lining.   Eggs : usually 2, sometimes 1 only, while 3 and 4 are on record.   Colour, white, only very rarely showing traces of markings.   Average size of 52 British eggs, 73.7 × 58.6 mm. (2.90 × 2.30 in.).   Laying begins early in April, but in South Europe in February to March.   Incubation period estimated at 35, 40, 45 days ; chiefly by female, but male takes part.   Single brooded.   (Plate 196, f. 3.)

IV. Food.—Largely fish of all kinds, living as well as stranded ; carrion, lambs, hares, rabbits, hedgehogs, poultry and sea-birds (Guillemot, Puffin, Kittiwake and other gulls), Ducks of various species, and Coot and Wood-Pigeon.

V. Usual Notes.—Little recorded.   According to O. von Riesenthal it utters a hoarse repeated " krak," to which it adds a note like the " yelping of a hound." [2]   Jourdain states that the cry is surprisingly weak for such a powerful bird, and that anxiety is shown by a querulous chatter.

---

[1] Seton Gordon, *The Charm of the Hills*, 127.   [2] Naumann, *Vögel Mitteleuropas*, v. 166.

PLATE 145.—GOLDEN-EAGLE : G. E. Lodge.

PLATE 146.—HEN-HARRIER, *Circus cyaneus cyaneus* (Linnæus)

I. Description.—Length, 21–21½ in. Its flight is like that of the Marsh-Harrier. The adult male is distinguished by pale slate-grey head and upper parts, with conspicuous white rump, breast and throat bluish grey, rest of under parts white ; primaries black. Females are larger and brown above ; buffish white below, streaked rufous ; rump white, streaked reddish ; five dark brown bars on tail. Young resemble female but are more rufous on back, and tail bars are also rufous.

II. Range and Habitat.—A local resident in the British Isles ; confined to the Devonian peninsula in England, the Outer Hebrides and Orkneys in Scotland, and some of the mountain districts in Ireland. Its haunts are open moorlands and heaths, but on the Continent it breeds also in cornfields. In Europe its range extends from the Arctic Circle south to the Cantabrian Mountains, North Italy, South Russia, and across Northern Asia to East Siberia, but it is replaced in North America and North-Eastern Siberia by an allied race.

III. Nest and Eggs.—A moorland rather than a marsh species, nesting in the British Isles among heather, making rather a slight nest of dead rushes in a hollow in the ground, with a few twigs of heather arranged round the cup. Eggs : usually 5–6, sometimes only 4, while 7 and even 8 have been recorded ; pale bluish white in colour, generally unmarked, but occasionally with light rusty or deep red brown markings. Average of 100 British eggs, 46.3 × 36.0 mm. (1.82 × 1.41 in.). Laying begins in May in Scotland ; earlier in Germany (end of April). Incubation period, about 30 days ; by female alone. One brood. (Plate 195, f. 3.)

IV. Food.—Chiefly birds taken by surprise on the ground or injured, young in the nest, and eggs : Meadow-Pipit, Skylark, Blackbird, Ring-Ouzel, Finches, and occasionally Ducks, Lapwing, Golden-Plover, Snipe, Dunlin, Grouse, or Partridge ; also rabbit, rat, water-rat, voles, and mice. Lizards, frogs, slow-worms, and small fish also recorded.

V. Usual Notes.—It utters a quick " hek hek hek " (Coward), which may be compared with a somewhat similar note of the Marsh-Harrier. These notes correspond no doubt to the " gegegegeg " and its variants given by Voigt, who had the species under frequent observation. The note seemed to be a kind of joy cry. Walpole Bond refers to the " squealing wail " of the hen, which corresponds probably to the " bleating " note described in Naumann's work, and to Voigt's " high, thin giä giä giä giä " (*ī = ee* ; *ä = a* in *care*). The hen, according to Voigt, also utters the ' gegegegeg." [1]

MARSH-HARRIER, *Circus aeruginosus aeruginosus* (Linnæus)

(No Plate)

I. Description.—Length, 21–23 in. All the Harriers have a characteristic low wavering flight, with occasional glides with rigid wings. The Marsh-Harrier is distinguished by its large size, and the adult male has ashy grey secondaries, tertials, and tail ; head creamy, with dark streaks. Females are more difficult to distinguish, but have creamy margin to shoulders, and light streaked heads, rest of plumage brown. Young birds are chocolate ; males have buffish crowns ; females only yellowish on nape, but there is a good deal of variation. Females larger than males.

II. Range and Habitat.—Recently a pair or two have bred in the Broad district of East Anglia. Its Irish status is uncertain, but possibly it still lingers there. Usually met with as erratic winter vagrant in marshy districts or river valleys. On the Continent its range does not extend north of Denmark, South Sweden, and the Baltic ; it extends south to South France, and eastward to the Mediterranean and some of its islands ; also into Western Asia. In North-West Africa, Spain, and possibly Egypt it is replaced by an allied race.

III. Nest and Eggs.—A fenland bird, generally seen beating low over reeds or water, and nesting in shallow water or on marshy ground among dead reeds or high growth of aquatic plants. Nest very bulky, built chiefly of dead reeds and sedge, but branches of sallow also worked in ; lined with dead grasses. Eggs : usually 4–5, rarely 6, or only 3, and 7 on record. Colour, dead white or bluish white ; often stained, but hardly ever showing genuine marking. Average size of 60 British and Central European eggs, 50.7 × 39.1 mm. (1.99 × 1.54 in.). Laying begins in May in Middle-Europe. Incubation period, 36–38 days (Vincent) ; almost entirely by female. Single brooded. (Plate 195, f. 2.)

IV. Food.—Largely frogs, toads, snakes, and eggs of many species of birds, as well as birds surprised among reeds and wounded birds, or young in the nest, especially of Coot and Moorhen and young of Ducks and Blackheaded-Gull ; rabbit and water rat also taken.

V. Usual Notes.—Droste-Hülshoff, who paid particular attention to this species, describes the usual call as a long-drawn shrill " kreeee " (anglicized).[2] He heard it when the birds were sporting and gliding in the air before roosting, also at times when snatching up prey. Naumann adds a sharp " wik, wik, wik," uttered sometimes after the capture of prey—" a ringing joy cry." The female (when uneasy) has a whining or squealing note : the male has a rather weak " chick à chick à ra," often repeated.

[1] *Op. cit.* (page 131 above), 201.　　　　　[2] *Vogelwelt der Nordseeinsel Borkum*, 75–78.

PLATE 146.—HEN-HARRIER (MALE): G. E. Lodge.

PLATE 147.—SPARROW-HAWK, *Accipiter nisus nisus* (Linnæus)

I. Description.—Length, 12–15½ in.; the male much smaller than female. Distinguished by short wings, long yellow feet, and barred under parts. The male has upper parts slaty grey, cheeks rufous, barred below with rufous; tail brown with dark bars. The female is barred below with ash brown, and has upper parts browner; rufous patch on flanks. Young have rufous edges to feathers of upper parts, and have under surface heavily barred with rufous, but this species shows much variation in plumage.

II. Range and Habitat.—Widely distributed resident in all wooded parts of the British Isles, but rare in the north of Scotland and Orkneys, and does not breed in the Shetlands or Outer Hebrides. On the Continent it ranges as far as the tree limit in Scandinavia, North Finland, and Russia, and south to the Mediterranean, also in Western Asia. In Corsica and Sardinia, North-West Africa, Madeira, the Canaries, and in Central and Eastern Asia it is replaced by allied forms.

III. Nest and Eggs.—Its favourite breeding haunts are plantations with some conifers among them, especially spruce, but it also breeds in deciduous trees, generally taking the remains of some old nest as a foundation and building on it a substantial nest of larch twigs, or branches of other trees, often with fragments of bark in the cup. Eggs: usually 4–6, occasionally 7 or 8 (larger sets almost certainly due to two females). Colour, pale bluish, sometimes unmarked, but generally with chocolate brown blotches, often forming a rough zone; occasionally tawny or reddish brown markings are met with, or the egg is almost suffused with reddish brown. Average of 100 British eggs, 39.7 × 31.7 mm. (1.56 × 1.24 in.). Laying begins in first half of May. Incubation period, normally 35 days, exceptionally 32–38 days; by female alone. One brood. (Plate 196, f. 1.)

IV. Food.—Chiefly smaller birds taken on the wing, including Starling, most of our resident Finches, Pipits, Skylark, Tits, Warblers, Thrushes, Robin, Redstart, Hedge-Sparrow, etc. Also recorded as killing Swift, Kingfisher, Cuckoo, Woodpecker, Wood-Pigeon, Turtle-Dove, Teal, Moorhen, Lapwing, Woodcock, Pheasant, Partridge, Greyhen, domestic fowls, young Lesser-Terns, and once Forktailed-Petrel. Mice and voles, bats and young rabbits, frogs, and occasionally beetles and grasshoppers on record.

V. Usual Notes.—The alarm cry heard when the nest is approached sounds like a loud, rapid " kep, kep, kep " or " kew, kew, kew," repeated several times. In moments of rising intensity this becomes " kyow, kyow, kyow." [1] The " kew, kew, kew " is also the call of the male bringing food; if the female does not come to where he has perched, he changes to " key-oo, key-oo, kew, kew, kew," the " key-oo " plaintive, and the " kew " shrill, and finally, to a soft " ki-ki-ki," if he has to go to the nest itself. [1] The cry of the male is the more high-pitched. [2] The young use the " kew " as an alarm note when about eighteen days old; they have a variety of other notes. [1] Another cry of the adults has been recorded, something like " ghu, ghu, ghu," [2] apparently a kind of love or sex note; it corresponds no doubt to the cry figured by Naumann as " gü."

MONTAGU'S HARRIER, *Circus pygargus* (Linnæus)

(No Plate)

I. Description.—Length, 18–19¼ in. It has the characteristic flight of the Harriers (see p. 146). Distinguished from the Hen-Harrier, which it somewhat resembles, by slimmer build, slightly smaller size; black bar across secondaries of closed wing; more ashy mantle; rufous streaks on lower parts, and less white on rump. Females, which are larger, are brown above; buffish white striped with rufous below. Young have upper parts dark brown, lighter and warmer below.

II. Range and Habitat.—Summer resident in England and Wales, much reduced in numbers of late years, breeding in East Anglia (?), Devonian peninsula, and in sporadic pairs in open plains, heaths, moors, and marshes north to Yorkshire, and possibly Northumberland. No definite proof of breeding in Scotland or Ireland, though it may have nested in both countries. On the Continent its range extends from about 57° N. in Russia south of the Baltic, south to the Mediterranean and North-West Africa, eastward to Bulgaria and South Russia; also in Western Asia to North Mongolia.

III. Nest and Eggs.—Even in England this species shows a tendency to breed not far apart, and, abroad, quite large colonies may be met with. It is found breeding in wet marshes, on dry heaths, on commons, and, abroad, in cornfields. Nest, a pad of grasses or rushes in a depression on the ground and surrounded by rank marsh plants, or heather, or sheltered by gorse. Eggs: usually 4–5, 6 rare, 8 once recorded; full clutches of 2 and 3 also occur. Colour, white or pale bluish white, generally unmarked, occasionally rusty or red brown markings. Average size of 80 eggs, 42.0 × 33.0 mm. (1.65 × 1.30 in.). Laying begins towards the end of May. Incubation period, 27–30 days; as a rule by female only, but a male has once been flushed from eggs. One brood. (Plate 195, f. 1.)

IV. Food.—Largely frogs, toads, snakes, and lizards; also small birds, nestlings, and eggs, especially Pipits, Skylarks, Yellow-Buntings, Stonechats, etc.; Thrushes, Blackbirds, and larger birds when injured; eggs of Moorhen and Coot, young game birds, etc. Also small mammals (young rabbits, hares, and field mice); insects (chiefly larger beetles) and earthworms.

V. Usual Notes.—The most ordinary note is a querulous " gek gek gek . . ." or " kek kek kek . . ." As to its other notes, detailed information is lacking.

---

[1] J. H. Owen in *British Birds* (Mag.), **x.** 27, 51, 84 (young), and *in litt.*   [2] Bertram Lloyd (*in litt.*)

PLATE 147.—SPARROW-HAWKS *(the bird on the nest is the female)* : G. E. Lodge.

PLATE 148.—BUZZARD, *Buteo buteo buteo* (Linnæus)

STEPPE-BUZZARD, *Buteo buteo vulpinus* Gloger

I. Description.—Length, 20–23 in. ; male smaller. Varies considerably in plumage ; conspicuously broad wings like Golden-Eagle, but much smaller, generally brown in colour ; adults show 12–13 darker bands on brown tail. Feet not feathered, which distinguishes it from the Roughlegged-Buzzard ; colour yellow. Young birds are generally paler on upper parts ; breast with brown blotches on white ground.

II. Range and Habitat.—Resident and common in Devonian peninsula, Wales, and Lakeland, and in smaller numbers in the Pennines ; breeds in all Scottish areas except Tweed, Dee, Outer Hebrides, Orkneys and Shetlands ; has been extinct in Ireland for half a century. Now chiefly confined to sea-coast cliffs and midlands, but formerly very general. On the Continent breeds from 66° N. in Sweden over middle Europe, south to Andalucia, and east from Prussia, the Carpathians to Macedonia ; but in Corsica and Sardinia, the Canaries, Azores, Madeira, and Cape Verdes, as well as in the greater part of Russia, North-East Sweden, Finland, Esthonia, Latvia, and the greater part of temperate Asia, it is replaced by other forms, one of which, the Steppe-Buzzard, has occurred here once.

III. Nest and Eggs.—Although on the Continent the Buzzard breeds freely in trees, most of the nests in Great Britain are on ledges of cliffs or on broken hillsides, on bushes growing out of rocks, though in some districts trees are the normal site. Nest bulky, built of sticks, heather stems, etc., solidified with earth ; inner cup decorated with fresh green branches of pine, ivy, larch, etc., as well as dead grass, bark, and woodrush. Eggs : normally 2–3 ; old birds may lay 1 only, while 4 is not rare in certain districts, and 5 have occurred a few times. Colour, white, sometimes with slight tinge of bluish, spotted and smeared with reddish brown, light or dark, and ranging from small spots to big blotches, with violet shellmarks in some cases. Average of 100 British eggs, 56.8 × 45.4 mm. (2.23 × 1.78 in.). Laying begins in latter part of April. Incubation period, 28 (to 31 ?) days ; by both sexes, but chiefly by female. One brood. (Plate 195, f. 4.)

IV. Food.—Carrion : dead sheep and lambs and placenta of ewes, rabbits, moles (occasionally hare, rat, field mice, shrew, stoat, weasel, and marten) ; also earthworms, snakes, frogs, toads, lizards, slow-worms ; and birds (Crow, Jackdaw, Finches, Tits, Pipits, Skylarks, Thrushes, Red-Grouse, once Pheasant, Partridge, Wood-Pigeon, Moorhen, Lapwing, chickens and young ducks, and young Shearwater). Also small mollusca, beetles and caterpillars.

V. Usual Notes.—The usual cry is a plaintive mewing, sometimes prolonged, sometimes short and repeated, uttered when the nest is approached. Other specific occasions which excited the mewing were the sound of a gunshot [1] and an attack by a Merlin.[2] A low chuckle or croak announces to the young the bringing of prey ; and the warning cry to the young, which reduces them at once to stillness, in whatever attitude they happen to be, is a shrill yelp.[1]

ROUGHLEGGED-BUZZARD, *Buteo lagopus lagopus* (Brünnich)

(No Plate)

I. Description.—Length, 23–26 in. ; male smaller. Distinguished from the Common-Buzzard by having the feet feathered down to the toes ; the basal part of the tail white, with a broad brown subterminal band ; under parts buffish white, with brown bars ; head and neck creamy white, streaked with brown ; mantle dark brown. Young birds are streaked on under parts, and show less white on the tail.

II. Range and Habitat.—Winter visitor, chiefly to the east side of Great Britain. On the Continent it breeds from North Scandinavia, Finland, and Russia, south to the high field of South Scandinavia ; but there is no satisfactory evidence of breeding south of the Gulf of Finland. Its breeding range extends to Siberia, from the Urals to Kamtschatka, and in North America it is replaced by allied forms. In winter it moves southward to Central Europe and the Balkans. It is a tundra-haunting species as a rule, though also found in wooded districts.

III. Nest and Eggs.—Does not breed in the British Isles. In Lapland it often nests on ledges of rocks ; sometimes on the ground, and in some districts on trees. Nest bulky, built of sticks, heather, turf, etc., the cup being lined with dead grass, also lichens, moorland plants, and pine shoots. Eggs : vary in number according to the food supply ; in ordinary years 2–3, but in lemming years 4–6. Colour, white, smeared or blotched and spotted with dark brown, sometimes almost unmarked. Average of 110 eggs, 55.0 × 43.5 mm. (2.16 × 1.71 in.). Laying begins in latter part of May. Incubation period about 31 days ; chiefly by female. One brood.

IV. Food.—In Lapland chiefly lemmings ; Ptarmigan and other birds, field mice and other rodents, frogs, lizards, insects, etc.

V. Usual Notes.—The usual cry is a cat-like mewing call : " pee-you " (Jourdain).

---

[1] *Wild Life*, December 1913, 347–363 (H. B. Macpherson).
[2] This last fact is recorded by R. H. Brown in *British Birds* (Mag.), xx. 125.

PLATE 148.—COMMON-BUZZARD: A. W. Seaby.

PLATE 149.—KESTREL

Falco tinnunculus tinnunculus Linnæus

I. Description.—Length, 13–15 in. ; male smaller. Recognizable in the field by its habit of hovering, and general tawny colour of upper parts. The male has head, neck, rump, and tail blue grey ; the latter with white tip and broad black subterminal bar ; back chestnut with black spots ; under parts buff streaked and spotted with black. Female has upper parts rufous, barred with black ; tail barred with black, and black tipped. Young much like female, but paler. Cere and feet yellow.

II. Range and Habitat.—Generally distributed resident in the British Isles, but only summer resident in the Shetlands, and many northern birds move southward in autumn. Does not range very high in mountains, but can exist almost anywhere if allowed. On the Continent ranges from about 68° in Scandinavia, and 61° in North Russia, south to the Mediterranean region, and North-West Africa ; is found also in Western and Northern Asia, but is replaced by allied forms in the Eastern and Western Canaries and Madeira, the Cape Verde Isles, North-East Africa, tropical Africa, North India, China, and Japan. The winter range extends farther south.

III. Nest and Eggs.—Nesting sites rather varied : most pairs breeding in old nests of Crow or Magpie, and occasionally other species, while ledges of sea cliffs and rocks and crevices in ruins or lofty buildings are also used ; also hollows in old trees ; occasionally also on the ground. No nesting material used. Eggs : 4–5, 6 at times, and 7–9 on record. Ground colour, white, blotched, spotted and smeared with varying shades of red brown ; exceptionally unmarked, sometimes no ground colour visible : in some sets violet grey shellmarks also noticeable. Average size of 100 British eggs, 39.7 × 31.7 mm. (1.56 × 1.25 in.). Laying begins early in April ; often not till mid-April. Incubation period, 27–32 days ; by both sexes, but chiefly female. One brood. (Plate 196, f. 2.)

IV. Food.—Largely small mammals : long- and short-tailed field mice, rat, shrew, mole, bank vole, bats ; once young rabbit ; also small passerine birds (Finches, Buntings, Pipits, Larks, Thrushes, Hedge-Sparrow, and Starling) ; occasionally young Snipe, Lapwing, and Wood-Pigeon and Hooded-Crow recorded. Individual birds will take game chicks ; also frogs, lizards, adder, slow-worm, earthworm, insects (especially beetles).

V. Usual Notes.—The usual cry is a loud, clear " ke " or " ke ke ke . . ." ; or variants of the same, notes not unlike the cry of the Lesser Spotted-Woodpecker. The species has also a cry figured by Voigt as a vibrating " wree " (anglicized) or " wree-wree-wre . . ." or " zee-ree-ree-ree . . ." This corresponds probably to the " rippling musical call used throughout the breeding season," described by Miss E. L. Turner.[1]

---

[1] *Broadland Birds*, 94 : " My captive birds often greeted me with this cry, and had a charming way of alighting on my arm and looking up inquiringly into my face while repeating the call."

PLATE 149—KESTRELS (*the male in the foreground*) : A. W. Seaby.

PLATE 150.—HOBBY, *Falco subbuteo subbuteo* Linnæus

I. Description.—Length, 12–14 in. ; male smaller. Much resembles Peregrine on small scale, but distinguished by extraordinary length of wing, black streaked breast, and rusty red thighs and vent. Upper parts bluish black ; black moustache ; cheeks white, passing upward into blackish ; throat white, breast tinged with buff, cere and feet yellow. Young have buff margins to feathers of back ; crown and cheeks marked buff ; pale tip to tail and thighs, and vent pale rufous.

II. Range and Habitat.—Summer resident in Southern England and somewhat local ; once recorded as breeding in Scotland. Not a mountain or moorland species, but haunts woodlands and plains or valleys with spinneys. On the Continent it breeds from North Sweden, Central Finland, and North Russia, south to the Mediterranean and some of its islands, also in Western Asia ; but is replaced by allied races in North-West Africa, Central and Northern Asia, and China. Winters in tropical and South Africa, and in Southern Asia.

III. Nest and Eggs.—Makes use of old nests of other species, generally Carrion-Crow's, but also occasionally those of Rook, Heron, Magpie, or even squirrel. Pines in small spinneys and elms in hedgerows are favourite sites. Eggs : usually 3, sometimes 2, very rarely 4, rather larger than those of Kestrel, nearly always much paler, being usually almost uniformly covered with small orange tawny or ochreous spots, exceptionally, fine reddish markings. Average size of 95 British eggs, 41.6 × 33.8 mm. (1.63 × 1.33 in.). Laying begins early in June. Incubation period, 28–32 days ; both sexes taking part. One brood. (Plate 196, f. 4.)

IV. Food.—Chiefly insects (beetles, dragon flies, grasshoppers, moths, ants, flies, etc.) ; and birds (Starling, Twite, Linnet, Sparrow, Meadow-Pipit, Blue-Tit, Song-Thrush, Blackbird, Swallow, House-Martin, Swift, once young Partridge) ; also bats.

V. Usual Notes.—The anger note has been variously rendered as a repeated sharp " keek," " kik," " ke," " gick," or " gück." Walpole Bond gives " quer-ic " as the call. The bird also utters a high-pitched " dew " or " tew." [1]

PLATE 116.—MERLIN, *Falco columbarius æsalon* Tunstall

I. Description.—Length, 10–12 in. ; male smaller. Recognized by small size ; male with crown and upper parts slaty blue with dark shafts, nape rufous, throat white ; under parts tinged rufous, striped black ; tail blue grey, barred blackish with white tip. Female has upper parts dark brown, tail brown with narrow lighter bands and white tip ; nape, cheeks, and under parts whitish, streaked with brown. Young like female, but more rufous. Cere and feet yellow.

II. Range and Habitat.—Resident and partial migrant ; breeding in the west from Somerset, Wales, and the Pennine spurs northward in Great Britain as far as the Shetlands, and also in Ireland. Haunts moorlands and hilly country in the summer, moving south and coastward afterwards. Breeds in the Faeroes, Scandinavia, Finland, North Russia, Esthonia, Latvia and Lithuania, but is replaced by allied races in Iceland, South-East Russia, various parts of Asia and North America. In winter found as far south as North Africa and North-West India.

III. Nest and Eggs.—Most nests in Scotland and Northern England are placed on hillsides among heather, occasionally among rocks, but in Wales old nests of Crows in trees are frequently made use of, and nests may be found among marram grass on sand-hills. On the moorlands there is little nest material beyond a few heather twigs, but among dunes marram grass and bents are used to form the cup. Eggs : generally 4, sometimes 5, or only 3, rarely 6 ; in most cases thickly and uniformly marked with fine stippling of dark brown, sometimes quite purplish ; occasionally rich red brown or tawny showing the white ground, and in rare cases almost unmarked. Average of 100 British eggs, 39.9 × 31.2 mm. (1.57 × 1.23 in.). Laying begins early in May. Incubation period, 29–30 days ; both sexes taking part, but chiefly the female. One brood. (Plate 196, f. 5.)

IV. Food.—Chiefly small birds ; especially Meadow-Pipit ; also Skylark, Linnet, Twite, Yellow-Bunting, Ring-Ouzel, etc. ; also occasionally most of our common small passerine birds, and occasionally Rock-Dove, Sandpiper, Dunlin, Snipe, Golden-Plover, Redshank, Lapwing, etc. Quite exceptionally young Grouse and Partridge ; also rabbits, voles, insects (beetles, moths, dragon flies, etc.), and lizards.

V. Usual Notes.—The note uttered when the nest is approached sounds like a shrill " kek, kek, kek." The " kek " of the male is stated to be higher pitched than that of the female (*cp.* Peregrine). The same " kek," with a difference understood by the hen, is the cry of the male bringing food. The call of the hen for food is a " long-drawn-out and frequently repeated ' eep-eep-eep,' " not unlike the whimpering call of the young. On alighting at the nest both sexes may utter a soft " tick." [2]

[1] For other notes see *British Birds* (Mag.), xxv. 200 (J. Walpole Bond).
[2] Most of the information supplied in this note is from the field observations of W. Rowan in *British Birds* (Mag.), xv. 223-4.

PLATE 150.—HOBBY AND ITS YOUNG: G. E. Lodge.

PLATE 151.—GREENLAND FALCON, *Falco rusticolus candicans* Gmelin

ICELAND FALCON, *Falco rusticolus islandus* Brünnich

I. Description.—Length, 20–21 in. (male) ; 23 in. (female). Recognized at once by general white colour with blackish markings on feathers of upper parts ; under parts only sparingly spotted. Immature birds have brownish markings which are heavier above, and drop-shaped below. Bill, cere, and feet yellow in adults, bluish in young birds.

II. Range and Habitat.—The Greenland race is met with in North-West and East Greenland and Arctic North America ; apparently also the Commander Isles and Arctic Siberia. Replaced by other forms in Scandinavia, Finland, North Russia, and in Asia and Canada. In the British Isles it is an irregular winter visitor, chiefly to the western coasts. The Iceland form, which apparently also breeds in South Greenland, has occurred in the British Isles.

III. Nest and Eggs.—Does not breed in the British Isles. In Arctic Greenland it nests on ledges of cliffs on the coast, using the same site year after year, and thus filling the ledge with disintegrated pellets, etc., on which the eggs are laid. Eggs : 3–4, 5 once recorded ; like all the Gyrfalcons' eggs, paler in colour than Peregrine's, being almost covered with brick red or yellowish tawny spots and freckles. Average size of 90 eggs, 58.8 × 45.7 mm. (2.31 × 1.80 in.). Laying begins in May. Incubation period, about 29 days ; chiefly, at any rate, by female. One brood.

IV. Food.—On its breeding ground, lemmings, Alpine hares, Ptarmigan, Guillemots, small waders, and Snow-Bunting ; in winter recorded as taking rabbit, water vole, domestic Pigeon, Rock-Dove, Golden-Plover, Snipe, Dunlin, Ringed-Plover, and Gulls, especially Kittiwake.

V. Usual Notes.—The ordinary cry is a loud, ringing " kyak." Hantzsch mentions a trilling " güü . . ." and the bird is said to utter a screaming note on taking prey.

PLATE 142.—PEREGRINE-FALCON, *Falco peregrinus peregrinus* Tunstall

AMERICAN PEREGRINE, *Falco peregrinus anatum* Bonaparte

I. Description.—Length, 15 in. (male) ; 18–20 in. (female). The largest of our breeding Falcons. Recognized by blackish crown, cheeks and moustachial stripe, slaty grey upper parts, barred with darker shade ; under parts white tinged with buff, spotted on chest, and barred with blackish below ; cere and feet yellow ; beak bluish. Young birds have buff edges to brown feathers of upper parts ; under parts yellowish with dark brown streaks ; cere and feet bluish.

II. Range and Habitat.—Has increased considerably in numbers of late years and now is resident (and also passage migrant), breeding mainly on cliffs by the sea in the south ; but also among mountains inland in Ireland, Wales, and Scotland. Absent as a breeder from the east coast of England south of Yorkshire. On the Continent breeds from North Scandinavia, Finland, and North Russia to the mountain ranges of Southern Europe, but the exact limits of this and the allied Mediterranean race not well defined. It is also replaced by other races in the interior of North-West Africa, Southern Africa, Siberia, Southern Asia, Malaysia, Australia, and America. The last named form has occurred twice.

III. Nest and Eggs.—Although on the Continent many pairs breed in old nests in trees, no case of this has been reported from the British Isles, and all the known nests have been on ledges of cliff or, exceptionally, on lofty buildings, on low islets among heather, or on the ground on a hillock on an open heath. The nest is a bare hollow scraped out in the turf. Eggs : normally 3–4, rarely 5, or 2 only. Ground, white, generally hidden or almost so by red brown markings, but occasionally showing a good deal of the ground, and sometimes violet blotches or cloudings. Average size of 100 British eggs, 51.8 × 41 mm. (2.04 × 1.61 in.). Laying begins occasionally at end of March, usually early in April. Incubation period, 28–29 days ; mainly by female, but male takes some part. One brood. (Plate 197, f. 2.)

IV. Food.—Varies according to locality ; Pigeons, Grouse, sea birds and, locally, Rooks and Jackdaws perhaps form staple diet. A long list of species of birds has been compiled from remains at plucking places and nests, including such surprising items as male Peregrine, Buzzard, Kestrel, Merlin and Sparrow-Hawk, Carrion-Crow, Jay, and Chough ; nearly all our small passerine birds, all our Doves ; most of our breeding Ducks and waders ; Gulls and Terns up to Lesser Black-backed and Herring ; all our Auks, Rails, and game birds which breed with us. Mammals include rabbit, young hare, water rat, shrew, and field mice ; also frogs, toads, and beetles.

V. Usual Notes.—The call of the male (tercel) returning with food has been rendered " e-eep, e-eep, e-eep." [1] The anger note, excited by intrusion, is a fierce, hard, repeated " kek, kek, kek . . ." or " hek, hek, hek," or, according to Jourdain, " kra, kra, kra," and Voigt, " gra . . ." Uttered by the male, it is stated to be " higher in pitch and shriller in tone " than the corresponding note of the female. [2] A cry heard in late autumn was an almost melodious " güü, güü . . ." (*ü*=French *u* ; *u*=*oo* in *poor*). [3]

[1] *British Birds* (Mag.), xxii., 199 (Ingram and Salmon).
[2] *Wild Life*, September 1916, 262 (D. A. Scott) and B. Lloyd (*in litt.*).
[3] Voigt, *op. cit.*, 194.

151

PLATE 151.—GREENLAND-FALCON AND PTARMIGAN (*see* Plate 140) : G. E. Lodge.

PLATE 152.—OSPREY, *Pandion haliætus haliætus* (Linnæus)

I. Description.—Length, 22 in. (male), 24 in. (female). Recognized by white head and nape, brown upper parts and white under surface, except for brown spots on breast ; cere and feet greenish blue. Dark stripe from eye to nape. Young birds have pale edges to feathers above ; tail distinctly barred.

II. Range and Habitat.—Formerly summer resident in many parts of west, central, and North Scotland, but has ceased to breed for nearly twenty years past, and is now an irregular passage migrant. Abroad it breeds from Lapland and North Russia locally to both north and south shores of the Mediterranean and its islands, the Atlantic groups south to the Cape Verde Isles, sparingly round the Black Sea, but commonly round the Red Sea, in North-East Africa, Arabia to India and Ceylon ; also in North Asia to Kamtschatka and Japan. Replaced by allied races in North America, the Malay Archipelago, and Australia. Haunts rocky coasts and islets ; also fresh-water lakes.

III. Nest and Eggs.—The Scotch sites were varied ; many were on rocks projecting from the surface of lochs ; others on big trees, usually Scots pines ; occasionally on ruins of buildings on islands. On the Continent nests are also found on ledges of sea cliffs. Nest bulky, built of sticks and driftwood, heather, seaweed, turf, etc. Eggs : 2–3, rarely 4 ; very beautifully blotched, and spotted with rich red or chocolate and ashy shell-marks on a white ground. Average of 33 British eggs, 62.2 × 46.7 mm. (2.45 × 1.84 in.). Laying begins about the end of April. Incubation period, 30–35 days ; male said to assist at times. One brood. (Plate 197, f. 3.)

IV. Food.—Mainly fish, both salt and fresh water species (sea trout, sole, brown trout, bream, perch, roach, carp, etc.). Exceptionally has been seen to take chicken ; beetles also recorded.

V. Usual Notes.—When the nest is approached the birds hover uttering a note like "killy, killy, killy." Anger is expressed by a penetrating "kee-kee-kee-kee-ich-ich-ich," the *ich* being a coughing or choking sound. The call is "fish-fish-fish," often uttered, appropriately, when a fish is being carried.[1]

KITE, *Milvus milvus milvus* (Linnæus)

(No Plate)

I. Description.—Length, 24–25 in. Distinguished at once from any other bird of prey here mentioned by its long and deeply forked tail, general rufous colouring, and a conspicuous dark patch on the white under side of the wing ; conspicuous in flight. Adults have head and neck whitish, striped with black ; mantle rufous ; primaries blackish ; tail red brown ; under parts rufous, striped brown. Female slightly larger, but not so bright. Young lighter and more spotted.

II. Range and Habitat.—A resident in small numbers in Southern Wales, formerly widely spread in Great Britain from the north of Scotland southward, but now confined to a restricted area of mountain, moor, and small cultivation, with oak woods. On the Continent it breeds in South Sweden, the Baltic republics, and Russia, south to North-West Africa (possibly a local race), on the Mediterranean coasts, and apparently also in Palestine and Asia Minor ; but is replaced by a local race in the Cape Verde Isles.

III. Nest and Eggs.—Usually nests in the fork of an oak in a wood on hillside in Wales ; in Scotland formerly bred in pines. Nest large, usually near the main stem, built of sticks, solidified with earth, and lined with rolls of wool, rags, or rubbish of all kinds. Eggs : 2–3, but 4 have been recorded ; shape variable, sometimes pointed oval, but not always ; white spotted and blotched rather sparingly with red brown, sometimes a dark hair streak or two. Average of 54 British eggs, 57.0 × 44.7 mm. (2.24 × 1.76 in.). Laying begins about mid-April. Incubation period, about a month ; chiefly by female. One brood. (Plate 196, f. 7.)

IV. Food.—Carrion ; small mammals (rabbit, leveret, squirrel, mole, rat, field mice, etc.) ; young birds (chicken, duckling, young Grouse, Lapwing, Curlew), and occasionally old birds taken unawares (Red-Grouse, Wood-Pigeon, Golden-Plover, Partridge, and Ducks) ; also frogs, snakes, blindworms, beetles, and earthworms.

V. Usual Notes.—Its usual note is rendered by Naumann as a high "hieh ! hi-hi-hieh !" (anglicized). He kept the bird in captivity and states that it has also a whistling note, a joy cry, and that this, together with other strange notes, compose a kind of song uttered in the breeding season.[2]

---

[1] Clinton G. Abbot, *Home Life of the Osprey* (1911).   [2] *Vögel Mitteleuropas*, v. 136.

PLATE 152.—OSPREY CATCHING FISH : A. W. Seaby.

Order : Anseriformes. Family : Anatidæ (Geese, Swans, and Ducks)

PLATE 153.—GREYLAG-GOOSE, *Anser anser* (Linnæus)

I. Description.—Length, 34–35 in. From the other three " Grey " Geese here de-scribed, it is distinguished from the Whitefronted by the almost entire absence of the white patch on the face and the black patches on the breast which mark the latter ; from the Bean and Pinkfoot by its flesh-coloured bill with white nail. In the field a good character is the light grey shoulder patches. Plumage greyish brown, under parts lighter with paler margins on the back, and dusky bars on under parts ; rump and wing coverts ash grey ; a few black marks on breast of old birds, and a little white round bill. Feet flesh-coloured. Belly dull white and white tip to tail.

II. Range and Habitat.—Resident in Scotland in Outer Hebrides, some of the Inner Hebrides, and the areas of West Ross, Sutherland, and North Moray. To the rest of the British Isles it is a winter visitor. It also breeds in Iceland and on the Continent from North Russia, Finland, and Scandinavia south to Holland, the Danube valley, Macedonia, and South Russia (exceptionally also in Spain and Algeria) ; also in temperate and Northern Asia to the Pacific. Winters south to the Mediterranean and Southern Asia. In Scotland it is found on moorlands generally not far from the sea or inland lochs, but in winter it is chiefly met with on the coast.

III. Nest and Eggs.—Breeds among heather in hollow on the ground, on open moor-lands, or on islands in lochs, but on the Continent may be found among reeds in marshes. Built of heather twigs, mosses, and grass mixed with down and feathers. Eggs : usually 4–5, but 3, and 6–8 recorded from Scotland, and abroad up to 14 and 15, probably due to two hens ; creamy white, often discoloured. Average of 60 British eggs, 85.4×58.3 mm. (3.36 × 2.29 in.). Laying begins latter part of April. Incubation period, 27–29 days ; by female only. One brood. (Plate 198, f. 6.)

IV. Food.—Vegetable matter only ; largely grass, but also green rye in spring, *Zostera*, tubers of *Scirpus maritimus*, water weeds, and in autumn, wheat, rye, and maize, peas, beans, lentils ; cloudberries and acorns also recorded. Insects, leeches, and crustacea also said to be taken.

V. Usual Notes.—Similar to those of the Domestic-Goose. The usual call in flight is a loud " gagagag " (Heinroth) or " kaah kah kak " (Naumann). The species utters the familiar goose-gabbling notes and the menacing hiss. The alarm note is described by Heinroth as a short nasal " gang," and the call to the young as a soft " gang gang gang." [1]

PLATE 153.—WHITEFRONTED-GOOSE, *Anser albifrons* (Scopoli)

I. Description.—Length, 27 in. Distinguished by its small size ; white frontal band round bill ; irregular black bars on breast ; orange yellow bill (with white nail), and feet. Upper parts brownish ash, under parts brownish white. Females have less black on the breast, while young lack the white on face in first plumage as well as the black on the breast ; bill and feet also paler and nail brown.

II. Range and Habitat.—Winter visitor to the British Isles, chiefly met with on the estuaries and coasts. On the Continent it breeds in North Russia and Siberia as well as the islands of Kolguev, Novaya Zemlya, etc., but the evidence of breeding farther west is not satisfactory. It crosses Iceland on passage and breeds in Greenland, but apparently this is the form which has been separated as *A . a. gambelli*, which breeds also in Arctic America. Winters south to the Mediterranean and Black Seas, Nile Valley, and Southern Asia. A tundra-haunting species.

III. Nest and Eggs.—Does not breed in the British Isles. Nests in hollow on ground in the Siberian tundra, using heather, mosses, lichens, and grass, with down and feathers, to make nest. Eggs : 4–6 ; white, but frequently stained. Material very scanty, but 23 eggs average 81.2 × 54.0 mm. (3.19 × 2.12 in.). Laying begins about end of May. Incubation period 27–30 days ; by female alone. One brood.

IV. Food.—Almost entirely vegetable ; grasses, especially from salt marshes, clover, green shoots of reed, sedge, etc., and at times grain. Young eat shoots of *Equisetum*. Beetles have been recorded by Naumann from stomach contents.

V. Usual Notes.—Information scanty. The call is characteristically abrupt, and, when uttered by a flock, sounds like laughter, hence a popular name of the species— Laughing-Goose.

[1] A. Voigt, *Excursionsbuch z. Studium der Vogelstimmen*, 254.

PLATE 153.—BEAN-GOOSE

Anser fabalis fabalis (Latham)

I. Description.—Length, 33–34 in. In size approaches the Greylag closely, and is distinguished by its black bill, with orange in the middle, nail black ; general plumage darker than Greylag ; no grey shoulder patches ; feet pinkish yellow ; no black on breast. Female smaller and young darker, with less distinct markings.

II. Range and Habitat.—Winter visitor to the British Isles, chiefly on the coasts. Breeds in Scandinavia, Finland, North Russia, Kolguev, Novaya Zemlya and eastward in Siberia to the Taimyr, but farther east is replaced by an allied race. In Russia it is said to range south to lat. 57° in the Urals, and on the east side of the Baltic to Livland. Winters south to the Mediterranean, Black Sea, and West Asia. More of a woodland bird than the other wild geese.

III. Nest and Eggs.—Does not breed in the British Isles. In Scandinavia and Finland often breeds at the foot of a birch near river or marsh, using dead leaves, moss, grass, and down in making the nest. Eggs : usually 4–5, sometimes only 3 or 6 ; creamy white and often stained. Average size of 51 eggs, 84.2 × 55.6 mm. (3.31 × 2.19 in.). Laying begins latter part of May. Incubation period, 28–29 days ; by female alone. One brood.

IV. Food.—Vegetable matter, but authorities somewhat contradictory ; Cordeaux says it is much more of a grain eater than the Greylag, but Saunders and others describe it as decidedly herbivorous, eating grasses and clover.

V. Usual Notes.—The flight call is loud and ringing ; it has been variously rendered as a repetition chiefly of " kīaks " or " kīcks," and " kīahs." The species has the usual hissing and gabbling notes of the genus.

PLATE 153.—PINKFOOTED-GOOSE

Anser brachyrhynchus Baillon

I. Description.—Length, 28 in. Decidedly smaller than Bean-Goose, which it somewhat closely resembles ; bill and nail black, pink in the middle ; feet pinkish ; shoulders rather lighter than rest of plumage, being dark blue grey ; head and neck lighter brown ; markings on the tail also broader.

II. Range and Habitat.—Winter visitor to the British Isles. Breeds in East Greenland, Iceland, and Spitsbergen, and winters in Western Europe from Scandinavia to France and Germany. In the Arctic haunts steep hillsides as a rule ; a shore bird in winter.

III. Nest and Eggs.—Does not breed in the British Isles. Prefers as a rule a site on the top of talus at foot of cliff, or on ledge on steep hillside, but occasionally well out in open ground. Nest, hollow used again and again ; lined lichens, mosses, etc., with down and feathers. Eggs : usually 3–6, occasionally 7 or 2 only, and 9 recorded in one nest (by two females) ; white. Average of 50 Spitsbergen eggs, 79.0 × 52.9 mm. (3.11 × 2.08 in.). Laying begins about end of May. Incubation period, 25–28 days (in confinement) ; by female alone. One brood.

IV. Food.—Frequents stubbles in autumn, but stomach contents show chiefly grasses, clover, trefoil, etc., and not as a rule grain. On its breeding grounds eats grass, *Cochlearia*, *Equisetum*, *Saxifraga*, *Cerastium*, etc.

V. Usual Notes.—Information scanty. The notes are said to be not unlike those of the Bean-Goose

For the other " Grey " Geese shown on Plate 153, see pages 153 and 153-A.

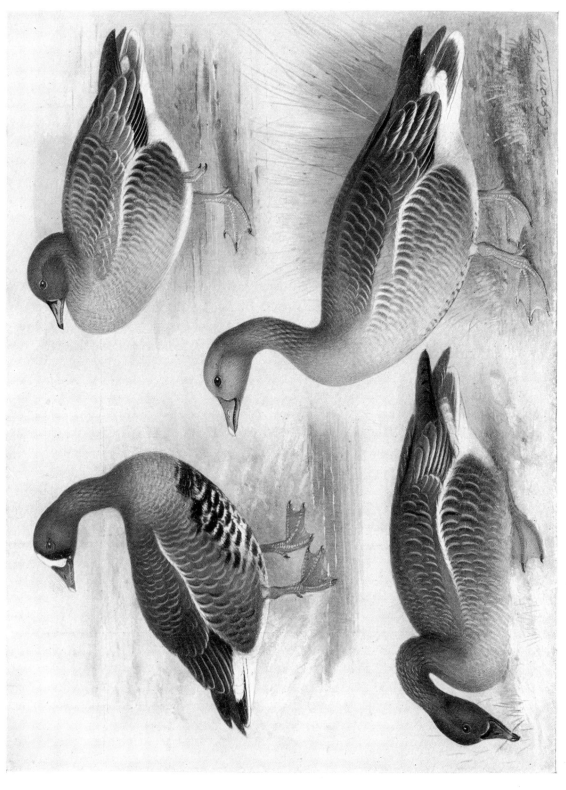

PLATE 153.—GREY GEESE—(*Upper*) WHITEFRONTED-GOOSE, PINKFOOTED GOOSE; (*Lower*) BEAN-GOOSE, GREYLAG GOOSE: H. Grönvold.

Plate 154.—BARNACLE-GOOSE

Branta leucopsis (Bechstein)

I. Description.—Length, 25–27 in. Recognized by white face and upper throat enclosed by surrounding glossy black of crown, neck, and upper breast; lores black; mantle and wing coverts lavender grey, with dark edgings with white rims. Bill, feet, tail, and wing quills black; breast and flanks whitish, the latter barred grey; tail coverts and belly white. Young have the white on the face tinged with dusky brown, and rufous edges to feathers of mantle.

II. Range and Habitat.—Winter visitor to the British Isles, chiefly on the west of Scotland and north-west of England. Breeds in North-East Greenland and Spitsbergen; also in Novaya Zemlya and apparently North-West Siberia; possibly in small numbers in Iceland, but no proof of this as yet. In winter seen on shores of Baltic and North Sea, rarely farther south. It haunts the estuaries in flocks, and is rarely met with inland; in summer breeds in rocky valleys.

III. Nest and Eggs.—Does not breed in the British Isles. Breeds on ledges of rock face or ridges of rock at high levels; nesting in circular hollow in ground (used year after year) and lined with thick pad of down and a few bits of lichen. Eggs: 3–5, exceptionally 6; white, but stained as incubation progresses. Average of 52 eggs, 76.5 × 50.4 mm. (3.01 × 1.98 in.). Laying begins about end of May. Incubation period, 24–28 days; by female alone. One brood.

IV. Food.—In winter mainly grasses from salt marshes, also Trefoil and *Ranunculus*, and small mollusca (*fide* Alpheraky); on its breeding grounds, Arctic willow and other plants, such as *Oxyria*.

V. Usual Notes.—Information inadequate. Voigt heard from it a soft " ga " or " gra," which seems to correspond to Naumann's soft, short " kak." It is credited also by Naumann with a hoarse, prolonged " kah," and he states that it hisses. Jourdain describes the usual note heard on the breeding ground as a loud, complaining " ark, ark."

PLATE 154.—BARNACLE GEESE : A. W. Seaby.

PLATE 155.—DARKBREASTED-BRENT

PLATE 155.—DARKBREASTED-BRENT

Branta bernicla bernicla (Linnæus)

LIGHTBREASTED-BRENT

Branta bernicla hrota (Müller)

I. Description.—Length, 22–24 in. Smaller than Barnacle, from which it is distinguished by its black head, neck, and upper breast, with small white patch on each side of the neck ; mantle dusky brown. In the Darkbreasted form the breast and belly are slate grey ; but in the Lightbreasted form these parts are varying shades of cinnamon brown, shading into white on the belly. Bill, feet, wing quills, and tail black. Young birds have no white on the sides of the neck.

II. Range and Habitat.—Winter visitor to the British Isles. The Darkbreasted form breeds from the Taimyr Peninsula in Siberia westward apparently to Kolguev and Novaya Zemlya ; while the Lightbreasted form breeds in Spitsbergen, Franz-Josef Land, Greenland, and Eastern Arctic America. Replaced by allied races in East Siberia and Western Arctic America. Winters in North Sea and Mediterranean. A marine species, only occasionally coming up rivers to breed, and often met with at sea in vast flocks or resting on mud flats.

III. Nest and Eggs.—Sometimes found nesting in colonies ; at other times in separate pairs, generally on small islets off the coast as a protection against foxes ; also on islands in bed of rivers or close to river bank. Breeds in hollow in ground, sometimes using any material at hand to make a nest ; at other times only lining with down. Eggs : usually 3–5, but 2, 6, and even 8, on record ; yellowish cream and glossy. Average of 50 eggs of Lightbreasted race, 71.8 × 47.2 mm. (2.82 × 1.86 in.). Laying begins early in June. Incubation period, about 28 days ; by female alone. One brood.

IV. Food.—In winter *Zostera marina*, also marsh grass and algæ ; on breeding grounds shoots of many species of Arctic plants. Seaweed and mussels found in stomachs.

V. Usual Notes.—Abel Chapman has described the great flights of Brents when they quit their feeding grounds on the tidal ooze for the open sea : " Out they go, full one hundred yards high, while their loud clanging defiance—' honk honk !— torròck, torròck ! ' and its running accompaniment of lower croaks and shrill bytones, resound for miles around." [1] The note uttered as they move about on the flats is a " hard, short ' raok ' or ' rott,' " according to Droste-Hülshoff, who was familiar with the species.[2] They are said to have the usual hiss.

---

[1] *Bird Life of the Borders*, 2nd edition, 333.
[2] *Vogelwelt der Nordseeinsel Borkum*, 270.

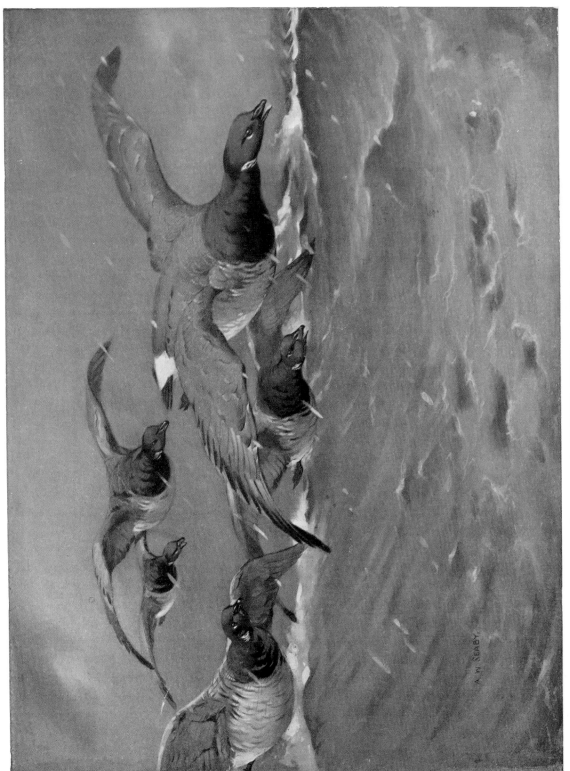

PLATE 155.—BRENT GEESE: A. W. Seaby.

PLATE 156.—WHOOPER

Cygnus cygnus cygnus (Linnæus)

I. Description.—Length, 60 in. (male) ; female smaller. All three species of Swan have white plumage when adult. This species is distinguished in the field by the stiff carriage of the neck, its loud ringing note, and from the Mute-Swan by its lemon yellow and black bill, without " berry " (see Mute-Swan). It is considerably larger than Bewick's Swan, which has also a yellow and black bill, but in the Whooper a tongue of yellow extends from the eye and the yellow base to beyond the nostrils, leaving the tip black ; feet black. Young birds are greyish brown, bill flesh-colour, tipped and edged with black.

II. Range and Habitat.—During recent years a pair or two have bred in Scotland (Forth and Tay areas, and pinioned birds in Shetlands). Chiefly a winter visitor to our shores. On the Continent breeds in North Scandinavia, Finland, and North Russia ; also in Siberia east to Kamtschatka. A smaller race also breeds in Iceland. In winter, south to the Mediterranean and Central Asia. Usually met with on larger lakes in summer ; frequents coasts in winter.

III. Nest and Eggs.—As the same sites are used over and over again, they become in time large mounds of earth with hollow in the middle, and much down and feathers scattered about. Eggs : usually 4–5, sometimes 6 or even 7 ; yellowish white, but often stained during incubation. Average of 75 eggs, 112.8 × 72.7 mm. (4.44 × 2.86 in.). Laying begins in May. Incubation period, estimated at 31, 40, and 42 days ; by female alone. One brood.

IV. Food.—Mainly vegetable : grasses, clover, and leaves, and roots of water-weeds such as *Glyceria*. Also, during summer, aquatic insects, worms, and snails.

V. Usual Notes.—The usual call, a loud, trumpeted double " whoop, whoop " gives the species its name. It is heard in flight, together with the swish of the powerful wings. The note uttered when the breeding place is invaded has been described by Hantzsch as a nasal " a " or " ang," and a higher " heh " (anglicized). Jourdain records " a low but musical song. . . . It was a phrase of about seven distinct notes, rising slightly, then falling and finally rising again." This was at the beginning of the breeding season.[1]

[1] *British Bird Book*, iv. 182.

Plate 156.—BEWICK'S SWAN

Cygnus bewickii bewickii Yarrell

I. Description.—Length, 46–50 in. Distinguished by its small size and black and orange yellow bill with no " berry " (see Mute-Swan). In this species the orange at the base of the bill does not extend below the nostrils, and there is black along the ridge of the upper mandible ; feet black. It is also noisy on the wing. Young birds are greyish brown.

II. Range and Habitat.—Winter visitor to the British Isles. Breeds in North Russia, Kolguev, Novaya Zemlya, and Northern Siberia east to the Lena, but in East Siberia is replaced by a larger race. In winter occasionally south to the Mediterranean and Central Asia. A haunter of the shallow lakes and pools of the tundra ; in winter on the coast chiefly.

III. Nest and Eggs.—Does not breed in the British Isles. From the size of the nest it is probably used for many years ; built up of weeds, turf, earth, etc., with hollow in the middle. Eggs : 3–5 ; creamy white, readily stained. Average of 25 eggs, 103.6 × 67.3 mm. (4.07 × 2.65 in.). Laying begins early in June. Incubation period unknown. One brood.

IV. Food.—Largely vegetable : grasses, clover, aquatic plants, etc. ; aquatic insects and small fish also recorded.

V. Usual Notes.—The call, uttered during flight at frequent intervals, resembles the " honking " of wild geese ; it is quite different from that of the Whooper, and has been figured by Dr. Patten : " tong, tong, bong, hong, ong, ongong "—" a varied din of honking notes " (Jourdain). The alarm note is said to be a soft goose-like " kuck, kuck " or " kueck, kueck " (Naumann).

PLATE 156.—MUTE-SWAN

Cygnus olor (Gmelin)

I. Description.—Length, 56–60 in. Distinguished by the graceful carriage of the neck ; reddish orange bill, with a large black " berry," or knob, at the base in the male, and smaller one in the female ; feet black. Young birds are dusky grey, lighter below, with lead-coloured bill and feet. Much more silent than the other species.

II. Range and Habitat.—An introduced species, now resident in a partially domesticated state. On the Continent it breeds in a wild state in Southern Sweden, Germany, Poland, Russia, the Danube valley, and in temperate Asia east to Mongolia. Now to be met with on lakes, pools, and quiet reaches of rivers almost everywhere.

III. Nest and Eggs.—May be found nesting by river banks, in marshes, on islands in lakes, sometimes (as at Abbotsbury) in great numbers. The nest is a large heap of aquatic vegetation, weeds, etc., with a depression for the eggs, generally quite close to water. Eggs : usually 5–7, but 8–12, and even 17, have been recorded, most of these undoubtedly by more than one female. Colour, bluish green, unlike any of the other British swans. Average size of 50 eggs, 114.5 × 73.1 mm. (4.50 × 2.88 in.). Laying begins usually in latter part of April. Incubation period, 34–40 days, extending occasionally to 43 ; almost entirely by female, but male apparently takes a small share. One brood. (Plate 199, f. 5.)

IV. Food.—Vegetable matter : water-weeds and confervæ, but more especially the stalks, rhizomes, and roots of aquatic plants (reed, arrowhead, and many other species). Young birds, frogs, and toads are occasionally killed but not eaten.

V. Usual Notes.—A relatively silent species. Both sexes utter occasionally low, not unmusical, notes, rendered by Naumann as " kgiurr " or " keiorr," varying with the sex. It is also stated by Naumann that wild individuals utter a loud trumpet-like cry, but this appears doubtful. That the species hisses when angry is well known. The alarm note is given by Heinroth as a sharp " chirr." Jourdain has frequently heard a snorting note from these birds when feeding.

PLATE 156.—SWANS—MUTE-SWAN (*red*) ; WHOOPER-SWAN (*middle*) ; BEWICK'S SWAN : G. E. Collins

PLATE 157.—SHELDUCK

Tadorna tadorna (Linnæus)

I. Description.—Length, 25–26 in. Recognized by its large size and the bold contrasts of its plumage, which is white, with head and neck blackish green, a broad chestnut band round the forepart of the body, and a dark stripe down the middle of the breast; scapulars and primaries black; tail tipped with black; wing spot green. Male has red bill with knob; feet pink. Female decidedly smaller, duller, and has no knob on bill. Young birds have bill flesh colour and feet leaden; no band on breast; face white.

II. Range and Habitat.—Resident in the British Isles, chiefly confined to wide estuaries with extensive mud-flats. Also winter visitor from the Continent. Abroad it breeds from about 70° N. in Scandinavia and 51° in North Russia to the North Mediterranean; but is scarce in the south, and chiefly confined to the coast, though breeding on the salt lakes of Central Asia to East Siberia. In winter south to the North African coast, the Sahara, North India, and East Asia.

III. Nest and Eggs.—Breeds among sandhills or in adjoining country to estuaries; occasionally near water far inland, making a nest chiefly of down with some grass several feet down in a rabbit hole or burrow; at times in hollow under boulder or beneath gorse bushes and thickets; occasionally in nearly open ground. Eggs: 8–14, but 16–18, and also higher numbers, evidently the product of more than one female, on record; white. Average size of 60 British eggs, 65.7 × 47.6 mm. (2.58 × 1.87 in.). Laying begins usually mid-May; sometimes early in the month. Incubation period, 23–30 days; by duck alone. One brood. (Plate 198, f. 2; 200, f. 1.)

IV. Food.—Almost entirely animal: marine mollusca (univalves, such as whelks, and bivalves), crustacea (small crabs, shrimps, and prawns), insects (beetles and larvæ of flies), fish spawn, and small quantities of vegetable matter.

V. Usual Notes.—The drakes utter a deep, rapid " ooh-ooh-ooh-ooh," heard frequently by the present writer during the breeding season, when they were excited by the approach of neighbouring pairs on the lake at Twigmoor. While uttering the note the birds may make violent forward and downward movements of the head and neck. According to H. Wormald [1] they also make these movements during the sex display, uttering at the same time a " beautiful trilling whistle " (apparently different from the note above described), and another note which Miss E. L. Turner has figured as " sos-thieu, sos-thieu," low and sibilant, heard by her when the drakes were flighting or flying about.[1] The duck is less vocal; she utters a harsh " quack-wack-wack-wack." [2]

[1] *In litt.*
[2] For a detailed account of displays and notes, see *British Birds* (Mag.), xxviii. 218 (H. Boase).

PLATE 157.—SHELDRAKE (*right hand*), SHELDUCK, AND DUCKLINGS: A. W. Seaby.

PLATE 158.—MALLARD, or WILD DUCK

Anas platyrhyncha platyrhyncha Linnæus

I. Description.—Length, 21–23 in. Recognized by purple speculum, margined white and black. Male (except from June to September) has head and neck glossy green, with white ring round neck; four middle tail coverts are longer and curled upwards; rump and tail black green; back brownish; scapulars, lower breast, and flanks greyish white with grey vermiculated lines; forebreast dark chestnut. In eclipse drake resembles the duck, but is more uniform on upper parts. Duck is dark brown, marked buff, and lacks the upcurled tail coverts. Young much like duck. Bill yellowish green; feet orange.

II. Range and Habitat.—Resident in the British Isles and generally distributed; also passage migrant and winter visitor. Abroad breeds throughout Europe from the Arctic Circle to North-West Africa, the Azores, Northern and temperate Asia, and North America, but is replaced by allied forms in Greenland and Iceland. Winters south to the Canaries, North Africa to Abyssinia, Southern Asia, and Central America. Occurs in marshy districts, river valleys, and shores of lakes, wherever cover is available.

III. Nest and Eggs.—Breeds in almost any kind of covert, within reach of water; in some districts frequently in pollarded willows or in old nests of other birds, or natural hollows in trees, and among ivy on old buildings. Nest of down, mixed with dead leaves or any material at hand, grass, etc. Eggs: usually 8–12, sometimes only 7, or 13–15; varying in colour from pale blue to greenish grey or buff. Average size of 70 British eggs, 57.2 × 41.4 mm. (2.25 × 1.63 in.). Laying begins usually in March, occasionally in February. Incubation period usually 25–26 days; by female alone. One or two broods. (Plate 199, f. 10; 200, f. 2.)

IV. Food.—Largely vegetable, including many species of aquatic plants such as small water-crowfoot (*Ranunculus*), starwort (*Callitriche*), *Potamogeton*, etc., and also seeds of grasses and other land plants; also seaweeds (*Zostera*), acorns, black-berries, corn, insects (water beetles, caddis worms, flies, etc.), small mollusca (marine and fresh-water), leeches, frogs, and worms.

V. Usual Notes.—The usual note of the duck is the familiar " quack," or better " qwark," sometimes repeated rapidly, and serving, with varying pitch and stress, to express various emotions. The drake's cry is less loud, and may be syllabled " rep." He has also piping notes, uttered only when in display. Both display and notes may be heard throughout the winter from October.[1]

[1] Naumann, *Vögel Mitteleuropas*, x 29; and H. Wormald *in litt*.

158

PLATE 158.—MALLARD ; TWO DRAKES PURSUING A DUCK : A. W. Seaby.

PLATE 159.—GADWALL

Anas strepera Linnæus

I. Description.—Length, 20 in. Recognized by the white speculum, bordered on the front with black. Drake has head, neck, breast, and mantle brown, with paler vermiculations; wings and tail sooty grey; median wing coverts chestnut, rump and tail coverts black; under parts whitish with paler vermiculations. In eclipse much like duck, but retains the chestnut on wing coverts. Female brown and grey, much like female of Mallard, but distinguished by white speculum. Bill blackish, feet orange.

II. Range and Habitat.—Resident, but very local in Great Britain, chiefly East Anglia and Scotland; also winter visitor to the British Isles, generally scarce. Abroad breeds in Iceland, South Sweden, the Low Countries, Spain, Algeria, Germany, and east through Russia to Kamtschatka; also in North America. In winter south to North-West Africa, Abyssinia, Southern Asia, the southern states of the U.S.A., and the West Indies. Haunts marshes and reed-grown banks of slow-flowing streams or lakes.

III. Nest and Eggs.—Breeds generally among thick growth of sedges and marsh vegetation near water. Nest mainly of white tipped down with bits of marsh plants mixed. Eggs: 7–10, but 11–12 and 16 on record; colour, warm creamy, much like those of Wigeon. Average of 41 British eggs, 53.9 × 39.4 mm. (2.12 × 1.55 in.). Laying begins in early part of May. Incubation period, 26–28 days; by female alone. One brood. (Plate 199, f. 8; 200, f. 3.)

IV. Food.—Mainly vegetable, but records somewhat scanty: water-weeds, seed, grain, etc. In winter quarters rice is freely taken; also berries of water plants, and once a mass of small white worms.

V. Usual Notes.—Voigt, writing from personal observation, states that the quacking of the duck is not unlike that of the Mallard duck, but usually higher pitched. When the birds are flying about the quacking passes into more rapid and deeper cackling notes, with which may be heard single whistling notes uttered by the drakes. The duck has also a very rapid chattering or gabbling note, which has given it one of its German popular names, " schnatterente." [1] According to Coward, the drakes, in amorous mood, utter " a clear and deliberate, though not loud ' ep, ep, pair.' " For the " ep " H. Wormald substitutes " ack, ack." [2]

PLATE 159.—TEAL, *Anas crecca crecca* Linnæus

AMERICAN GREEN-WINGED TEAL, *Anas crecca carolinensis* Gmelin

I. Description.—Length, 13–15 in. Recognized by small size; speculum half glossy black and half glossy green, bounded on either side by buff. Drake has chestnut head with a band of glossy blue green running backward from the eyes, and bordered above and below with buff, which also continues to the bill; mantle and flanks finely pencilled grey and white; hinder scapulars forming band of black and white; breast white, spotted black; belly white; rump and tail coverts dusky to black. In eclipse male resembles female, but has larger speculum and fine buff markings on mantle. Duck is generally golden buff streaked with dark brown, below whitish. Bill blackish; feet brown grey. Young resemble duck, but have paler edges to wing coverts and darker centres to under feathers.

II. Range and Habitat.—Resident, fairly generally distributed, in the British Isles; also passage migrant and winter visitor; less numerous in south and east than in north and west of Great Britain. Haunts drier ground than most Ducks, but within reach of water. Abroad it nests in Iceland, and from about 70° N. in North Europe south to Italy and the central Balkan countries; in Asia from the Southern Urals to Japan, the Kuriles, and North China. Winters south to North Africa, the Nile valley, Southern Asia, and the Philippines. Replaced by an allied form in North America. which has occurred two or three times.

III. Nest and Eggs.—Often nests in open commons under cover of bushes or thickets, among bracken in woodlands, etc. Nest, hollow lined with material at hand: grass, dead bracken, etc., and down. Eggs: 8–12, but 13–16 recorded; light buffish with tinge of green as a rule. Average of 70 British eggs, 45.2 × 33.2 mm. (1.78 × 1.31 in.). Laying begins in latter half of April. Incubation period, 21–22 days; by female alone. One brood. (Plate 199, f. 1; 200, f. 6.)

IV. Food.—Animal as well as vegetable: seeds, carpels, and roots of water plants and grasses, algæ, etc.; also rice in winter quarters. Insects include larvæ of flies, caddis worms, etc.; worms, slugs, and fresh-water molluscs also taken.

V. Usual Notes.—The usual spring cry of the drake is a soft double whistle, syllabled variously as " krlik " or " pripp-pripp." He utters various other notes during his displays. The alarm note of the duck surprised with her brood, sounded, as heard by Coward, like " whelp, whelp." Her quack is sharper and shorter than that of the Garganey duck

[1] *Op. cit.* (p. 131 above), 259.   [2] *In litt.*

PLATE 159.—TEAL (*right hand*) AND GADWALLS (*left*) : A. W. Seaby.

PLATE 160.—SHOVELER

Spatula clypeata (Linnæus)

I. Description.—Length, 20 in. Recognized by the large dilated leaden-coloured bill and green speculum, bordered by white stripes in front and behind. Drake has shoulders pale blue, greater wing coverts white ; head and neck dark glossy green ; forebreast and scapulars white ; rest of under parts chestnut ; flanks freckled brown on pale ground ; vent white ; back dark brown. In eclipse head and neck much like those of duck ; is duller on under parts. Female has grey blue shoulders ; mantle dark brown with paler edges ; under parts and head mostly pale brown, with dusky streaks on breast and flanks and finer streaks on head. Young much like duck. Feet orange.

II. Range and Habitat.—Resident and partial migrant in the British Isles, now very general. Also winter visitor. On the Continent breeds from the Arctic Circle in Europe south to the Mediterranean, but irregularly and sporadically ; also across temperate Asia to the Commander Isles and probably Japan. Winters south to North-West Africa, East and South Africa, and Southern Asia. Also breeds in North America, wintering south to the West Indies, Colombia, and the Sandwich Isles. A haunter of marshes and lagoons rather than deep lakes, and more of an inland than marine species.

III. Nest and Eggs.—Breeds in marshes or meadows near water : nesting in hollow, sometimes close to bush, lined down, with bits of dry grass, etc., intermixed. Eggs : 7–12, but 13–14 recorded. Colour, rather variable, some olive buff, some greenish olive. Size of 80 British eggs, 52.4 × 38.1 mm. (2.06 × 1.50 in.). Laying begins about mid-April. Incubation period, 23–24 days ; by female alone. One brood only. (Plate 199, f. 4 ; 200, f. 4.)

IV. Food.—Both animal and vegetable : mollusca, both fresh-water and marine ; also snails, crustacea, worms, tadpoles, frog and fish spawn ; insects (chiefly water beetles) ; also seeds and leaves of many aquatic plants, and on the coast, *Zostera marina*.

V. Usual Notes.—The drake has a somewhat deep note which has been variously rendered as a double " voak, voak," " chock, chock," " gog, gog," or " thuck, thuck." According to Naumann, he utters in his spring flights a peculiar, not very loud, clinking note syllabled as " peckn, peckn." What seems to be a similar note is referred to by others. The duck's quack is shorter and much less loud than that of the Mallard duck.

PLATE 160.—GARGANEY

Anas querquedula Linnæus

I. Description.—Length, 15–16 in. Rather larger than the Teal, the drake is at once recognized by his conspicuous broad white stripe from the eye and ear coverts to the sides of the neck ; the duck has also a light band over the eye ; wing spot green between two white bars. Male has crown and nape dark brown, cheeks and neck lighter brown ; wing coverts bluish grey ; breast brown, with dark crescents ; belly white ; two broad bands on flanks, and dark transverse lines ; back dark brown ; tail and primaries brown ; bill black ; feet greenish leaden. Female generally less strikingly coloured. Young much resemble females.

II. Range and Habitat—Summer resident in Great Britain, and vagrant to British Isles. Has greatly increased its range recently, and now breeds in many districts of England, and has bred in Forth area in Scotland. On the Continent breeds 60° N. in Scandinavia and North Russia south to the northern Mediterranean and probably Marocco ; also across Asia to Kamtschatka and the Commander Isles. Winters south to tropical Africa, South Asia, and the Malay Archipelago. Haunts marshes, heaths, and meadows near water.

III. Nest and Eggs.—Breeds in hollow among long meadow grass within reach of water. Nest well concealed, down, white tipped. Eggs : 7–11, but 13 and 14 also on record ; warm creamy buff, lacking the greenish tinge present in eggs of Teal. Average size of 41 British eggs, 46.3 × 33.7 mm. (1.82 × 1.32 in.). Laying begins late in April. Incubation period, about 22–24 days ; by female alone. One brood. (Plate 199, f. 2 ; 200, f. 7.)

IV. Food.—Both animal and vegetable : seeds, leaves and buds of many species of water plants ; also on coasts seaweed, and in winter quarters rice ; spawn and young of fish and frogs ; leeches, worms, and insects, chiefly aquatic, including water beetles, caddis flies, water boatman, etc., and fresh-water mollusca.

V. Usual Notes.—The " quack " of the duck resembles that of the Teal, but is not so sharp and short ; it sounds like " knek," hence the German name of the species " Knäkente." The drake utters a peculiar strident clacking or rattling note, " klerrep," that has been compared to a stick drawn across iron railings, and to the grinding of teeth. H. Wormald describes it as a " grating crackle," and states that, during an experience of thirty years, he has heard no other note from the drake.[1] Both sexes are said to utter, by way of love notes, a clear, very rapid " yeck, yeck, yeck "[2] (anglicized).

[1] *In litt.*　　　　[2] *Vögel Mitteleuropas*, x. 88. Voigt heard it as " dyü, dyü, dyü " (anglicized).

PLATE 160.—SHOVELERS (*upper pair*) AND GARGANEYS: A. W. Seaby.

PLATE 161.—PINTAIL

Dafila acuta acuta Linnæus

I. Description.—Length, 24–29 in., but this includes two tapering tail feathers of drake, which are sometimes 8½ in. long. In addition to this the drake is recognized by brown head and neck ; but a white stripe extends from the breast up each side of the neck ; belly also white ; flanks and back delicately vermiculated with grey on whitish. Greater wing coverts buff ; speculum bronze green, margined black and white ; tail black ; bill and feet slate grey. In eclipse drake resembles duck, but retains the speculum. Duck mottled brown above, and greyish white below ; has shorter tail than male, but slender neck like his. Young much resemble female.

II. Range and Habitat.—Very local resident and winter visitor, breeding in Norfolk (1929) ; in Scotland regularly in Forth, Moray, and Orkney areas ; has bred also in Tweed, Tay, North-West Highlands, Outer Hebrides, and Shetlands ; also in North Ireland. On the Continent it breeds from about 70° N. in Europe south to Andalucia and the Camargue ; also across Asia to Kamtschatka, and in Iceland, wintering south to Central and East Africa and Southern Asia. Replaced in North America by an allied race, wintering south to Central America and the West Indies. Haunts usually marshes and fresh-water lakes.

III. Nest and Eggs.—Breeds among heather or grass in hollow on ground, well sheltered, using dead grasses or heather, as well as down. Eggs : usually 6–9, at times 10–12 recorded. Colour, variable, ranging from yellowish green to pale olive yellowish. Average size of 40 British eggs, 53.0 × 37.1 mm. (2.08 × 1.46 in.). Laying begins in May. Incubation period, 22–23 days ; by female alone. One brood. (Plate 199, f. 3 ; 200, f. 5.)

IV. Food.—Animal and vegetable : including small fish (once), spawn and young of frogs, insects (water beetles, flies, etc.), mollusca (marine and fresh-water univalves) ; also roots and seeds of aquatic plants and seeds of land plants, acorns, and, on the coast, *Zostera marina.*

V. Usual Notes.—The drake's usual note, frequent in the spring, is a single, sometimes double, flute-like whistle, which seems to give the bird some trouble to utter, judging from the accompanying movements. When flighting he utters a peculiar, rather faint wheezing note. The duck's quack is sharp and short.[1]

PLATE 161.—WIGEON

Anas penelope Linnæus

I. Description.—Length, 18½–20 in. The drake is recognized by the chestnut of head and neck, contrasting with the conspicuous light buff of forehead and crown ; back white, vermiculated with black ; speculum green, tipped black below ; forebreast greyish pink ; wing coverts white ; belly whitish ; wing and tail quills brown ; flanks pencilled grey ; bill leaden, tipped black ; feet dark brown. In eclipse more like female, but brighter. Female has upper parts mottled grey brown ; shoulder nearly white ; speculum grey green ; under parts buffish. Young resemble female.

II. Range and Habitat.—Resident in the northern part of Great Britain ; also passage migrant and winter visitor to the British Isles. In Scotland breeds in all areas except Dee, but only occasionally in Shetland, Orkneys, Hebrides, Clyde, and Solway. Exceptionally has nested in the northern counties of England ; once Wales. Abroad breeds in Iceland, Faeroes, and Northern Europe south to the Baltic ; locally in Germany, in Finland, North Russia and East Russia ; in Asia east from Turkestan to Kamtschatka. Winters south to North Africa, the Nile valley, Southern Asia, and the southern states of the U.S.A. More a shore than inland water species.

III. Nest and Eggs.—Breeds on the moorlands, often nesting close to the little becks on the hillsides, in hollow among heather or rough grass, lined with down and a little grass, etc. Eggs : usually 7–9, sometimes only 6 or 10 ; warm cream colour. Average size of 50 British eggs, 54.3 × 38.4 mm. (2.13 × 1.51 in.). Laying begins about May 10–15. Incubation period, 24–28 days ; by female alone. One brood. (Plate 199, f. 6 ; 200, f. 8.)

IV. Food.—All records give vegetable matter : grasses and aquatic plants such as *Glyceria, Equisetum, Polygonum, Potamogeton, Ranunculus,* etc. ; at sea, chiefly *Zostera.* Blackberries and grain also recorded.

V. Usual Notes.—The familiar cry of the drake is distinctive : a musical piping or whistling double " whee-you " or " whee-oo," uttered with the beak wide open, and heard both by day and night. When flighting the drake utters a short note like " whip, whip " (H. Wormald), as well as the " whee-oo." The latter is used as a call, an alarm note (Voigt), and during the sex display (Millais) ; it. and the purring note of the ducks, are heard in winter when the birds are resting in flocks on the mud-flats. " These single notes are incessant," writes Abel Chapman, " but at intervals the whole pack bursts out into a simultaneous chorus which lasts perhaps half a minute and then subsides." [2] The purring note is the call cry of the duck ; the alarm cry appears to be different : a strident (schnarrender) " trr " (Hantzsch), or a " harsh growling ' kraak, kraak ' " (Coward). Droste-Hülshoff adds another sound to the call cry of the duck, which he figures " hooik " or " hooek," which may change to " hooekrrrr " (anglicized), the *r*'s representing, presumably, the purr.[3]

---

[1] The whole of this note is based on the direct observations of H. Wormald.
[2] *Bird Life of the Borders*, 312. [3] *Vogelwelt der Nordseeinsel Borkum*, 292.

PLATE 161.—WIGEON (*lower*); PINTAILS COURTING (*upper four*) : A. W. Seaby.

PLATE 162.—POCHARD

Nyroca ferina ferina (Linnæus)

I. Description.—Length, 17–19 in. The drake is recognized by his chestnut red head and neck ; ash grey speculum ; also has broad lobe to hind toe ; breast and upper back black ; mantle whitish, pencilled with fine grey wavy lines ; under parts whitish ; tail coverts black ; bill black with bluish bar in middle ; iris red ; feet blue grey. Female has head dull chestnut ; back dark brown, mixed greyish ; under parts brownish white ; iris brown. Young birds resemble duck, but are darker below.

II. Range and Habitat.—Resident (also winter visitor), locally in the British Isles, chiefly in eastern and southern counties of England, but in small numbers ; also in the north and west ; also irregularly in Scotland, and reported as breeding in Ireland. Usually haunts lakes and pools where there is high growth of reeds or sedge. On the Continent breeds from South Finland and mid-Sweden and Russia (60° N.), south to Spain, Algeria, and the Balkan Peninsula. Also in Western Asia east to Lake Baikal. Winters south to the Atlantic Isles, the Mediterranean region, and Southern Asia. Replaced by an allied race in North America.

III. Nest and Eggs.—Unlike many Ducks, this species frequently builds its nest in shallow water among dead reeds, flags, or sedges, using the dead leaves as material. Eggs : usually 6–10, but 11, 13, and 14 recorded in England, and higher numbers on the Continent ; greenish grey, or olive greenish. Average size of 60 British eggs, 61.0 × 43.9 mm. (2.40 × 1.73 in.). Laying begins mid-April in England. Incubation period, 24–26 days as a rule ; by female only. One brood. (Plate 198, f. 5 ; 200, f. 9.)

IV. Food.—Partly vegetable matter, but some animal also : seeds of grasses, rushes, etc., and buds, roots and leaves of many aquatic plants (*Glyceria, Bidens, Potamogeton, Polygonum,* etc.), and grain. Animal matter includes small fish, worms, tadpoles, insects (water beetles, etc.), and marine univalves and bivalves as well as fresh-water snails.

V. Usual Notes.—During the sex display the duck, according to J. G. Millais, utters a harsh " kurr-kurr-kurr," and the drake a groaning note to which he may add a soft, low whistle, heard only a short distance away. The groaning note seems to be the effect of release of air from the distended windpipe. The alarm notes and calls of the sexes do not seem to have been clearly differentiated, but something like the " kurr " note has been heard from both when swimming and flying.

PLATE 162.—TUFTED-DUCK

Nyroca fuligula (Linnæus)

I. Description.—Length, 17–17¼ in. The drake is recognized by his striking black and white colouring and crest; head, mantle, and breast being black, purplish on the head ; the belly and flanks white ; narrow white wing bar ; iris yellow ; bill and feet slaty. In eclipse male resembles female, which is sooty brown instead of black ; under parts brown, barred with grey. Young birds have the forehead marked with white.

II. Range and Habitat.—Now resident (but also passage migrant and winter visitor) in many parts of the British Isles, including the Orkneys and Hebrides, but still scarce in North-West Scotland. Haunts inland waters, large or small ; also coastal. Abroad it nests in Iceland, the Faeroes, Russia (50° N.), Finland, North Scandinavia, and south to Germany, Jugo-Slavia, Bulgaria, and the lower Volga in Russia ; also in Cyprus. Also across Asia to the Commander Isles. Winters south to North Africa, Abyssinia, South Asia, and the Malay Archipelago.

III. Nest and Eggs.—Nests on islands in lakes, under cover of bushes or in grass, or near the shore ; occasionally in marshy ground, some distance inland. Eggs : variable in number, 7–12, but all numbers from 13–18, 20–24, and, when several ducks lay together, even 28 and 40 ! Eggs : elongated in shape, olive or greenish grey. Average size of 61 British eggs, 57.7 × 40.4 mm. (2.27 × 1.59 in.). Laying begins in latter part of May in England, rather later in Scotland. Incubation period, 24–28 days ; by female alone. One brood. (Plate 198, f. 4 ; 200, f. 10.)

IV. Food.—Animal matter chiefly, but also some vegetable matter : fish and frog spawn, small frogs and tadpoles ; both marine and fresh-water mollusca, univalves as well as bivalves ; insects (water beetles, diptera, water boatman, etc.). Also grasses, duckweed, aquatic plants of many species, and berries of hawthorn.

V. Usual Notes.—The alarm cry, which appears to be used also as a call, has been variously rendered as " curragh," " karr karrkarr," " arrr," and is common to the sexes. The drake's notes, when displaying to the duck, are described as " a soft, liquid, several-syllabled utterance, rarely penetrating to any distance," and often uttered in chorus by several drakes together.[1] Renderings of this " song " have been attempted, of which the most complete is the following by Whitaker : " tuc tuc, tuck, quit, quitta, wheeo, whit, quit, quit, quie." [2] During the performance " the whole body quivers " (H. Wormald).

---

[1] *Scottish Naturalist,* 1912, 266 (S. E. Brock). [2] Seebohm, *History of British Birds,* iii. 585.

PLATE 162.—TUFTED-DUCKS (*centre bird and two left*) AND POCHARDS (*right*) : A. W. Seaby.

PLATE 163.—SCAUP, *Nyroca marila marila* (Linnæus)

I. Description.—Length, 18–19 in. Resembles the Tufted drake, but has no crest, while the duck is distinguished by white band round the base of the bill. The drake has head, neck, upper back and forebreast black, with purple green gloss; rest of back, scapulars and upper wing coverts white, pencilled with grey; flanks and rest of under parts white; rump, tail, and quills dull brown. Speculum white, with greenish black border; bill grey blue; nail black; feet leaden blue. In eclipse drake resembles the duck, but head and breast are darker. The duck has head, neck, and breast rufous brown; some white on sides of head; mantle and flanks pencilled grey on brownish ground; rest as in male. Young birds much like duck.

II. Range and Habitat.—Resident in small numbers in Scotland (Outer Hebrides, Sutherland, and Orkneys); also passage migrant and winter visitor to coasts of British Isles. Breeds abroad in Iceland, the Faeroes, Scandinavia, Finland, North Russia, south to Bornholm in the Baltic; also in Siberia, but is replaced by an allied race in East Siberia and Bering Isles, also in North America. Winters south to the Mediterranean region, North-West Africa, and Southern Asia, the American race moving to the southern states of the U.S.A. In winter haunts estuaries and flat coasts.

III. Nest and Eggs.—Breeds in hollow in ground sheltered by grass tussocks; often many pairs nesting in company near water. Eggs: 6–11; 19 and 22, evidently by two females; olive grey in colour. Average size of 100 eggs, 61.9×43.6 mm. (2.43×1.71 in.). Laying begins latter part of May. Incubation period, 27–28 days; by female only. One brood. (Plate 199, f. 9; 200, f. 11.)

IV. Food.—Chiefly animal, but includes some vegetable matter: mollusca, marine bivalves (mussels and cockles) and univalves, and small fresh-water univalves; crabs and other crustacea; small fish and insects, chiefly flies. Also aquatic plants and seaweeds.

V. Usual Notes.—The call, which appears also to be the alarm note, is usually rendered " karr, karr, karr." What are presumably variant renderings of the same alarm note are given by Hantzsch: " brr, brr " or " hrr, hrr," and, more intense, " br räh " (*ä*=*a* in *care*).[1] J. G. Millais describes a variety of notes uttered during the spring sex display. The chief utterance of the drake is made with greatly distended windpipe, and sounds like a not very impressive " pa-whoo." It suffices, however, to impress the duck, who responds appropriately with a dulcet " chup-chup," to which she may add, as an afterthought, " cherr-err." The duck contributes other harmonies to the performance, these being a crooning " tuc-tuc-turra-tuc," and " scaar-scaar." [2]

PLATE 163.—EIDER, *Somateria mollissima mollissima* (Linnæus)

I. Description.—Length, 23–25 in. Sexes very different, but in both feathering extends along sides of bill some distance. The drake has upper back, wing coverts and scapulars white; long secondaries buffish white; head white, except black patch on crown and sea-green patch on each side of nape; bill greenish; primaries shorter; secondaries, rump, and tail brownish black, but white patch on each side of rump; breast rosy buff; belly black; feet dull green. In eclipse generally rusty brown mixed with white. The duck has mantle dark brown, broadly edged with rufous; under parts brown barred grey or light brown, and two white bars on wing. Young like female, but less white on wings. Males have black on sides of head.

II. Range and Habitat.—Resident in northern part of Great Britain, south to Northumberland on the east side, and has bred in Clyde and Solway areas on west side. Also breeds in co. Donegal in Ireland. Otherwise winter visitor, scarce in south. Abroad breeds in West France, Holland, Sylt, and the coasts of Denmark and Scandinavia northward to North Finland and North Russia; but the Norwegian form has been separated, as has also the Faeroe birds and the Spitsbergen, possibly Iceland and Greenland to East North America; other forms inhabit North America and East Siberia. Winters off coasts of Europe, only occasionally on the Mediterranean. Very marine in its habits, rarely penetrating inland.

III. Nest and Eggs.—Breeds on islets in sea or on the coast, nesting in hollow sometimes on open shingle or sandhill, sometimes sheltered by boulder or wall or grass, freely lined brownish down. Eggs: usually 4–6, sometimes 3 only, or 7–9; higher numbers probably due to two ducks; greenish grey; rarely deep bluish or light olive grey, with often oily spots. Average size of 84 British eggs, 77.5 × 50.8 mm. (3.05 × 2.00 in.). Laying begins in early May. Incubation period, 26–28 days; by female only. One brood. (Plate 198, f. 3; 200, f. 12.)

IV. Food.—Almost entirely animal: chiefly marine mollusca, up to a great size, both bivalves and univalves, including large razor-shells, mussels, whelks, cockles, and periwinkles, etc. Also crustacea (crabs), sea urchins, starfish, remains of fish refuse, and small fish; also, in fresh water, beetles. Vegetable matter, seaweed only.

V. Usual Notes.—The drake utters frequently a loud moaning cry syllabled variously as " wow, wouw, wouw " (Jourdain); " aah-ou " or " ah-ee-ou " (C. W. Townsend); [3] " hoo-a-ow " (Voigt, anglicized). This cry may form part of the sex display. The drake also utters " a nasal ' ha ' or loud ' hauwa, hahauwa ' at the nest, and a long-drawn ' gag ' while resting on the water." [4] The note of the duck when driven off the nest is a grunting " krrr " or " korrr."

---

[1] *Beitrag zur Kenntnis der Vogelwelt Islands*, p. 185.
[2] *Auk*, 1910, 179.
[3] J. G. Millais, *British Diving Ducks*.
[4] *British Bird Book*, iv. 282 (Jourdain).

PLATE 163.—SCAUPS (*left top*) AND EIDER-DUCKS : A. W. Seaby.

PLATE 164.—GOLDEN-EYE

Bucephala clangula clangula (Linnæus)

I. Description.—Length, 16–19 in. The drake is recognized by the conspicuous white spot in front of the eye, contrasting with the glossy green black of the head and throat ; white under parts ; black back ; lower neck, scapulars, and wing-patch white ; bill blue black ; feet yellow, with black webs ; iris yellow ; slight crest. In eclipse, much like the duck, but has still some white on the head and also on the wings. The female has head umber brown with no spot ; back, breast, and flanks greyish, mixed with darker grey ; under parts white ; white patch on wing divided by two black stripes. Young much like female.

II. Range and Habitat.—Passage migrant and winter visitor to the British Isles, chiefly on coasts, occasionally on lakes inland. Breeds from tree limit in Scandinavia, Finland, and North Russia, south to the southern high fjeld in Norway, South Sweden, locally in North Germany. Apparently also in Jugo-Slavia and Roumania ; also across Asia in wooded districts east to Kamtschatka and Saghalien. Replaced by an allied form in North America. Winters south to the Mediterranean, West Asia, North India, and China, and in America to Mexico. In the breeding season it haunts forested banks of rivers and lakes.

III. Nest and Eggs.—Does not breed in the British Isles. Breeds in holes of trees, but also lays in boxes put up for the purpose, lining the interior with light greyish down. Eggs : 6 or 7–14, but 15–16 also on record ; greenish, with slight tinge of blue. Average size of 100 eggs, 61.7 × 44.8 mm. (2.43 × 1.76 in.). Laying begins about mid-April in Middle Europe ; a month later in Lapland. Incubation period, 26–30 days ; by female alone. One brood.

IV. Food.—Chiefly animal, but some vegetable matter recorded : small fish ; mollusca, fresh and salt water, chiefly univalves ; crustacea (small crabs, shrimps, sandhoppers, etc.) ; worms, leeches, insects (water beetles, flies, caddis worms, and larvæ of dragon flies) ; also frogs and tadpoles. Vegetable matter recorded includes seeds, seaweed, and once corn.

V. Usual Notes.—During the sex display, at the stage when his neck is stretched straight up, the drake utters a rasping double " zzee-at." [1] A usual note, apparently common to both sexes, has been syllabled " kr " or " krrah " or " arrr," and certainly expresses alarm if not other emotions. The duck utters a rapid " quack quack . . ." Characteristic of the species is the unusually loud rattling or whistling noise made by the wings in flight ; hence the popular names Rattlewing and Whistler. Coward describes the sound as being like " thin ice cracking under the bows of a boat," and states that he has heard it from fully half a mile away.

PLATE 164.—LONGTAILED-DUCK

Clangula hyemalis (Linnæus)

I. Description.—Length, 22–26 in. The drake in summer has middle tail feathers long, slender, and black ; outer feathers white ; cheeks whitish buff ; rest of upper parts and breast blackish brown, with rufous margins on back and scapulars ; flanks and belly white. In winter the tail as in summer, but head and neck more or less white or greyish with large dark brown patch on side, shading into paler brown ; back, breast, wing coverts, and quills dark brown ; long scapulars, inner secondaries, belly and flanks white ; bill blackish, but pink in middle ; feet leaden, dark webs. Females lack long tail feathers and white scapulars ; upper parts brownish ; sides of head greyish white, also ring round neck ; forebreast rusty brown ; rest of under parts pale brown. Young much like duck, but darker on back.

II. Range and Habitat.—Resident in very small numbers in Orkneys and Shetlands, but mainly winter visitor to coasts of British Isles, and scarce in South England and South Ireland. A tundra-haunting and marine species, breeding beyond tree limits. Abroad it nests in Iceland, Faeroes, Spitsbergen, and the islands off North Russia, south to the high fjeld of South Norway, North Sweden, and in Russia to Lake Onega ; also in Siberia east to Kamtschatka and the Commander Isles, and in Arctic North America from Alaska to Greenland. Winters south to South France, North Italy, the Black and Caspian Seas, and in Asia to Lake Baikal and China ; in America to the southern states of the U.S.A.

III. Nest and Eggs.—Nests in hollow in ground, sheltered by grass tussocks or dwarf bushes, on islet or near water. Eggs : 6–9, occasionally 10 ; greenish grey in colour. Average size of 130 eggs, 53.3 × 38.0 mm. (2.10 × 1.49 in.). Laying begins latter part of May. Incubation period about 3½ weeks ; by female alone. One brood. (Plate 199, f. 7.)

IV. Food.—Almost entirely animal : chiefly mollusca (marine bivalves and univalves) ; also crustacea (small crabs, shrimps, sandhoppers, etc.) ; insects (larvæ of flies, etc.), and small worms. Vegetable matter includes grain from wrecks, seaweed, mosses, etc.

V. Usual Notes.—A lively and noisy bird. The loud musical call of the drake has been rendered in various ways difficult to reconcile : " coal an can'le licht " (Scotch) ; " our, o, u, ah " (R. Gray) ; " ow, owh, lik a a a owh lik," or " ah a gleck a ah gleck " (Naumann, anglicized) ; " kao, kao, kaogleck " (Droste-Hülshoff), or simply " kalloo, kalloo . . ." from which the species derives one of its popular Scotch names. The quack of the duck is not unlike that of the Golden-Eye.

[1] *Auk*, 1910, 177.

PLATE 164.—GOLDEN-EYES (*upper*) AND LONGTAILED-DUCKS (*right*) : A. W. Seaby.

PLATE 165.—SCOTER

Oidemia nigra nigra (Linnæus)

I. Description.—Length, 20–21 in. Recognized by the uniformly dark plumage ; the drake has orange yellow ridge on the black bill and a black knob ; knob and orange are absent in the duck, which has also a grey chin and dusky cheeks. Males are blacker than females, which are rusty brown ; feet dusky olive. Young have cheeks, chin, and neck greyish white ; rest of under parts mottled white and brown.

II. Range and Habitat.—Resident in the north of Scotland and Ireland ; otherwise passage migrant and winter visitor. In breeding area haunts moorlands with scattered lochs and larger lake shores ; in winter mainly found on estuaries and coasts. Abroad breeds in Iceland, and from North Russia, Novaya Zemlya, Waigatz, Spitsbergen, Finland, and Northern Scandinavia south to mid Scandinavia ; also in West Siberia to the Taimyr Peninsula. Replaced by an allied form in North-East Siberia and North America. Winters south to the Atlantic isles, the Baltic, Caspian, and Black Seas, and Eastern Mediterranean ; the American form south to the southern states.

III. Nest and Eggs.—Breeds near edges of lochs on bare, open moorlands, or on islets in larger lakes, making a nest in hollow among heather or grass, with grass, moss, lichen, etc. Eggs : 5–8, but 9 and 10 on record ; warm pinky cream when fresh. Average of 47 British eggs, 64.4 × 44.7 mm. (2.53 × 1.76 in.). Laying begins in latter part of May. Incubation period, 27–28 days ; 32–33 also recorded ; by female alone. One brood. (Plate 198, f. 1 ; 200, f. 13.)

IV. Food.—Mainly animal : mollusca, chiefly marine bivalves, such as mussels, cockles, razor-shells, etc., also fresh-water bivalves, etc. ; crustacea (shrimps, crabs, and sand-hoppers), worms, insects, small fish, etc. Vegetable matter includes aquatic plants, beans, and grain from wrecks.

V. Usual Notes.—Not much is recorded. Droste-Hülshoff, who must have known the species well as it was present in great numbers round Borkum, describes the usual cry as a hoarse " korr, korr, korr," and a less common spring cry as " tu-lük " ($u = oo$; $\ddot{u}$ = French u).[1] He does not distinguish the notes of the sexes. Faber writes the drake's note as " tü-tü, tü-tü," and Naumann as " skrück lück," which suggests that the " tu-lük " is the note of the male.

PLATE 165.—VELVET-SCOTER

Oidemia fusca fusca (Linnæus)

I. Description.—Length, 21–22 in. Resembles Common-Scoter in dark colouring, but is distinguished at once by the white bar across the wing, which is smaller in the female and young ; bill of drake apricot yellow with black knob and black line running diagonally to the nail ; feet orange, black webs ; plumage velvet black. Female is sooty brown ; under parts lighter ; two white patches on each side of the head ; bill dark leaden, knob small ; feet red. Young birds resemble the duck.

II. Range and Habitat.—Passage migrant and winter visitor to the British Isles, occurring chiefly on the east, and, to a less extent, on the southern coasts. Breeds in North Russia, Novaya Zemlya, Finland, and Scandinavia, south to South Norway and the Baltic isles, Esthonia, the Pinsk Marshes ; also in Siberia from Transcaucasia to the Yenisei. Replaced by an allied form in East Siberia. Winters south to the North African coast and North Persia ; the eastern form to China and Japan.

III. Nest and Eggs.—Does not breed in the British Isles. Breeds in hollow in ground, well sheltered by tussock or low bush, sometimes in deep cracks in the peat. Eggs : large, creamy white, 5–8 as a rule, but 9–11 also recorded. Average size of 130 eggs, 71.1 × 48.2 mm. (2.80 × 1.89 in.). Laying begins in June in North Europe. Incubation period, 27–28 days ; by female alone. One brood.

IV. Food.—Mainly animal, especially marine mollusca (mussels, cockles, razor-shells, whelks, etc.) ; occasionally small fish ; crustacea, worms, insects, and fresh-water univalve mollusca. Tubers, buds, etc., of water plants also taken.

V. Usual Notes.—Little recorded. Appear to be the same as those of the Scoter.

[1] *Vogelwelt der Nordseeinsel Borkum*, 309.

PLATE 165.—COMMON SCOTERS (*right hand*) AND VELVET-SCOTERS (*left*) : A. W. Seaby.

PLATE 166.—GOOSANDER

Mergus merganser merganser Linnæus

I. Description.—Length, 26 in. All three " Sawbills " have straight, slender bills, with saw-like teeth directed backwards. The Goosander is the largest, and is distinguished from the Merganser by its ashy grey rump and tail, and white lower neck and breast ; also no definite crest. The drake has head and upper neck glossy black green ; mantle black ; under parts white with salmon pink tinge ; outer scapulars and wing coverts also white ; bill and feet red. In eclipse the drake is like the female but is darker above, and has a more or less complete black ring round the neck between the chestnut and whitish areas. The duck has the head chestnut red, throat white, upper parts slate grey ; white on major coverts and inner secondaries ; under parts white, with rosy tinge ; flanks greyish ; crest thick and bushy. Young female resembles duck ; young male, drake in eclipse. No crest.

II. Range and Habitat.—Resident in Scotland ; scarce in Orkneys and Shetlands, also Outer Hebrides, but nests south to Argyll and Tay areas. Otherwise winter visitor to coast and large pieces of water inland. Abroad breeds in Iceland, Faeroes (rare), North Russia, Finland, and Scandinavia, south to Denmark, North Germany (local), Bavaria, Switzerland, Bosnia, perhaps Roumania. Also in Asia east to Kamtschatka and the Kuriles, but is replaced by an allied race in the mountains of Southern Asia, and a third in North America. Winters south to the Baltic and occasionally to the Mediterranean, the Black and Caspian Seas, the Persian Gulf, while other races migrate to Southern Asia and the southern states of the U.S.A. Haunts banks of streams and lakes, generally wooded, in the breeding season.

III. Nest and Eggs.—Nests well inside a deep hole, often in some decayed tree, many feet from the entrance ; also in burrows among peat. Eggs : usually 7–12, but 6, 13, 15, and 17 on record ; smooth and white, tinged creamy. Average of 54 British eggs, 66.7 × 46.5 mm. (2.62 × 1.83 in.). Laying begins latter half of April in Scotland. Incubation period, 32 days ; by female only. One brood. (Plate 198, f. 7 ; 200, f. 14.)

IV. Food.—Mainly fish : most recorded being fresh-water species, small trout, salmon, barbel, eel, and coarse fish ; also frog, caterpillars and cockchafers, worms, etc., recorded.

V. Usual Notes.—The usual note, uttered by both sexes, is syllabled " krrra " or " karr." From two drakes engaged in chasing one the other Voigt heard a note like " gagaga " and " rrga," and Hesse, also from the drake, and often, the combination " kragagaga . . ." The last-named observer heard the duck utter the " krrra " as a call to the young.[1]

PLATE 166.—REDBREASTED-MERGANSER

Mergus serrator Linnæus

I. Description.—Length, 22–24 in. Smaller than Goosander, and distinguished by reddish throat in both sexes. The drake has black green head with double crest of long slender feathers ; iris red ; white ring round neck ; upper breast red brown, streaked darker ; sides of neck base black ; scapulars black, edged white ; upper wing coverts white, edged black, making bold triangular patches ; wing coverts and secondaries mostly white, making broad white band on each side of body when wings are closed, crossed transversely by two black bars ; under breast and belly white, tinged rosy ; bill and feet red. In eclipse resembles the duck, but is darker above, and has wing coverts white. The duck has head, neck, and throat chestnut, mixed with brown ; upper parts mostly dusky brown with pale margins ; wings barred white ; under parts whitish, streaked on breast brownish grey ; crest shorter than in drake ; bill and feet reddish.

II. Range and Habitat.—Resident in Scotland south to the Clyde and Tay areas, and in most of Ireland, haunting river banks and lakes, also islets in sea lochs. Otherwise passage migrant and winter visitor chiefly to coasts. Abroad it breeds in Iceland, the Faeroes, North Russia, Finland, and Scandinavia, south to Denmark, East Germany, Esthonia, Latvia, and, apparently, the Caucasus. In Asia it occurs across the continent to the Pacific ; also in North America from Alaska to Greenland. Winters south to the North African coast, the Atlantic isles, the Persian Gulf, and in small numbers to South-East Asia ; in America to the southern U.S.A. and Cuba.

III. Nest and Eggs.—Usually well concealed under bushes, brambles, grass tussocks, but at times disclosed by approach trodden down by the sitting bird ; also in hollows among boulders or in hole in bank. Eggs : usually 7–11, but 12–17 also recorded ; greenish drab or stone buff in colour. Average size of 60 British eggs, 65.5 × 44.8 mm. (2.58 × 1.76 in.). Laying begins after mid-May. Incubation period, about 4 weeks ; by female alone. One brood. (Plate 198, f. 8 ; 200, f. 15.)

IV. Food.—Mainly a fish eater (small salmon and trout, eel, plaice, blenny, coal fish, pike, roach, dace, gudgeon, sand eel, etc.) ; crustacea (crabs and shrimps), worms and insects (cockchafers, caterpillars, and aquatic larvæ).

V. Usual Notes.—The note of the duck, heard by Hantzsch at the breeding place, is a deep " grrr." The same observer gives the cries uttered on the wing as " rä " (*ä=a* in *care*), passing, with growing excitement, to " raprap " and " rowp " (anglicized). During the sex display the male utters a rough, loud, purring note, syllabled by C. W. Townsend as " da-ah." [2]

---

[1] Quoted by A. Voigt (*op. cit.*, p. 131), 267.   [2] *Auk*, 1911, 341–5 (" Courtship of the Redbreasted-Merganser ").

PLATE 166.—GOOSANDERS: A. W. Seaby.

MERGANSERS: A. W. Seaby

PLATE 167.—SMEW

Mergus albellus Linnæus

I. Description.—Length, 14–17½ in.   Bill much shorter than in other Sawbills.   The drake is brilliant black and white ; black at end of crest, eye patch, on back, wing coverts, and secondaries ; also black lines cutting the white in front of wings ; rump, tail coverts, and quills grey ; flanks finely pencilled grey ; beak and feet grey ; rest of plumage white.   In eclipse much like duck, which is smaller, and is chestnut on head and nape ; upper parts, breast, tail, and coverts grey ; belly, throat, and sides of neck white ; black eye patch.   Young like female, but lack eye patch.

II. Range and Habitat.—Winter visitor to the east coast of Great Britain, less common in south, rare elsewhere.   Breeds from about tree limit in North Russia and Finland to North-East Scandinavia, Lake Onega, and apparently the Dobrogea in East Romania.   Also in Asia east to Kamtschatka.   Haunts wooded banks of rivers and lakes in breeding season ; coasts and lakes in winter.   Ranges south in winter to the Mediterranean, the Swiss lakes, the Black and Caspian Seas, and Persia, North India, and China.

III. Nest and Eggs.—Does not breed in the British Isles.   Nests in holes of stumps and trees near rivers or lakes, and in nesting boxes where provided, adding down.   Eggs : 6–9, but 5, 10, 11 and 14 on record ; warm creamy, but smooth and hard-shelled.   Average size of 107 eggs, 52.4 × 37.4 mm. (2.06 × 1.47 in.).   Laying begins in May. Incubation period unknown ; probably by female only.   One brood.

IV. Food. — Chiefly   animal, especially fish (including   young salmon, trout, eel, roach, gudgeon, minnow, bleak, sand eel, coal fish, and stickleback) ; small crustacea (shrimps, sandhoppers, etc.) ; frogs, fresh-water mollusca, and water beetles.

V. Usual Notes.—Nothing recorded worth mention.

PLATE 167.—SMEWS (*the drake being the nearer*) : A. W. Seaby

PLATE **168**.—GLOSSY-IBIS

Plegadis falcinellus falcinellus (Linnæus)

I. Description.—Length, 22 in. Distinguished by long decurved bill, bare face, and general dark red brown plumage ; back much glossed metallic purple and green ; bill dark brown ; feet bronze brown ; female rather smaller. Young have no metallic gloss, and show patches of greyish white on head and neck.

II. Range and Habitat.—Autumn visitor to the British Isles, chiefly in the south. Abroad breeds in the Lower Danube valley, South Russia, and in small numbers in South Spain ; also in Central Africa, Southern Asia, and the southern states of the U.S.A., but replaced by allied races in Malay Archipelago, Australia, and the western states of the U.S.A. Migrates south to Southern Africa and Southern Asia in the Old World. A sociable species, generally in flocks or small parties.

III. Nest and Eggs.—Does not breed in the British Isles. Breeds in colonies, close to other swamp-breeding birds, such as Lesser-Egrets, Buffbacked-Herons, Night-Herons, Pygmy-Cormorants, etc., making a slight nest of twigs or reeds on bushes or heaps of dead vegetation. Eggs : 3–4, or occasionally 5 and 6 ; very deep blue in colour. Average size of 80 eggs, 52.1 × 36.9 mm. (2.05 × 1.45 in.). Laying begins in first part of May. Incubation period, 21 days. One brood.

IV. Food.—Animal and some vegetable matter : mollusca, chiefly fresh-water univalves, but also bivalves, small amphibia and reptiles, insects (beetles, flies, locusts, dragon flies, etc., and their larvæ) ; also scorpions and small crustacea, as well as unidentified vegetable matter.

V. Usual Notes.—A relatively silent species. It utters at times a harsh heron-like note, figured by Naumann as " rrha." This agrees with the observations of Jourdain ; also of Lord Lilford, who kept a number in confinement.

Order : Ciconiiformes. Suborder : Ciconiæ. Family : Ibididæ

SPOONBILL

Platalea leucorodia leucorodia Linnæus

(No Plate)

I. Description.—Length, 32–36 in. Distinguished by white plumage and spatulate bill, black at the base and yellow at the tip, barred with black ; feet black. In spring male has long and bushy crest ; shorter in the female, and absent in winter ; slight yellow tinge on crest and fore-neck ; iris red. Young birds have no crest ; iris black ; bill at first flesh colour, afterwards blackish ; shafts and ends of quills black.

II. Range and Habitat.—Formerly bred in England, but has long ceased to do so, and is now only passage migrant, chiefly to southern and south-eastern coasts ; haunting mud-flats and marshes. Abroad breeds in Denmark (1928), Holland, Spain, Hungary, the Lower Danube valley, and South Russia ; also in Western and Southern Asia to Japan and Corea ; but the birds breeding from Egypt, east to India, China, and Japan, belong to an allied race. European birds are migratory, wintering in Africa.

III. Nest and Eggs.—Does not now nest in the British Isles. Breeds in colonies, generally making large nests of reeds in shallow water among standing reeds ; also on bare islets in lagoons, on big cork oak trees, or on tamarisk bushes, when a more flimsy nest is made of dead branches. Eggs : 3–4 as a rule, exceptionally 5, or even 6 ; dull white, with some spots or smears of reddish or yellowish brown. Average size of 88 eggs, 67 × 45.4 mm. (2.64 × 1.78 in.). Laying begins latter part of April in Southern Europe. Incubation period estimated at 21 days ; both sexes taking part. One brood.

IV. Food.—Both animal and vegetable : remains of aquatic plants and grasses in stomachs ; also small fresh-water fish, frogs, mollusca, newts, leeches, worms, and insects (chiefly aquatic, such as water beetles, dragon flies, caddis flies, etc., and larval forms). Also crustacea.

V. Usual Notes.—A relatively silent species. Jourdain, when visiting one of their breeding places, noted " that an occasional low grunting note, which might be written ' ur,' or ' urd,' was uttered by one or two of the birds which were flying about, and seemed to denote anxiety on their part." [1] A more elaborate sequence of notes was heard at one breeding colony, amounting to a song : " hooh, hooh, hooh, hooroom, hōōk, hōōk, hōōk, hōōk, hoor, hoor, hoom, hoom " (anglicized).[2] The species clacks with the mandibles of its beak like a stork ; this is said to express anger, also surplus energy, and possibly sex emotion.

[1] *British Bird Book*, iv. 312.
[2] *Ornis*, i. 513 (Szikla), quoted in Naumann's *Vögel Mitteleuropas*, vii. 10, where also the note of the young is given as " pierr, pierr."

PLATE 168.—GLOSSY-IBIS: Winifred Austen.

Family : Ardeidæ

PLATE 169.—HERON

Ardea cinerea cinerea Linnæus

I. Description.—Length, 36 in. Recognized by its large size, long yellow beak, long feet, and general grey and white plumage. In flight the head between the shoulders, with recurved neck, slow flapping flight and broad rounded wings, helps recognition. The male has upper parts from base of neck to tip of tail light ashy grey ; quills dark slaty blue ; long pendent crest and nape black ; forehead, cheeks, and neck white, streaked dark bluish, with long white terminal feathers ; under parts white. Female resembles male, but is smaller, and plumes shorter. Young lack crest and pendent breast feathers.

II. Range and Habitat.—Resident in most parts of the British Isles, but only a passage migrant to the Shetlands. (For results of census of English and Welsh Heronries in 1928, and some information on Ireland, see E. M. Nicholson, *British Birds* (Mag.), xxii., pp. 270, 334.) On the Continent breeds locally in all countries ; also in the Canaries, and in parts of Africa and in Western Asia, but replaced by allied races in Madagascar and Southern Asia. Migratory in northern localities. Haunts river valleys, marshy districts, and shores of lakes.

III. Nest and Eggs.—Breeds in colonies, building large nests of sticks usually high up in trees ; also, where trees are scarce, on low bushes on islets in lakes, or on bush-grown cliff sides, and occasionally on the ground or in shallow water among reeds, where the nest is also built of reeds. Some grass is often used as lining. Eggs : 3–5 as a rule, but 6 and even 7 have been recorded ; pale bluish green. Average of 101 eggs, 60.2 × 43.0 mm. (2.37 × 1.69 in.). Laying begins in February, but many birds lay in March. Incubation period, 23–28 days ; shared by both sexes ; probably one brood as a rule, but two in some cases. (Plate 197, f. 6.)

IV. Food.—Extremely variable ; but chiefly fish, usually fresh-water species such as eel, trout, coarse fish, lamperns, sticklebacks, etc. ; also mammals, including water vole, brown rat, field mice, shrews, mole, rabbit and bat (once) ; birds are occasionally taken, such as Waterhen, young Coot, Water-Rail, Dunlin, Snipe, young Terns, etc. ; mollusca, chiefly fresh-water species, worms, small crustacea and insects (water beetles, flies, caddis flies, etc., and their larvæ) ; also small quantities of mosses, algæ, seeds, and other vegetable matter.

V. Usual Notes.—The various utterances of the Heron have still to be systematically studied. The usual cry is the harsh " frank," which gives the bird one of its local names, " Old Franky ; " it is uttered chiefly in flight. The bird has several notes in the breeding place. Those with a definite sexual significance have been rendered by E. Selous as (1) a prolonged guttural " choo-oo-orr," frequently repeated, and (2) a clear liquid " koop." These may be mixed with clickings of the mandibles. The anger note, excited by another heron's trespass, was a " hoarse, grating, shrieking cry," and the alarm note, uttered by a pair on seeing the observer, " a peculiar thin quavering cry." [1]

[1] E. Selous, *Realities of Bird Life*, chap. ii.

PLATE 169.—HERONS: A. W. Seaby.

PLATE 170.—BITTERN, *Botaurus stellaris stellaris* (Linnæus)

I. Description.—Length, 28–29 in. Distinguished by its general buff and brown coloration, erectile ruff on neck, and long green feet. Crown and nape black; upper parts irregularly barred with black and streaked with black on lower parts; quills barred black and chestnut; bill greenish yellow; ten feathers in tail. Sexes alike. Young birds have almost uniformly coloured quills.

II. Range and Habitat.—Winter visitor to most parts of the British Isles, and now again resident in Norfolk, where it became re-established in 1911. A bird of marshland, requiring extensive reed beds and swamps with shallow water. Breeds on the Continent from 60° in Sweden, Finland, and Russia (57°) locally south to North Algeria; also in Northern Asia east to Japan. In winter south to the Mediterranean region, South-West Asia, and Eastern Africa. Replaced by allied races in tropical and South Africa, Madagascar, and Australia.

III. Nest and Eggs.—Breeds singly, unlike the Herons, making a smallish nest in a grass tussock or among thick growth of dead reeds, built of stems of reed, etc., and not far from water, sometimes practically in it. Eggs: usually 4–6; uniform olive brown colour. Average size of 82 eggs, 52.7 × 38.5 mm. (2.07 × 1.51 in.). Laying begins late in March, but usually in April. Incubation period, 24–26 days; by female alone. One brood. (Plate 197, f. 4.)

IV. Food.—Chiefly animal matter: fish (fresh-water species, chiefly coarse fish, including pike up to 14 in., and eel to 15 in.), mammals (water vole, mice, and shrews), young birds, frogs, newts, crustacea, insects (water beetles, flies, water boatmen, etc.). Also vegetable matter: grass, water weeds, and algæ.

V. Usual Notes.—The usual call of both sexes is a raucous " aark, aark," sometimes " auk, auk." It is also the note uttered when the nest place is approached. The call of the young for food is a bubbling note that can " easily be imitated by blowing through a straw into a glass of water." What may be described as the song of the male is the famous " booming." It has been likened to bellowing and lowing, but is quite distinguishable, once heard. The Welsh term " bwmp," repeated, is said to represent the sound better than " boom." It may be heard three miles off. One has to be closer to hear the usual prelude of short grunts; also the long-drawn inspiration which precedes each successive boom. During the prelude of grunts the head and neck are horizontal, and the whole body vibrates; during the booming the head and neck are raised. The prelude is followed, normally, by three to six booms. The performance may be heard from the end of January usually to mid-June, but sometimes as late as mid-July. Before incubation begins, the female sometimes utters a " subdued ' wumph,' " like the " first seasonal efforts of the male before his voice is in training." [1]

LITTLE-BITTERN, *Ixobrychus minutus minutus* (Linnæus)

(No Plate)

I. Description.—Length, 12–13 in. Much smaller than Common-Bittern; the male has crown, nape, and back black with greenish gloss; primaries and tail brownish black; wing coverts buffish white; cheeks, neck, throat, and under parts buff, streaked on breast and flanks, lower neck feathers elongated; upper breast blackish, margined buff; bill yellow with dark brown ridge; feet green. Female has crown blackish brown; above chestnut, margined with buff; cheeks and hind neck rufous; wing coverts brownish buff; under parts buff, streaked brown. Young are like female, but duller.

II. Range and Habitat.—Vagrant to the British Isles, chiefly at migration periods, and most frequently in the south; no definite proof of breeding. On the Continent nests from France, Holland, Germany, the Baltic Republics and Russia, south to Northern Africa; also in Western Asia to Kashmir and Sind. Winters south to Southern Africa, and in small numbers in Southern Asia. Replaced by allied forms in tropical Africa, Madagascar, and Australia. Haunts smaller swamps and pieces of water as well as more extensive marshes, and is at home among trees.

III. Nest and Eggs.—Does not nest in the British Isles, though it may have done so formerly. Does not breed in colonies, but two or three nests may be met with not far apart. Built of dead sedges and reeds in somewhat varied sites: on heaps of dead aquatic vegetation, or on low branches of trees, on old willows, etc. Eggs: 5 or 6 as a rule, but 7–10 have been recorded, and even 12, probably by two females; dull white in colour. Average size of 100 eggs, 35.2 × 26.1 mm. (1.38 × 1.03 in.). Laying begins early in May in South Europe, about the end of May in the north. Incubation period, 16–19 days; shared by both sexes. One brood. (Plate 197, f. 5.)

IV. Food.—Chiefly, if not altogether, animal: smaller fish, frogs, newts, fresh-water mollusca and insects (water beetles, water-boatmen, etc.). Also said to take young of Great Reed-Warbler from the nest.

V. Usual Notes.—The note corresponding to the Bittern's booming resembles " the noise made by the impact of a heavy mallet on a pile more closely than anything else " (Jourdain and Lodge).[2] It is heard from May to July. A note heard by Hantzsch from birds disturbed with young sounded like " gick, gick," and a similar note was heard by Voigt.[3] But disturbed birds frequently rise without utterance.

---

[1] The above account summarizes Miss E. L. Turner's observations recorded in her *Broadland Birds*, chap. i.
[2] *British Bird Book*, iv. 348.   [3] *Op. cit.* (p. 131 above), 215.

PLATE 170.—BITTERNS: A. W. Seaby.

Suborder : Steganopodes. Family : Phalacrocoracidæ

PLATE 171.—CORMORANT [1]
Phalacrocorax carbo carbo (Linnæus)

SOUTHERN CORMORANT
Phalacrocorax carbo sinensis (Shaw and Nodder)

I. Description.—Length, 36 in. This and the next two species have all four toes webbed. Distinguished by straight, hooked bill, short feet, and purplish black plumage ; larger than Shag, and has 14 tail feathers. In breeding plumage it has a crest of scattered hair-like white plumes, a continuous white band from the throat upward to the back of the eyes, and a white patch on the thigh ; gular patch yellow. Male larger. Young birds are brownish ; under parts dull white, with brownish mottling ; iris at first brown instead of bright green.

II. Range and Habitat.—Resident on the coasts of Great Britain and Ireland except on south and east coasts of England from the Isle of Wight to Yorkshire. Habitat usually rocky coasts, but also in the west locally, lakes inland. Abroad it breeds in Greenland, Iceland, the Faeroes, Norway, Finland, and North Russia. and east to the Kola peninsula ; also in Eastern North America in small numbers to Labrador. Replaced by an allied race (*Phalacrocorax c. sinensis*) from Holland and the Baltic to the Balearic Isles, Italy, the Black Sea, and thence east to Japan and China ; a rare straggler to our southern coasts ; also by other races in Africa. Australia, and New Zealand.

III. Nest and Eggs.—Breeds in colonies, sometimes on the ground on islands or rocks at sea ; also on ledges of sea cliffs, and, in some districts, in trees on islands in lakes. On the coast the usual material is seaweed, but in trees, sticks and heather are used, lined with rushes, grass, straw, etc. Eggs : usually 4–5, but sometimes only 3 or 6, while 8 and 9 are probably due to two females. The ground colour is pale greenish blue, but it is almost concealed by heavy overlying deposits of soft white chalky matter, so that often the eggs are apparently dull white. Average of 100 British eggs, 65.8 × 40.7 mm. (2.59 × 1.60 in.). Laying begins in latter part of April. Incubation period, 23–28 days ; shared by both sexes. One brood (Plate 201, f. 2.)

IV. Food.—Fish, both marine and fresh-water, sometimes of astonishing size, such as conger eel $2\frac{1}{2}$ feet long, while in another case the bird died from exhaustion after trying to swallow an immense mullet. In addition to fish, crustacea (crabs) are sometimes taken.

V. Usual Note.—The usual note heard from birds disturbed at the breeding place is a harsh croak. Voigt states that the Cormorants kept in the Zoological Garden at Leipzig uttered, when squabbling, a sound like a bleating (*meckernden*) " hähähähä " (*ä*=a in *care*).[2] The call note of the old returning to the nest and young has been syllabled " kwank, kwank." [3]

---

[1] Or Black-Cormorant.   [2] *Op. cit.* (p. 131 above), 268.
[3] *Wild Life*, September 1915, 91 (G. T. Atchison).

PLATE 171.—CORMORANTS IN BREEDING PLUMAGE:: A. W. Seaby.

PLATE 172.—SHAG[1]

Phalacrocorax aristotelis aristotelis (Linnæus)

I. Description.—Length, 27 in. Resembles Cormorant in general appearance, but has only 12 tail feathers, is decidedly smaller, and has dark green head, neck, and under parts. In spring a curved crest is assumed on the forehead. Male larger; iris green. Young birds have very slender bills; upper parts brownish green; under parts brownish ash, mottled with brown.

II. Range and Habitat.—Resident on the coasts of the British Isles, except on the south and east coasts of England from the Isle of Wight to Northumberland; also rare on the east coast of Ireland. Confined to rocky coasts, and does not breed inland on lakes like the Cormorant. Abroad it breeds in Iceland, the Faeroes, and from Norway south to the Portuguese coast, but is replaced by an allied form in the Mediterranean and Black Seas, and possibly on the west coast of Marocco.

III. Nest and Eggs.—Breeds in company or singly, often in holes in the roof of sea caves, or on ledges of cliffs; occasionally among boulders on shore, making a nest of seaweeds or using sticks, heather stems, etc. Eggs: 2–5, but 6 and even 8 (? by two females) recorded; with pale blue undershell and overlying deposit of white chalk, as in the Cormorant. Average size of 100 British eggs, 62.9 × 38.4 mm. (2.47 × 1.51 in.). Laying period strangely irregular; sometimes March or even earlier, but more frequently April and May. Incubation period, 24–27 days, performed by both sexes. Probably single brooded, but young have been seen in the nest as late as September. (Plate 201, f. 1.)

IV. Food.—Marine fishes, including eels up to 2 feet in length, sillock, plaice, flounders, wrasse, herrings, garfish, etc. Crabs and mussels have also been recorded.

V. Usual Notes.—Little recorded. A relatively silent species. The usual note is a harsh croak, which is heard at the breeding place both as a call uttered on return to the nest place and as a nuptial cry.[2]

---

[1] Or Green-Cormorant.
[2] E. Selous, *Realities of Bird Life*, 59.

172

PLATE 172.—SHAGS OR GREEN-CORMORANTS: A. W. Seaby.

PLATE 173.—GANNET

Sula bassana (Linnæus)

I. Description.—Length, 30–34 in. Recognized in adult plumage by its strong, straight bill, pale leaden blue, with darker slate longitudinal lines ; white plumage, with buff tinge on crown and nape ; primaries very dark brown. Young in the first year are blackish brown, speckled with white, diminishing year by year till the white adult plumage is attained. When first hatched, black and naked, but soon covered with white down, which is retained on head and neck for some time, giving the appearance of a wig.

II. Range and Habitat.—A local resident in the British Isles. Breeding colonies exist at Grassholm (Wales), Ailsa, the Bass Rock, the Outer Hebrides (2), Orkneys and Shetlands in Scotland, and in co. Cork and Kerry (Ireland). Also breeds in Iceland, the Faeroes, and in Eastern North America south to Newfoundland. In winter it ranges south to the Atlantic islands and the Maroccan coast ; on the west side to the Gulf of Mexico. A marine species, only coming to land in the breeding season.

III. Nest and Eggs.—Breeds in colonies, the nests so close that they almost touch one another on cliff sides or grassy slopes where undisturbed. Nesting material mainly seaweeds, but grasses and marine plants are also used, and objects picked up on the sea are added. Egg : 1 only in most cases ; a few cases have been observed where 2 are found in one nest, but it is uncertain whether by one female. Colour, pale blue, with overlying deposit of white chalky matter which rapidly becomes stained. Average size of 90 eggs, 78.8 × 50.0 mm. (3.10 × 1.96 in.). Laying begins occasionally at the end of March, usually in April. Incubation period, 39–45 days ; shared by both sexes. One brood. (Plate 201, f. 3.)

IV. Food.—Fish (marine) : herring, mackerel, cod, sarthe, pollack, whiting, haddock, salmon, sea trout, pilchard, sand eels, etc. Also cuttlefish.

V. Usual Notes.—The usual cry at the breeding place is a hoarse "wrow" or "urrah," the sound varying with distance. Heard by the writer within a few inches of the bird's beak it resolved itself into a strident " arrrr ! " It is the note that accompanies the bird's inrushing flight to the nest ledge, and the violent displays that frequently follow, being then uttered by both sexes either while they stand erect, beaks colliding or wagging, wings waving, tails deflected, or while they make deep, sidelong, backward bows. The cry also expresses anger. When flying over the sea or sailing near the cliff, the Gannet is silent. Often, on quitting the ledge for the air, it utters a long-drawn, snoring note, like " yorrrr." This is the effect of an expulsion of air, strong enough at times to blow the mandibles apart, and has possibly to do with the air-sacs with which the species is so liberally provided. The young in down utter a high-pitched, yapping " uk." [1]

[1] The account here given is based on several weeks' stay on the Bass Rock, recorded in the *British Bird Book*, iv. 367 (Kirkman).

PLATE 173.—GANNETS : Winfred Austen.

Plate 174.—STORM-PETREL

Hydrobates pelagicus (Linnæus)

I. Description.—Length, 5½–6½ in. All the Petrels have prominent external tube-shaped nostrils and webbed feet. This species is distinguished by its small size, dark coloration, and slightly rounded tail ; beak (which has hooked tip), feet, and entire plumage black, except the upper tail coverts and sides of vent ; also narrow light edges to major wing coverts.

II. Range and Habitat.—Species breeds locally on islets off the western and northern coasts of Great Britain and Ireland, from the Scillies to the Shetlands, and in Ireland south to the islands off the Kerry coast. Abroad it breeds in the Westmann Isles, the Faeroes (but not in Norway), Brittany, and the Western Mediterranean east to Filfola (Malta) ; possibly also in the Canaries. Marine species, chiefly east North Atlantic and Western Mediterranean.

III. Nest and Eggs.—Breeds in colonies of varying size on rocks off the coast, nesting at times in crevices of boulders or even in loose stone walls, or in burrows in the peat ; the only nest material used being a little dry grass. Egg : 1 ; white without gloss, sometimes unmarked or with fine red brown speckles, often in a zone near the big end. Average of 100 eggs, 27.9 × 21.2 mm. (1.10 × .83 in.). Laying begins about the end of May or June. Incubation period, 36–42 days ; shared by both sexes. One brood. (Plate 201, f. 6.)

IV. Food.—Evidence scanty. Thick yellow oily matter, fragments of fish liver, otoliths and other remains of fish, minute shells, seeds and fragments of seaweed, also insects when obtained inland, are recorded from stomach contents.

V. Usual Notes.—When out at sea this Petrel appears to be a relatively silent bird, uttering but occasionally a sharp twittering note (Hartert).[1] At the breeding place, on the contrary, it is noisy, both during its nocturnal flights (it is absent in the daytime), and in its nest hole. The cry during the nocturnal flights has been syllabled " kekerek-i," the " *i* " being loud and shrill, the rest subdued.[1] The notes heard proceeding from the nest holes are a singular churring, punctuated by a gulping sound, " like a fairy being sick," the combination being something like " chúrk-chet ; chúrk-chet . . ."[2]

Plate 174.—LEACH'S PETREL, or FORKTAILED-PETREL

Oceanodroma leucorrhoa leucorrhoa (Vieillot)

I. Description.—Length, 7¼–8 in. Much resembles the Storm-Petrel, but is rather larger, and has a long and deeply forked tail ; also grey on wing coverts and secondaries. It is darker below than above, and also has white upper tail coverts.

II. Range and Habitat.—Local breeding species on islets off the west coast of Scotland and Ireland (Flannans, St. Kilda, and North Rona in Scotland, Kerry and Mayo in Ireland), otherwise irregular autumn visitor, storm driven. Abroad it breeds on the Westmann Isles, the east coast of North America, and in the North Pacific. Replaced by allied forms on the west coast of North America. A marine species, only coming to land during the breeding season. Frequents normally North Atlantic and North Pacific.

III. Nest and Eggs.—Breeds in colonies, usually in burrows in peaty soil, but also in hollows under rocks and crevices in ruins ; sometimes dry grass is found in the nest. Egg : 1 only ; white, without gloss, considerably larger than that of the Storm-Petrel, but similar, sometimes with wreath of fine red brown speckles near big end. Average of 100 eggs, 32.7 × 23.9 mm. (1.28 × .94 in.). Laying begins early in June. Incubation period, at least 6 weeks, probably longer ; apparently by both sexes. Only one brood reared. (Plate 201, f. 7.)

IV. Food.—Records scanty. Picks up oily or greasy matter from the sea surface ; copepoda and crustacea also recorded from stomach contents.

V. Usual Notes.—Appears, like the Storm-Petrel, to be noisy at the breeding place, and elsewhere relatively silent, but information is scanty.

[1] Naumann, *Vögel Mitteleuropas*, xii. 44.
[2] Ch. Oldham and B. Lloyd (*in litt.*). See also *British Birds* (Mag.), xxv. 207.

PLATE 174.—STORM-PETREL: A. W. Seaby

LEACH'S FORKTAILED-PETREL: A. W. Seaby.

Plate 175.—FULMAR

Fulmarus glacialis glacialis (Linnæus)

I. Description.—Length, 19 in. Distinguished from the other Petrels by its yellowish bill and white and grey plumage. Mantle and tail grey; quills mostly dusky; rest of plumage white or pale grey; feet ash-coloured. Young birds have darker bills.

II. Range and Habitat.—Resident chiefly on the northern coasts of the British Isles, but has greatly increased its range of late years, and now breeds from the Shetlands south, on the east side of Great Britain, to Yorkshire; on the west side it breeds only in the Outer and one of the Inner Hebrides south of the Sutherland coast; in Ireland on Donegal, Mayo, and Kerry coasts. A marine species; only comes to land at its breeding places. Abroad it breeds in Spitsbergen, Bear Island, Franz Joseph Land, Iceland, the Faeroes, Novaya Zemlya, recently at one locality in Norway, and in Arctic America. Replaced by an allied race in the North Pacific. Moves southward to some extent in winter months.

III. Nest and Eggs.—Breeds in colonies, usually on ledge or in recess in the face of steep sea cliff, but also on the flat tops of stacks or edges of cliffs abroad where undisturbed. Nest, merely a few small bits of stone in a hollow scratched out by the birds; often no extraneous material. Egg: 1 only, 2 recorded, but perhaps due to two birds; white, the reddish spots are probably due to food stains. Average size of 100 eggs, 73.6 × 50.2 mm. (2.89 × 1.97 in.). Laying begins about mid-May. Incubation period, variously estimated at about 6–8 weeks; shared by both sexes. One brood. (Plate 201, f. 4.)

IV. Food.—Varied; whale blubber and carcasses; also wounded birds (up to size of Puffin and smaller Gulls), but in British waters mainly small crustacea and cephalopoda (cuttlefish). Also floating oil and fish refuse, and remains of vegetable food (algæ, and in breeding season, remains of plants).

V. Usual Notes.—The bird is, as far as known, silent when on the wing. If the sitting bird is approached it utters a low crooning note, which may be the prelude to a sudden discharge from the mouth of yellowish, evil-smelling oil. It is stated by E. Selous that when pairs are displaying they utter " a series of hoarse coughs or grunts," and that the same utterances express anger.[1]

[1] *The Bird-watcher in the Shetlands*, 125

175

GREAT-SHEARWATER

Puffinus gravis O'Reilly

(No Plate)

I. Description.—Length, 18–19 in. Distinguished by large size, ashy brown head and nape ; chin, throat, sides of neck and breast white ; back of neck whitish, upper parts dark brown ; feathers edged with greyish, and upper tail coverts brown and white, mottled ; pale brown in middle of belly and thighs ; rest of under parts white ; feet pinkish white.

II. Range and Habitat.—Autumn visitor to the coasts of the British Isles, chiefly on the west side. Breeds in the Tristan da Cunha group, and probably at other localities in the southern hemisphere, migrating northwards in the southern winter to the North Atlantic. Marine in its habits like the other Petrels.

III. Nest and Eggs.—Does not breed in the British Isles. Hardly anything is known of the breeding habits of this species except that it is known to nest in crevices of the rocks on Inaccessible Island, Tristan da Cunha. Egg : 1 only ; white, no markings. Average size of 7 eggs, 77.0 × 48.7 mm. (3.03 × 1.91 in.). Eggs laid September. No details as to incubation.

IV. Food.—In the North Atlantic will take fish refuse thrown out from boats, and has been caught by baited hooks. Information scanty.

V. Usual Notes.—No information found.

Plate 175.—MANX-SHEARWATER
Puffinus puffinus puffinus (Brünnich)

W. MEDITERRANEAN SHEARWATER
Puffinus puffinus mauretanicus Lowe

I. Description.—Length, 14–15 in. Smaller than Great-Shearwater, and much larger than the two Petrels ; has upper parts, crown, and nape sooty black ; chin, throat, and under parts white, with brownish mottling on sides of neck and brown behind the thighs ; feet flesh-coloured. Young much like adult.

II. Range and Habitat.—Resident locally on islands off the western and northern coasts of Great Britain and Ireland, from the Shetlands to the Kerry coast in Ireland and the Scillies in England. The only other known breeding places are the Westmann Isles, the Faeroes, and apparently Madeira, the Salvages, and Azores, but further evidence desirable. A movement southward takes place in the autumn, and the bird then frequently occurs exhausted inland.

III. Nest and Eggs.—Breeds in colonies, sometimes on steep grassy cliffs ; at other times on broken ground on large or small islands, making use of rabbit holes or natural hollows, and enlarging them and constructing a slight nest of grass, bracken, feathers, etc. Egg : 1 only ; white, unmarked. Average size of 100 British eggs, 60.8 × 42.2 mm. (2.39 × 1.66 in.). Laying begins in early May. Incubation period, 52–54 days ; shared by both sexes. One brood. (Plate 201, f. 5.)

IV. Food.—Small fish, taken near the surface, such as sprats ; also small cephalopoda (cuttlefish), and fish refuse thrown overboard by boats.

V. Usual Notes.—There does not appear to be any record of its diurnal utterances when out at sea. During its nocturnal flights at the breeding place it is very noisy, there being a continuous concert of guttural crows in all pitches, the regular formula being " kuk kuk káw kaw," the penultimate being strongly stressed. The crow is repeated ; it may be broken off abruptly, or else end with a guttural gulp.[1] Another rendering : "kŭk-kŭk-kŭk-ōō.[2]

[1] Ch. Oldham and B. Lloyd *in litt.*
[2] *British Birds*, xxiv. 204 (R. M. Lockley).

PLATE 175.—FULMARS: A. W. Seaby.

MANX-SHEARWATERS: A. W. Seaby.

PLATE 176.—GREAT CRESTED-GREBE

Podiceps cristatus cristatus (Linnæus)

I. Description.—Length, 20–24 in. All the Grebes have lobed feet, and tail practically absent. This species is recognized by its large size, dark brown crown, crest tufts, and upper parts ; tippets below face chestnut, with blackish margin ; white eye stripe and cheeks ; white under parts and white secondaries conspicuous in flight. Female smaller, with less developed crest and tippets. In winter they are scarcely perceptible in the adults ; and in the young they are absent. Feet olive, iris crimson.

II. Range and Habitat.—Resident where fairly large pieces of water are available in Great Britain and Ireland, but local in Wales and in Scotland north to Clyde and Tay areas ; also in Morayshire, but elsewhere only an occasional visitor. Haunts coastal as well as inland waters ; but, like other Grebes, avoids the open sea. On the Continent it breeds from about 60° N. in Scandinavia, Finland, and Russia, south to the Mediterranean and Northern Africa. Also in Asia from Palestine to East Siberia and Japan. In northern localities migratory, wintering south to the Mediterranean, the Persian Gulf, India, Burma, etc. Represented by allied races in Africa, Australia, and New Zealand.

III. Nest and Eggs.—Breeds generally among reeds and sedge growing near margins of inland waters ; sometimes on large lakes almost socially. Nest is composed of water-weeds and aquatic plants procured by diving, and is built up in shallow water till the cup is well above water-level. Eggs : 3, or 4–5, but 6–9 on record ; dull chalky white, rapidly becoming stained by wet nest material. Average of 100 British eggs, 54.8 × 36.7 mm. (2.15 × 1.44 in.). Laying begins in latter part of April, sometimes not till May. Incubation period, 25–28 days ; shared by both sexes. Normally one brood, occasionally two. (Plate 202, f. 2.)

IV. Food.—Chiefly small fish, such as perch and dace ; also newts, fresh-water molluscs and insects (water beetles, water boatman, etc.). On coasts also small crustacea (*Gammarus*). Some vegetable matter also taken (grasses, seeds of rushes, etc.), and feathers are often found in stomachs.

V. Usual Notes.—The following summarizes descriptions given by Julian S. Huxley.[1] (1) An oft-repeated loud bark, rolling, rather shrill with less loud variant, not shrill or rolling ; a call to the mate or sign of hostility to other pairs.   (2) " A rapid alternation of two sounds on two notes : ' k'p ' or ' t'c ' on the low note, and an indefinite vowel sound about a tone higher."   Accompanies display taking the form of side to side head shakes.   (3) A guttural " Double Trumpet " note : the first half like " ah " or " aw," 3–4 times repeated ; the second like " kwaaa-aa-ah," sinking rapidly. Heard from reeds. Meaning not stated.   (4) A sound like " erick " ; a call ; often heard. Two other rarer notes described, heard from birds in the reeds : a " groan " and a sound like the whirring of a dentist's drill, often associated—appropriately enough—with the " groan."
   The young keep up a continuous dulcet piping like the " jingling of far-away silver bells." [2]

---

[1] *Proceedings of the Zoological Society*, 1914, 492–562.
[2] E. L. Turner, *Broadland Birds*, 122.

PLATE 176.—GREAT CRESTED-GREBE AND YOUNG IN DOWN : A. W. Seaby.

PLATE 177.—BLACKNECKED-GREBE

Podiceps nigricollis nigricollis Brehm

I. Description.—Length, 12 in. Distinguished at all seasons by slightly upturned bill; four inner primaries white. The male in breeding plumage has head and neck black, with a patch of golden reddish feathers on the ear coverts; upper parts dark brown, breast and belly white, flanks chestnut; white on secondaries. Female rather smaller. In autumn the black throat and golden ear-tuft disappear, but a dusky band remains on the throat. Young much resemble winter birds.

II. Range and Habitat.—A very local resident in England, North Wales, and Ireland; only at present definitely known to be in about half a dozen localities, but may have escaped notice elsewhere. Also winter visitor chiefly to east coasts. On the Continent breeds from Denmark and the Baltic republics to the Mediterranean and North Africa, but replaced by an allied race in the rest of Africa; also found in Asia east to China and Japan, and represented by an allied race in western North America. Northern birds winter in Southern Europe.

III. Nest and Eggs.—Nests in lagoons, small pools or lakes, but generally where covert is plentiful, and often in colonies, making the usual heap of wet water-weeds and plants in shallow water. Eggs: 3–5 normally, but 6–8 also on record; chalky white with dull surface, sometimes stained very dark brown when incubated. Average size of 100 eggs, 43.9 × 30.2 mm. (1.72 × 1.19 in.). Laying begins late in April in South Europe. Incubation period, 20–21 days; shared by both sexes. One brood. (Plate 202, f. 4.)

IV. Food.—Chiefly insects (water beetles, *Notonecta*, caddis grubs, ants, etc.); also mollusca, small fish, and some crustacea in winter. Feathers often found in stomachs.

V. Usual Notes.—According to Voigt, who watched the species frequently, the usual note is a squeaky, piping sound like "hao-eet" (anglicized). It may be followed by a louder blast or flourish (*ein kräftiger Stoss*) of several notes variously figured—*e.g.* "chrrr-ihbib-dob-rick." Hesse adds the combination "pit pit hoo-eet hoo-eet." [1]

PLATE 177.—DABCHICK, OR LITTLE-GREBE

Podiceps ruficollis ruficollis (Pallas)

I. Description.—Length, 8–9½ in. Recognized by smaller size than any of the other Grebes. In summer the male has chin black; cheeks, sides, and front of neck chestnut red; rest of head and neck dark brown; upper parts dark brown; under parts whitish; flanks dusky; feet dull green; a little white on the secondaries. The female is smaller. In winter the chin becomes white and the chestnut, brown. Young are duller, and are streaked on the sides of the head.

II. Range and Habitat.—Generally distributed, resident on most small pieces of water and slow-flowing rivers and streams, but absent from rapid streams in hilly districts and scarce in North Scotland. Partial migrant, moving to the coast in hard weather. Abroad breeds from about 62° in Scandinavia south through Europe to North-West Africa. Replaced by many other forms in Asia, Japan, the Philippines, the Malay Archipelago, Australia, and New Zealand.

III. Nest and Eggs.—Frequently breeds on slow-flowing streams as well as small pools, under shelter of overhanging branches, rushes, reeds, etc. Nest, a small edition of those of the other Grebes; built of water-weeds, and often anchored by branches or plants in the water. Eggs: usually 4–5, occasionally only 3, or 6 to 8 recorded, once 10; white with usual chalky surface, becoming stained as incubation progresses. Average of 100 British eggs, 37.8 × 26.2 mm. (1.48 × 1.03 in.). Laying begins in April, exceptionally in March. Incubation period, estimated variously at 18 or 20 to 26 days; shared by both sexes. Probably double brooded, but many nests come to grief. (Plate 202, f. 3.)

IV. Food.—Insects (water beetles, *Notonecta*, larvæ of dragon-flies and flies, etc.); small fishes; many species of fresh-water mollusca, chiefly univalves; vegetable matter, and in winter crustacea. Feathers seldom found, but pebbles recorded.

V. Usual Notes.—The note has been well compared to the "neigh or hinny of a horse heard very faintly in the distance," and rendered thus: "chēē-lee, lēēlee, lēēlee, lēēlee . . ." [2] It is heard in and out of the breeding season, and may be preceded by other notes described by different observers as a series of "whits," or of "queeks," or of "bibs." The alarm call has been figured as a "sharp little 'wit, wit.'" [3]

---

[1] Voigt (*op. cit.*, p. 131), 279.   [2] E. Selous, *Bird Life Glimpses*, 262.
[3] Trans. Herts Natural History Society, 1937, 114 (B. Lloyd).

PLATE 177.—REDNECKED-GREBE
Podiceps griseigena griseigena (Boddaert)

HOLBÖLL'S GREBE
Podiceps griseigena holboellii (Reinhardt)

I. Description.—Length, 16½–18 in. Comes next in size to the Great Crested. Adults in spring have crown, nape, and hind neck black ; chin, cheeks, and throat grey ; neck in front rich chestnut, no tippet ; upper parts dark brown, with white patch on the secondaries, under parts white. In winter the neck becomes grey in front. Young are similar but duller. Iris yellowish.

II. Range and Habitat.—Winter visitor to the British Isles, chiefly on the east side. Breeds on the Continent from Finland and Northern Russia to Sweden, Denmark, Germany, Hungary, Roumania, and South Russia ; also in Western Asia. Winters south to the North African coast and Persia. Replaced by another larger race (*Podiceps g. holboellii*) in Eastern Asia and North America. Habitat : inland and coastal waters.

III. Nest and Eggs.—Does not breed in the British Isles. Nests on larger sheets of water where there is covert from growing reeds or other vegetation, making a heap of weeds and other vegetable matter in shallow water, with hollow above water-level but wet. Eggs : usually 4 or 5, occasionally 3 only, or 6 ; white, with soft chalky surface like other Grebes' eggs. Average size of 100 eggs, 50.6 × 33.9 mm. (1.99 × 1.33 in.). Laying begins late in April, later in the north. Incubation period, 23–25 days ; shared by both sexes. One brood.

IV. Food.—Small coarse fish, frogs, insects (water beetles, *Notonecta glauca*, etc.) ; some vegetable matter and also feathers. In winter small crustacea also taken.

V. Usual Notes.—According to Voigt the male utters in the breeding time, from April onwards, a loud repeated double cry composed of alternate short and long notes. The short, which he figures as " ööö " (ö = the vowel sound in French *neuf*), resembles almost a neigh, hence the local German name " Hengst " (stallion) given to the species. The long note is strongly nasal, and, according to Naumann, like the squeaking of a frightened piglet. Both observers stress the singularity of the cry. Naumann ascribes it to both sexes, and states that it is heard by night and day. He adds another note, the usual call, which he syllables as " keck, keck." Both notes, he states, may be heard occasionally in the autumn.[1]

[1] Voigt (*op. cit.,* p. 131), 278 ; Naumann, *Vögel Mitteleuropas,* xii. 82.

Plate 177.—SLAVONIAN-GREBE

Podiceps auritus (Linnæus)

I. Description.—Length, 13–13½ in. Distinguished at all seasons from the Blacknecked-Grebe (which is slightly smaller) by its straight bill. The male in breeding plumage has tufts of elongated chestnut feathers on each side of the head: crown, forehead, chin, and tippet black; neck, breast, and flanks chestnut; upper parts dark brown; secondaries chiefly white, and belly white; iris red; feet greenish and yellowish. Female has head tufts less conspicuous. In autumn the head tufts disappear, and throat and flanks are white streaked with grey. Young birds are like winter adults, but flanks and belly are browner.

II. Range and Habitat.—A local resident in Scotland (Moray area), otherwise passage migrant and winter visitor to the British Isles. Breeds on inland lochs; in winter is generally on coast, occasionally inland waters. Breeds abroad in Iceland, and on the Continent from Scandinavia, Finland, and Russia, to Denmark and the Baltic; also in the Baltic republics; in Asia east to the Pacific; in Alaska and Canada. Winters south to the Mediterranean, Asia (lat. 24°), and in North America to the southern states of the U.S.A.

III. Nest and Eggs.—Breeds on edges of lochs, among growing *Equisetum*, etc., or in marshes, generally in company with other pairs. Nest like that of other species, composed of water-weeds and plants in shallow water reaching just above the surface. Eggs: 3–5 or 6, but 7 and 8 recorded; chalky white, with soft surface. Average size of 100 eggs, 44.5 × 30.7 mm. (1.75 × 1.21 in.). Laying begins from mid-May or later. Incubation period, 24–25 days, both sexes taking part. One brood. (Plate 202, f. 1.)

IV. Food.—Small fish, small fresh-water mollusca, insects (water beetles, larvæ of crane flies, etc.), and more vegetable matter than the other Grebes (roots, confervæ, seaweed, etc.). Also, in winter, shrimps.

V. Usual Notes.—The usual note is "ko-wee, ko-wee" repeated at regular intervals. "It might be compared to the squeak of a dry wheelbarrow, producing one double squeak at each revolution of the wheel. It has, however, a clearer quality than this comparison might indicate. Each 'ko-wee' has a rising inflection, and its two syllables are run closely together, with the accent on the latter."[1] According to Riemschneider. the note resembles that of the Rednecked-Grebe.[2]

[1] This description is given by A. D. Du Bois in *British Birds* (Mag.), xiv., 10.
[2] *Ornith. Monatsschrift*, 1896, 319.

For the other species shown in the Plate see pages 177, 177-A.

PLATE 177.—REDNECKED GREBE (*largest*), BLACKNECKED-GREBE (*left*), AND
SLAVONIAN-GREBE: A. W. Seaby.

LITTLE-GREBE OR DABCHICK UNCOVERING EGGS: A. W. Seaby

PLATE 178.—GREAT-NORTHERN DIVER
Colymbus immer immer Brünnich

WHITE-BILLED DIVER
Colymbus immer adamsii Gray

I. Description.—Length, 30–33 in.   The adult is recognized by its large size, black bill, black head and neck, with purple and green gloss, broken on throat and neck by two parallel bands of white with downward streaks ; mantle black, with conspicuous cross-bands of white spots ; under parts white but some streaking near the neck ; feet blackish ; iris red.   Female smaller.   In autumn the black throat-bands disappear.   Young birds have upper parts blackish with paler margins ; under parts white ; bill brownish horn.

II. Range and Habitat.—Winter visitor to the coastal waters of the British Isles, chiefly in the north, where some non-breeders remain all the year.   A marine species, but also met with on lochs.   Breeds in Iceland, but not on the Continent of Europe ; also in Greenland, Jan Mayen, Bear Island, and in eastern North America ; but replaced by a smaller race in western North America, and by a white-billed form (*C. i. adamsii*) in North-West America and Siberia west to Finland.   Winters chiefly in the North Sea and Western Mediterranean ; also off the American coasts south to the southern U.S.A.

III. Nest and Eggs.—Does not breed in the British Isles.   Haunts larger lakes where there is little covert in Iceland, and makes hardly any nest, merely flattening a slight hollow in a big tussock, though in America nests are sometimes built up in the water of vegetable matter.   Eggs: 2 ; varying in colour from deep umber brown to greenish olive, with usually a few dark brown blotches or spots.   Average size of 100 eggs, 89.8 × 57.6 mm. (3.53 × 2.26 in.).   Laying begins early in June. Incubation period, 29–30 days ; shared by both sexes.   One brood.

IV. Food.—Mainly fish, especially small flatfish such as flounders, sand eel, and herring, but including also many others ; also crustacea, including crabs $2\frac{1}{2}$ in. across the carapace ; mollusca (razor shells), cuttlefish up to 8 in. across, and some vegetable matter.

V. Usual Notes.—Like its two congeners, the species utters a weird, wailing cry, described by some as a blood-curdling scream ; it is heard by night and day. This wail, but more abrupt, is used as an alarm note.[1]   Another cry, uttered by a pair when on the water, sounded to Jourdain " like a deep loud note followed by three high-pitched ones : ' yooo, wee wee wee.' "[2]   Jourdain heard besides a " loud resonant ' hooo-hoo-hoo-hoo,' " presumably distinct from the above-mentioned wail. The usual flighting note is a quacking note, also described as a barking " yup." E. B. Dunlop has recorded a shrill whistled " whee-whew," repeated several times, but this may be the same note as one of those already described.   He also notes the clucking call to the young, and still others.[1]

[1] *British Birds* (Mag.), ix. **142–7** (E. B. Dunlop).
[2] *British Bird Book*, iv. 447

PLATE 178.—GREAT NORTHERN-DIVER (*breeding plumage*) : A. W. Seaby.

PLATE 179.—BLACKTHROATED-DIVER, *Colymbus arcticus arcticus* Linnæus

I. Description.—Length, 25–27½ in. Larger than Redthroated but smaller than Great Northern-Diver. Male in breeding plumage has ash-grey head and neck; throat purplish black, with longitudinal white stripes at sides of neck and upper breast; upper parts blackish, with rows of rectangular white spots; under parts white, bill black, iris red, feet brown. Female rather smaller. In autumn chin and throat become white; upper parts ashy brown. Young have grey margins to feathers of upper parts.

II. Range and Habitat.—A somewhat local resident in Scotland, breeding from Argyll and Tay areas northward, but doubtful whether it has bred in the Shetlands. A marine and fresh-water species; haunts deeper lochs than the Redthroated-Diver. Breeds in Scandinavia, Finland, North Russia, south to Northern Germany and middle Russia. Replaced by allied races in South-East Russia and West Siberia, also in East Siberia and Alaska and Northern Canada. Winters south to the Mediterranean and Black Seas; also the Caspian and North Pacific, south to the Lower Californian coast.

III. Nest and Eggs.—Breeds either on islet or peninsula on shore of a loch, generally deeper and larger than those haunted by the next species, making, as a rule, hardly any nest beyond a flattened hollow close to the water, though good-sized nests constructed in the water near the shore have been recorded. Eggs: 2, but 3 also on record, varying from deep umber brown to lighter olive, generally with a few blackish markings. Average of 100 British eggs, 83.7 × 52.5 mm. (3.29 × 2.06 in.). Laying begins towards latter part of May. Incubation period, 28–30 days; shared by both sexes. One brood. (Plate 202, f. 6.)

IV. Food.—Mainly fish, but also crustacea (crabs and prawns). Naumann records frogs.

V. Usual Notes.—Like its two congeners, it utters a weird, wailing cry, and also the note described by some as yelping or yapping, and by others as quacking, uttered chiefly in flight. The descriptions of its other utterances vary somewhat, but the evidence points to a harsh alarm note, likened by Collet to a Raven's croak—apparently a distinctive utterance.[1]

PLATE 179.—REDTHROATED-DIVER, *Colymbus stellatus* Pontoppidan

I. Description.—Length, 21–24 in. The smallest of the three Divers. The adult male in summer has a patch of dark chestnut on the throat, rest of the head and neck slate grey; upper parts ash brown, under parts white, with spots of dark grey on flanks. There is some streaking of white and brown on the nape and sides of the breast. Female smaller. The chestnut throat is lost in autumn, and the upper parts spotted and streaked with white. Young birds have feathers margined with white.

II. Range and Habitat.—Resident in Scotland from Argyll and Moray areas northward to Shetlands, and has bred in Arran and Islay; also at one locality in Ireland (co. Donegal). Abroad breeds in Iceland, the Faeroes, Spitsbergen, Novaya Zemlya, Kolguev, North Russia, Finland, and Scandinavia, south to Southern Sweden and middle Russia, also in Asia to Kamtschatka and the Commander Isles, and from Alaska to Greenland. A marine and fresh-water species; haunts smaller lochs and shallower waters than the Blackthroated-Diver. Winters in the North Atlantic, the Mediterranean and Black Seas, and the North Pacific south to Formosa and California.

III. Nest and Eggs.—Breeds on edges of lagoons, on islets in small lochs, or even pools, occasionally at close quarters with other pairs; sometimes making no nest beyond a flattened hollow, and at other times collecting moss and weeds to build a substantial nest near the water's edge. Eggs: 2, but 3 on record; olive or olive greenish to umber brown, with some blackish blotches as a rule. Average size of 100 British eggs, 74.9 × 45.3 mm. (2.94 × 1.78 in.). Laying begins latter part of May. Incubation period, 24–29 days; shared by both sexes. One brood. (Plate 202, f. 5.)

IV. Food.—Chiefly fish, both marine and fresh-water species; also mollusca (mussels, etc.), crustacea, and insects. Some vegetable matter (water-weeds) also recorded.

V. Usual Notes.—A detailed account has been given of the utterances of this species by E. Selous.[2] Its most remarkable cry is the generic, long-drawn-out melancholy mewing wail, described by another observer (M. D. Haviland) as the " hoarse voice of a woman calling out in agony." It is uttered by the male when waiting (April or earlier) for the female to come to the pool or part of a loch chosen for the nest " territory "; in his " territorial " disputes with other males, both to challenge and to triumph; on the approach of Gulls, Crows, or Hawks. It may be uttered by the female. When terrified by the approach of a large bird of prey (species of Eagle) one pair was seen to dive, uttering a sound " something between a gasp and an interjection wonderfully expressive of terror." The species has also a " nuptial clamour or jubilee . . . a strange wild duet of metallic ringing, harsh, clanging cries, which either may or may not be ushered in by the melancholy wailing mew " above described. In uttering both cries, the birds stretch their necks upon the water, then raise their heads, so that the tips of the mandibles—about an inch apart— just touch the surface. The clanging duet may be uttered on the wing; whether the mewing wail is, seems uncertain. The cry in flight is a quacking " uck " or " kark."

---

[1] The scanty facts are collected by Jourdain in the *British Bird Book*, iv. 451.
[2] *Wild Life*, 1914 (March, April). See also *Realities of Bird Life*, by the same author, and *British Birds* (Mag.), xxxi. 75 (D. B. Keith).

PLATE 179.—BLACKTHROATED-DIVER AND YOUNG IN DOWN: A. W. Seaby.

REDTHROATED-DIVER AND YOUNG IN DOWN: A. W. Seaby.

PLATE 180.—EGGS OF THE CROW FAMILY.

1. Magpie. 2. Jay. 3. Jackdaw. 4. Carrion-Crow. 5. Chough. 6. Hooded-Crow. 7. Rook. 8. Raven.

PLATE 181 —EGGS : H. Grönvold.

1. Greenfinch. 2. Goldfinch. 3. Siskin. 4. Hawfinch. 5. House-sparrow. 6. Tree-sparrow. 7. Chaffinch. 8. Linnet. 9. Lesser-redpoll. 10. Twite. 11. Bullfinch. 12. Crossbill. 13. Corn-bunting. 14. Yellow-bunting. 15. Cirl-bunting. 16. Reed bunting. 17. Snow-bunting. 18. Skylark. 19. Woodlark. 20. Pied-wagtail. 21. White-wagtail. 22. Grey-wagtail 23. Blueheaded-wagtail. 24. Yellow-wagtail. 25. Tree-pipit. 27. Meadow-pipit. 28. Rock-pipit.
(Natural Size.)

PLATE 182.—EGGS: H. Grönvold.

1. Tree-creeper. 2. (*a*) Wren ; (*b*) St. Kilda Wren. 3. Mistle-thrush. 4. Blackbird. 5. Song-thrush. 6. Ring-ouzel. 7. Wheatear. 8. Whinchat. 9. Stonechat. 10. Redstart. 11. Robin. 12. Nightingale. 13. Hedge Sparrow. 14. Whitethroat. 15. Lesser-whitethroat. 16. Blackcap. 17. Garden-warbler. 18. Dartford-warbler. 19. Goldcrest. 20. Chiff-chaff. (*Natural Size.*)

PLATE 183.—EGGS.

1. Willow-warbler.   2. Wood-warbler.   3. Reed-warbler.   4. Marsh-warbler.   5. Sedge-warbler.   6. Grasshopper-warbler.
7. Savi's warbler.   8. Starling.   9. Oriole.   10. Longtailed-tit.   11. Coal-tit.   12. Crested-tit.   13. Marsh-tit.   14. Great-
tit.   15. Blue-tit.   16. Nuthatch.   17. Bearded-reedling.   18. Redbacked-shrike.   19. Woodchat-shrike.   20. Flycatcher.
21. Pied-flycatcher.   22. House-martin.   23. Sand-martin.   24. Swallow.

PLATE 184

EGGS OF CUCKOO, CUCULUS CANORUS

By H. GRÖNVOLD

Figs. 1 to 12, Eggs of Cuckoo, together with those of foster parents :

1, + Hedge-sparrow (Leatherhead, Brit. Mus.). 2, + Sedge-warbler (England, Brit. Mus.). 3, + Wren (Northampton, F. Jourdain coll.). 4, + Pied-wagtail (Berks, Brit. Mus.). 5, + Pied-wagtail (Tenby, Brit. Mus.). 6, + Reed-warbler (Arlington, Surrey, Brit. Mus.). 7, + Tree-pipit (Salop, Brit. Mus.). 8, + Meadow-pipit (Hayes Common, Brit. Mus.). 9, + Tree-pipit (Odiham, Hants, Brit. Mus.). 10, + Greenfinch (Suffolk, F. Jourdain coll.). 11, + Redstart (Valkenswaard, Holland, Brit. Mus.). 12, + Blackbird (Staffordshire, F. Jourdain coll.).

Figs. 13 to 30 represent eggs of Cuckoo alone :

13 (+ Nightingale, Surrey, Brit. Mus.). 14 (+ Robin, Churt, Brit. Mus.). 15 (+ Robin, Moravia, Brit. Mus.). 16 (+ Robin, England, Brit. Mus.). 17 (+ Chiffchaff, Churt, Brit. Mus.). 18 (+ Reed-warbler, Arlington, Brit. Mus.). 19 (+ Grasshopper-warbler, Brighton, Brit. Mus.). 20 (+ Hedge-sparrow, S. Cadbury, Somerset, R. H. Read coll.). 21 (+ Reed-bunting, England, Brit. Mus.). 22 (+ Redbacked-shrike, Moravia, Brit. Mus.). 23 (+ Whitethroat, Epping, Brit. Mus.). 24 (+ Reed-warbler, Holkham, Brit. Mus.). 25 (+ Dartford-warbler, Churt, Brit. Mus.). 26 (+ Linnet, Churt, Brit. Mus.). 27 (+ Whinchat, Otterbourne, Brit. Mus.). 28 (+ Spotted-flycatcher, Salop, Brit. Mus.). 29 (+ Skylark, Salop, Brit. Mus.). 30 (+ Stonechat, Twyford, Brit. Mus.).

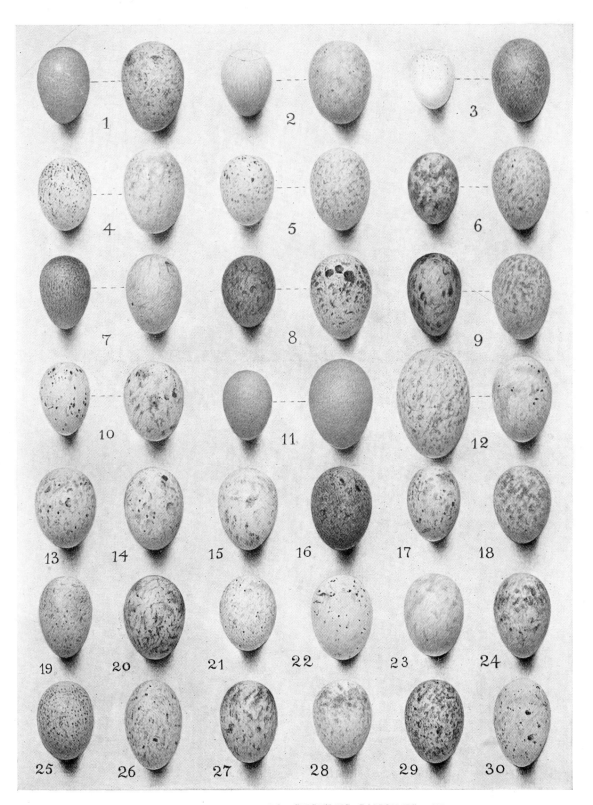

PLATE 184.—EGGS OF CUCKOO, CUCULUS CANORUS: H. Grönvold.

PLATE 185.—EGGS.

1. Nightjar (2 figures). 2. Hoopoe (1 figure). 3. Pallas's sandgrouse (2 figures). 4. Puffin (1 figure). 5. Razorbill (3 figures). 6. Black-guillemot (2 figures).

PLATE 186.—EGGS: GUILLEMOT (5 figures).

PLATE 187.—EGGS : H. Grönvold.

1. **Roseate-tern.** 2. Common-tern. 3. Little-tern. 4. Arctic-tern. 5. Sandwich-tern. 6. Black-tern.

PLATE 188.—EGGS : H. Grönvold.

1. Blackheaded-gull.   2. Common-gull.   3. Herring-gull.   4. Lesser blackbacked-gull.

PLATE 189.—EGGS : H. Grönvold.
1. Kittiwake. 2. Great blackbacked-gull. 3. Arctic-skua. 4. Great-skua.

PLATE 190.—EGGS: H. Grönvold.
1. Woodcock. 2. Snipe. 3. Kentish-plover. 4. Stone-curlew. 5. Ringed-plover. 6. Oyster-catcher.

PLATE 191.—EGGS : H. Grönvold.

1. Dotterel.   2. Common-sandpiper.   3. Golden-plover.   4. Wood-sandpiper.   5. Lapwing.   6. Avocet.

PLATE 192.—EGGS: H. Grönvold.

1. Rednecked-phalarope.   2. Dunlin.   3. Ruff.   4. Redshank.   5. Greenshank.   6. Whimbrel.

PLATE 193.—EGGS: H. Grönvold.

1. Curlew. 2. Great-bustard. 3. Waterhen. 4. Coot. 5. Corncrake. 6. Spotted-crake. 7. Baillon's crake.
8. Water-rail.

PLATE 194.—EGGS: H. Grönvold.

1. Partridge.   2. Redlegged-partridge.   3. Red-grouse.   4. Ptarmigan.   5. Pheasant.   6. Quail.   7. Capercaillie.
8. Black-grouse.

1

2

3

4

4

5

PLATE 195.—EGGS : H. Grönvold.

1. Montagu-harrier. 2. Marsh-harrier. 3. Hen-harrier. 4. Buzzard. 5. Golden-eagle.

PLATE 196.—EGGS: H. Grönvold.

1 Sparrow-hawk. 2. Kestrel. 3. Whitetailed-eagle. 4. Hobby. 5. Merlin. 6. Goshawk. 7. Kite.

PLATE 197.—EGGS: H. Grönvold.

1. Honey-buzzard. 2. Peregrine-falcon. 3. Osprey. 4. Bittern. 5. Little-bittern (upper egg soiled by bird). 6. Heron.

PLATES 198–9

The eggs of the Ducks, Geese, and Swans are either white or uni-coloured; they have no markings. Coloured plates are of little use for their identification, and have been omitted. Shape and size are more helpful. These are shown by the outlines here given. The feather and down patterns on Plate 200 are also of some use. It may be added that to have given coloured plates of these eggs would have involved the sacrifice of two of the other coloured plates, for the total is strictly limited.

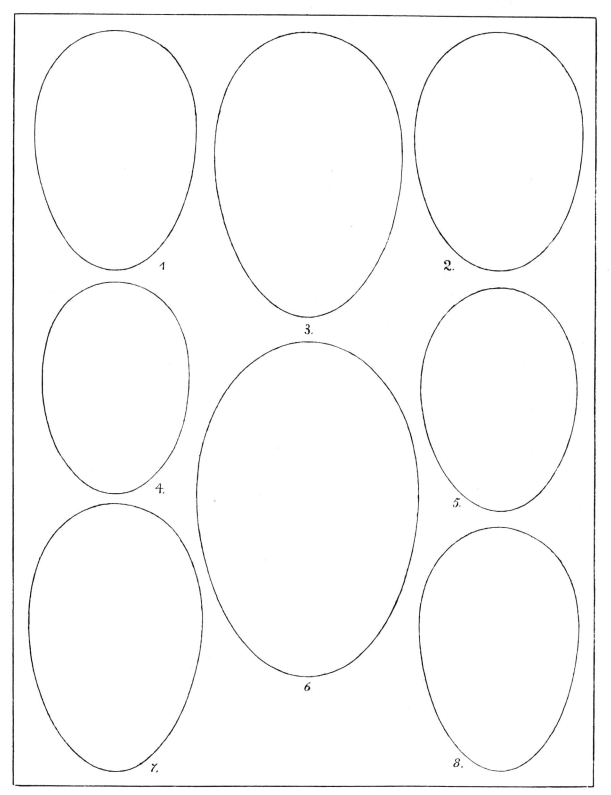

PLATE 198.—EGGS

1. Black-scoter. 2. Shelduck. 3. Eider. 4. Tufted-duck. 5. Pochard. 6. Greylag-goose. 7. Goosander.
8. Redbreasted-merganser.

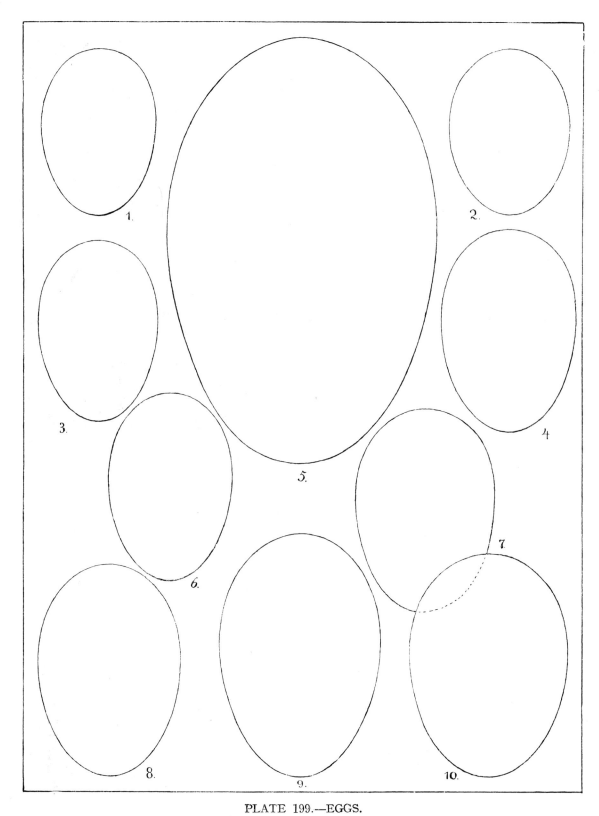

PLATE 199.—EGGS.

1. Teal. 2. Garganey. 3. Pintail. 4. Shoveler. 5. Mute-swan. 6. Wigeon. 7. Longtailed-duck. 8. Gadwall.
9. Scaup. 10. Mallard.

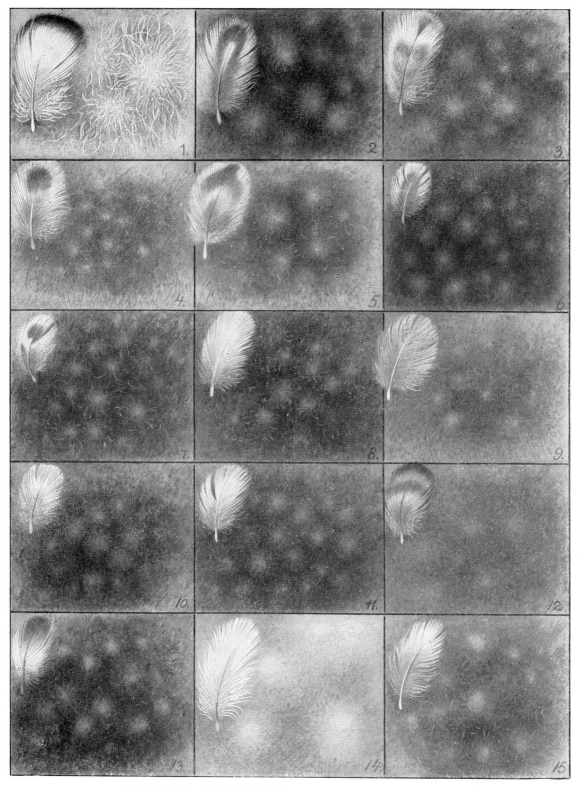

PLATE 200.—NEST FEATHERS AND DOWN OF DUCKS.

[The feather and down patterns should be used in conjunction with the descriptions in the Classified Notes by which they are in some cases slightly modified.]

1. Shelduck.   2. Wild-duck or mallard.   3. Gadwall.   4. Shoveler.   5. Pintail.   6. Teal.   7. Garganey.   8. Wigeon.
9. Pochard.   10. Tufted duck.   11. Scaup.   12. Eider-duck.   13. Scoter.   14. Goosander.   15. Redbreasted-merganser.

PLATE 201.—EGGS : H. Grönvold.

1. Shag. 2. Cormorant. 3. Gannet. 4. Fulmar. 5. Manx-shearwater. 6. Storm-petrel. 7. Leach's forktailed-petrel.

PLATE 202.—EGGS : H. Grönvold.

1. Slavonian-grebe. 2. Great crested-grebe. 3. Little-grebe. 4. Blacknecked-grebe. 5. Redthroated-diver.
6. Blackthroated-diver.

FORMS OMITTED ON ACCOUNT OF RARITY

THE following forms are on the British List, but on account of their rarity have been omitted from the body of the work:

Order I. : Passeriformes.
FAM. : CORVIDÆ.
Thickbilled-Nutcracker, *Nucifraga caryocatactes caryocatactes* (Linnæus).
Thinbilled-Nutcracker, *N. c. macrorhynchos* Brehm. Brown with white-spotted plumage, about size of Jay, occurring in winter. Over 50 records of Thinbilled (Siberian) race ; Thick billed (European) much rarer.

FAM. : FRINGILLIDÆ.
Greenland, Hornemann's, and Coues's Redpolls, *Carduelis flammea rostrata, C. h. hornemanni,* and *C. h. exilipes,* are all Arctic forms of Redpoll which have occurred in winter ; larger and paler than the other races, while the two last-named have white rumps.
Citril-Finch, *Carduelis c. citrinella* (Linnæus). Once recorded.
Serin, *Serinus canarius serinus* (Linnæus). Small yellow-breasted Finch (4½ in. long). Has occurred over 30 times.
Scarlet-Grosbeak, *Carpodacus e. erythrinus* (Pallas). Occurs chiefly in north in autumn. Males rosy red ; hens and young brown ; 5½ in. long.
Pine-Grosbeak, *Pinicola enucleator* (Linnæus). Very rare Arctic straggler ; few authenticated. Cocks show much crimson ; hens yellowish and grey ; about 8–9 in. long.
Twobarred-Crossbill, *Loxia leucoptera bifasciata* (Brehm), has double white wing bar. Few records.

FAM. : EMBERIZIDÆ.
Pine-Bunting, *Emberiza leucocephala* Gmelin. Whiter than Yellow-Bunting. 1 record.
Blackheaded-Bunting, *E. melanocephala* Scopoli. Male has black head ; yellow beneath. About 12 records.
Redheaded-Bunting, *E. bruniceps* Brandt. 1 record. Brown replaces black on head.
Yellowbreasted-Bunting, *E. aureola* Pallas. About 7 recorded. Has white wing bar.
Ortolan, *E. hortulana* Linnæus. Green-headed ; bill reddish ; autumn visitor ; 6 in. long.
Rock-Bunting, *E. cia cia* Linnæus. Only 6 recorded. Head grey, black stripes.
E. Siberian Meadow-Bunting, *E. cioides castaneiceps* Moore. 1 straggler. Head grey ; brown and black markings.
Rustic-Bunting, *E. rustica* Pallas. Chestnut breast band on light breast ; smallish. Under 20 records.
Little-Bunting, *E. pusilla* Pallas. Very small (4¾ in.). Most records on migration Scotland.
Largebilled Reed-Buntings, *E. s. compilator* Mathews and Iredale, and *E. s. tschusii* Reiser and Almasy. Both these thick-billed races have occurred, but only 3 records altogether.

FAM. : PLOCEIDÆ.
Snow-Finch, *Montifringilla n. nivalis* (Linnæus). About 6. Black and white alpine stragglers.

Fam. : Alaudidæ.

Whitewinged-Lark, *Melanocorypha leucoptera* (Pallas). About 12 recorded. White secondaries ; chestnut on wings ; 7 in.

Black-Lark, *M. yeltoniensis* (Forster). 6–7 recorded. Male black and very large.

Calandra-Lark, *M. c. calandra* (Linnæus). Another large bird ; black on collar ; white on secondaries. 2 records.

Shorttoed and Eastern Shorttoed-Larks, *Calandrella b. brachydactyla* (Leisler) and *C. b. longipennis* (Eversmann). Small sandy birds, underparts not spotted. About 25 records of first and 3 of second.

Crested-Lark, *Galerida c. cristata* (Linnæus). About 9 records. Long crest ; short tail ; 6¾ in

Fam. : Motacillidæ.

Masked-Wagtail, *Motacilla alba personata* Gould. 1 record. Much black on throat and neck.

Grey, Ashy, and Blackheaded-Wagtails, *M. flava thunbergi, cinereocapilla,* and *feldegg* have all occurred. First has dark crown, no eye stripe ; second more white on chin ; third has upper part of head black. First has occurred oftenest.

Petchora-Pipit, *Anthus gustavi* Swinhoe.

Redthroated-Pipit, *A. cervinus* Pallas. Has reddish breast and throat in spring and summer.

Scandinavian and American Rock-Pipits, *A. spinoletta littoralis* Brehm and *A. s. rubescens* Tunstall. Former is pinker on breast in spring and summer than Rock-Pipit. Latter has once occurred.

Fam. : Certhiidæ.

Wall-Creeper, *Tichodroma muraria* (Linnæus). 6 obtained and 2 seen. Crimson and white on wings.

Fam. : Turdidæ.

White's Thrush, *Turdus dauma aureus* Holandre. Has occurred in winter nearly 30 times. Bold crescent markings on under side.

Dusky-Thrush, *T. eunomus* Temminck. Another Asiatic straggler with black breast. 7 records.

Blackthroated-Thrush, *T. ruificollis atrigularis* Temminck. Has throat as well as breast black. 4 records.

Rock-Thrush, *Monticola saxatilis* (Linnæus). Has blue head and orange breast in male. At least 5 recorded.

Desert-Wheatear, *Œnanthe deserti deserti* (Temminck), *Œ. d. homochroa* (Tristram), and *Œ. d. atrogularis* (Blyth). All three races of this sandy, desert species have occurred, but very rarely.

Blackeared-Wheatear, *Œ. hispanica hispanica* (Linnæus) and *Œ. h. melanolenca* (Güldenstadt). Both eastern and western races of this boldly contrasted bird have occurred ; nearly 20 records altogether.

Pied-Wheatear, *Œ. l. leucomela* (Pallas). Twice only, in Scotland.

Isabelline-Wheatear, *Œ. isabellina* Temminck. A sandy coloured species which has occurred 4 times.

Black-Wheatear, *Œ. l. leucura* (Gmelin) and *Œ. l. syenitica* (Heuglin). A large black species, with white rump and on tail, of which two races have occurred, but only on about 4 occasions.

Thrush-Nightingale, *Luscinia luscinia* (Linnæus). A rather darker bird, and with traces of spots on breast. Only recorded 2 or 3 times.

Fam. : Sylviinæ.

Icterine-Warbler, *Hippolais icterina* (Vieillot). Has bred once at least, and recorded about 40 times.

Melodious-Warbler, *H. polyglotta* (Vieillot). Only about half a dozen records.

Booted-Warbler, *H. c. caligata* (Lichtenstein). Once, Fair Island.

Olivaceous-Warbler, *H. pallida elæica* (Lindermayer). Once, in Sussex.

Barred-Warbler, *Sylvia nisoria nisoria* (Bechstein). Occurs on migration on east coast England and Scottish coasts ; rare Ireland.

Orphean-Warbler, *S. h. hortensis* (Gmelin). Only 5 records.

Rüppell's Warbler, *S. rüppeli* Temminck. 2 from Sussex.

Sardinian-Warbler, *S. m. melanocephala* (Gmelin). 1 (or 2) only recorded.

Subalpine-Warbler, *S. c. cantillans* (Pallas). 4 from Scotland and Ireland.

Rufous and Brownbacked-Warblers, *Agrobates g. galactotes* (Temminck) and *A. g. syriacus* (Hemprich and Ehrenberg). Both races have occurred in England, 5 and 4 times.

Greenish-Warbler, *Phylloscopus nitidus viridanus* Blyth. Once in Lincolnshire.

Eversmann's Warbler, *Ph. b. borealis* (Blasius). About 11 recorded.

Yellowbrowed-Warbler, *Ph. i. inornatus* (Blyth). Passage migrant, but scarce.

Pallas's Warbler, *Ph. p. proregulus* (Pallas). Only 1 record (Norfolk).

Dusky-Warbler, *P. h. fuscatus* (Blyth). Twice obtained.

Radde's Bush-Warbler, *Herbivocula schwarzi* (Radde). 1 record, Lincolnshire.

Cetti's Warbler, *Cettia cetti* (Temminck). 3 from Sussex.

Moustached-Warbler, *Lusciniola m. melanopogon* (Temminck). Once only.

Savi's Warbler, *Locustella l. luscinoides* (Savi). Formerly bred. Only 2 actually obtained since 1900.

Pallas's Grasshopper-Warbler, *L. certhiola* (Pallas). Once only, Ireland.

Lanceolated-Warbler, *L. lanceolata* (Temminck). 4 occurrences.

Great and Eastern Great Reed-Warblers, *Acrocephalus a. arundinaceus* (Linnæus) and *A. a. orientalis* (Temminck and Schlegel). The former about a dozen times ; latter once.

Blyth's Reed-Warbler, *A. dumetorum* Blyth. About 9 records.

Paddyfield-Warbler, *A. a. agricola* (Jerdon). Once only.

FAM. : PRUNELLIDÆ.

Alpine-Accentor, *Prunella c. collaris* (Scopoli). Occasional straggler chiefly to south and east. Has throat greyish, spotted.

FAM. : LANIIDÆ.

Lesser Grey-Shrike, *Lanius minor* Gmelin. About 22 records. Has black stripe across eyes.

Woodchat and Corsican-Woodchat, *L. s. senator* Linnæus and *L. s. badius* Hartert. These have chestnut crown. Woodchat has occurred about 50 times. Corsican race, with white wing bar, once.

Masked-Shrike, *L. nubicus* Lichtenstein. Only once obtained, in Kent.

FAM. : MUSCICAPIDÆ.

Brown-Flycatcher, *Muscicapa latirostris* Raffles. Only 1 record.

Collared-Flycatcher, *M. albicollis* Temminck. Has complete white collar, and has occurred 4 times.

Redbreasted-Flycatcher, *M. p. parva* Bechstein. Has occurred about 50 times on passage. Male like small Robin, but base of tail white.

FAM. : HIRUNDINIDÆ.

Redrumped-Swallow, *Hirundo daurica rufula* Temminck. Has tawny rump. 4 records.

Order : Coraciiformes.

FAM. : APODIDÆ.

Alpine-Swift, *Apus m. melba* (Linnæus). Rare summer visitor. Large, white-bellied species.

Needletailed-Swift, *Chætura c. caudacuta* (Latham). 2 authentic records.

FAM. : CAPRIMULGIDÆ.

Egyptian Nightjar, *Caprimulgus æ. ægyptius* Lichtenstein. A pale desert form. Once recorded

Rednecked-Nightjar, *C. ruficollis desertorum* Erlanger. With broad rufous collar. 1 record.

American Nighthawk, *Chordeiles m. minor* (Forster). A transatlantic straggler. 1 record.

FAM. : MEROPIDÆ.

Bee-eater, *Merops apiaster* Linnæus. Bronze on back and green on breast. Over 70 occurrences.

FAM. : STRIGIDÆ.

European and American Hawk-Owls, *Surnia u. ulula* (Linnæus) and *S. u. caparoch* (Müller). 8 records of these two forms.

Tengmalm's Owl, *Ægolius f. funereus* (Linnæus). Nearly 30 occurrences in Great Britain.

Eagle-Owl, *Bubo b. bubo* (Linnæus). Some records may be due to escapes ; but others genuine.

Scops Owl, *Otus s. scops* (Linnæus). Over 50 occurrences. Smallest species on our list.

Order : Cuculiformes.

FAM. : CUCULIDÆ.

Great Spotted-Cuckoo, *Clamator glandarius* Linnæus. Has occurred 5 times.

American Yellowbilled-Cuckoo, *Coccygus a. americanus* (Linnæus). About 12 records.

American Blackbilled-Cuckoo, *C. erythrophthalmus* (Wilson). 2 records.

Order : Charadriiformes.

FAM. : COLUMBIDÆ.

Eastern Rufous Turtle-Dove, *Streptopelia o. orientalis* (Latham). Once only recorded.

FAM. : ALCIDÆ.

Brunnich's Guillemot, *Uria l. lomvia* (Linnæus). A northern species ; white line on edge of upper bill. Only rare winter vagrant.

FAM. : LARIDÆ.

Whiskered-Tern, *Chlidonias h. hybrida* (Pallas). Whitewinged Black-Tern, *Ch. leucopterus* (Temminck). Both these Marsh-Terns are rare vagrants, with red bills and feet. Former larger ; latter black and white.

Gullbilled-Tern, *Gelochelidon n. nilotica* (Gmelin). Black bill and feet. Nearly 30 recorded.

Caspian-Tern, *Hydroprogne caspia* (Pallas). Largest of Terns. Red bill. Nearly 30 occurrences.

Sooty-Tern, *Sterna f. fuscata* Linnæus. Accidental visitor. About 10 records.

Lesser Sooty-Tern, *S. anæthetus* Scopoli. Accidental. 1 definite record.

Sabine's Gull, *Xema sabini* (Sabine). Small ; black cap in summer ; forked tail. Scarce winter visitor.

Wedgetailed-Gull, *Rhodostethia rosea* (McGillivray). 1, England. Pinkish white ; narrow neck ring. An Arctic species.

Bonaparte's Gull, *Larus philadelphia* (Ord). An American straggler.

Adriatic-Gull, *L. melanocephalus* Temminck. Black head in summer. About 10 recorded.

Great Blackheaded-Gull, *L. ichthyaetus* Pallas. Very large ; head black.

Ivory-Gull, *Pagophila eburnea* (Phipps). An Arctic species. Adults pure white ; black feet.

FAM. : GLAREOLIDÆ.

Creamcoloured-Courser, *Cursorius c. cursor* (Latham). About 30 occurrences.

Pratincole, *Glareola p. pratincola* (Linnæus). About 25 recorded.

Blackwinged-Pratincole, *G. nordmanni* Nordmann. 8 recorded.

FAM. : CHARADRIIDÆ.

Caspian-Plover, *Charadrius a. asiaticus* Pallas. 4–5 records.

Semi-palmated Ringed-Plover, *Ch. semipalmatus* Bonaparte. 1, Sussex.

Little Ringed-Plover, *Ch. dubius curonicus* Gmelin.   About 10 authentic records.

Kildeer-Plover, *Ch. vociferus* Linnæus.   About 10 occurrences.

American and Asiatic Golden-Plovers, *Ch. dominicus dominicus* Müller and *Ch. d. fulvus* Gmelin.
4 or 5 American and some 15 Asiatic recorded.

Sociable-Plover, *Chettusia gregaria* (Pallas).   About 10 obtained and others seen.

Blackwinged-Stilt, *Himantopus h. himantopus* (Linnæus).   Rare vagrant, chiefly to S. and E.

Broadbilled-Sandpiper, *Limicola f. falcinellus* (Pontoppidan).   About 16 records.

American Pectoral-Sandpiper, *Calidris melanotos* (Vieillot).   Has occurred at least 60 times.

Siberian Pectoral-Sandpiper, *C. acuminata* (Horsfield).   4 Norfolk records.

Baird's Sandpiper, *C. bairdii* (Coues).   5 occurrences.

Bonaparte's Sandpiper, *C. fuscicollis* (Vieillot).   16 or 17 recorded.

American-Stint, *C. minutilla* (Vieillot).   4 records.

Temminck's Stint, *C. temminckii* (Leisler).   Has bred twice ; rare passage migrant.

Buffbreasted-Sandpiper, *Tryngites subruficollis* (Vieillot).   About 19 records.

Semipalmated-Sandpiper, *Ereunetes pusillus* (Linnæus).   Once, Kent.

Bartram's Sandpiper, *Bartramia longicanda* (Bechstein).   About 14 records.

Marsh-Sandpiper, *Tringa stagnatilis* (Bechstein).   6 obtained.

Spotted-Sandpiper, *T. macularia* Linnæus.   About 8 records admitted by Witherby.

Solitary-Sandpiper, *T. s. solitaria* Wilson.   7 recorded.

Greater-Yellowshank, *T. melanoleuca* (Gmelin).   2 records accepted ; 1 doubtful.

Yellowshank, *T. flavipes* (Gmelin).   6 records.

Dusky-Redshank, *T. erythropus* (Pallas).   Passage migrant, chiefly east coast ; rarely winters
on south coast.

Terek-Sandpiper, *Terekia cinerea* (Güldenstadt).   7 records (Kent and Sussex).

Redbreasted-Sandpiper, *Limnodromus g. griseus* (Gmelin).   Some 23 recorded.

Slenderbilled-Curlew, *Numenius tenuirostris* Vieillot.   4 at least ; others seen, Kent.

Eskimo-Curlew, *N. borealis* (Forster).   7 or 8 records.

Order : Gruiformes.
FAM. : OTIDIDÆ.

Eastern and Western Little-Bustards, *Otis t. orientalis* Hartert and *O. t. tetrax* Linnæus.   A
good many obtained, but few critically examined.   All Eastern race but one (Yorks).

Macqueen's Bustard, *Chlamydotis undulata macqueenii* (Gray and Hardwicke).   4 records ; all
east coast.

FAM. : GRUIDÆ.

Crane, *Grus g. grus* (Linnæus).   Formerly bred in the Fens ; now rare casual.

FAM. : RALLIDÆ.

Little-Crake, *Porzana parva* (Scopoli).   About 45 recorded.

Baillon's Crake, *P. pusilla intermedia* (Hermann).   Has been recorded as breeding, and also as
vagrant.

Carolina-Crake, *P. carolina* (Linnæus).   5 authentic records, mostly from west coasts.

Order : Accipitres.
FAM. : VULTURIDÆ.

Griffon-Vulture, *Gyps f. fulvus* (Hablizl).   1 obtained ; 3 seen.

Egyptian-Vulture, *Neophron p. percnopterus* (Linnæus).   2 immature birds obtained.

FAM. : BUTEONIDÆ.

Great Spotted-Eagle, *Aquila clanga* Pallas.   About a dozen records.

Pallid-Harrier, *Circus macrourus* (Gmelin).   1, Fair Island.

Goshawk and American-Goshawk, *Accipiter g. gentilis* (Linnæus) and *A. g. atricapillus* (Wilson).
Now rare vagrants.   European race may have once bred.   About 5 American race recorded.

Honey-Buzzard, *Pernis a. apivorus* (Linnæus). Used to breed very sparingly ; may do so now
Black-Kite, *Milvus m. migrans* (Boddært). 2 only.
Gyr-Falcon, *Falco r. rusticolus* Linnæus. 2 definite records.
Redfooted-Falcon, *F. v. vespertinus* Linnæus. Under 50 occurrences.
Lesser-Kestrel, *F. n. naumanni* Fleischer. Has occurred about 11 times.

Order : Anseriformes.

FAM. : ANATIDÆ.

Lesser Whitefronted-Goose, *Anser erythropus* (Linnæus). 1 certain, other possible records.
Snow-Goose, *A. h. hyperboreus* Pallas. Records of small parties from Ireland probably
authentic ; about 7 obtained.
Greater Snow-Goose, *A. h. nivalis* (Forster). 2 or 3 definite records.
Redbreasted-Goose, *Branta ruficollis* (Pallas). 5 or 6 obtained.
Canada-Goose, *B. c. canadensis* (Linnæus). Naturalized, and breeds.
Ruddy-Shelduck, *Casarca ferruginea* (Pallas). An invasion in some numbers in 1892 ; other
wise rare.
American Bluewinged-Teal, *Anas discors* Linnæus. About 6 records.
American Wigeon, *Anas americana* Gmelin. Few satisfactory records, but 2 or 3 probably
genuine.
Redcrested-Pochard, *Netta rufina* (Pallas). Some occurrences in flocks must be wild birds.
Ferruginous-Duck, *Nyroca n. nyroca* (Güldenstadt). About 100 occurrences, mostly on east side.
Buffleheaded Duck, *Bucephala albeola* (Linnæus). 3 reliable records.
Harlequin-Duck, *Histrionicus h. histrionicus* (Linnæus). Rare ; 4–5 records.
King-Eider, *Somateria spectabilis* (Linnæus). A few records from Scotland, Ireland, and
east coast England.
Steller's Eider, *Polysticta stelleri* (Pallas). 2 only.
Surf-Scoter, *Oidemia perspicillata* (Linnæus). Rare straggler to Orkney ; about 25 elsewhere.
Hooded Merganser, *Mergus cucullatus* Linnæus. 4 authentic records ; others seen.

Order : Ciconiiformes.

FAM. : PHŒNICOPTERIDÆ.

Flamingo, *Phœnicopterus ruber roseus* Pallas. Many seen may have been escapes, but some
wild.

FAM. : ARDEIDÆ.

Purple-Heron, *Ardea purpurea* Linnæus. A smaller, darker bird than the Grey. 50–60 records.
Great White-Heron *Egretta a. alba* (Linnæus). About 7 definite records.
Little-Egret, *E. g. garzetta* (Linnæus). Also white, bill black. 1 certain record ; others
possible.
Buffbacked-Heron, *Ardeola i. ibis* (Linnæus). 2 authentic ; recently turned down.
Squacco-Heron, *A ralloides* (Scopoli). Much smaller. About 70 recorded.
Night-Heron, *Nycticorax n. nycticorax* (Linnæus). Frequently recorded.
American-Bittern, *Botaurus lentiginosus* (Montagu). Some 45 records.
White-Stork, *Ciconia c. ciconia* (Linnæus). Recorded from South-East England about 30
times ; elsewhere rarely.
Black-Stork, *C. nigra* (Linnæus). About 20 recorded.

Order : Procellariiformes.

FAM. : PROCELLARIIDÆ.

Madeiran Forktailed-Petrel, *Oceanodroma castro* (Harcourt). 4 records.
Wilson's Petrel, *Oceanites oceanicus* (Kuhl). About 13 obtained and others seen.
Frigate-Petrel, *Pelagodroma m. hypoleuca* (Webb, etc.). Twice only.

Mediterranean Great-Shearwater, *Puffinus k. kuhlii* (Boie).   1 obtained.
North Atlantic Great-Shearwater, *P. k. borealis* Cory.   1 obtained.
Sooty-Shearwater, *P. griseus* (Gmelin).   Autumn visitor.
Little Madeiran-Shearwater, *P. assimilis baroli* Bonaparte.   9 recorded.
Cape Verde Shearwater, *P. a. boydi* Mathews.   2 occurrences.
Bermuda Shearwater, *P. a. l'herminieri* Lesson.   1 record, Sussex.
Kermadec-Petrel, *Pterodroma neglecta* (Schlegel).   Once only, Cheshire.
Capped-Petrel, *P. hasitata* (Kuhl).   1, Norfolk.
Collared-Petrel, *P. brevipes* (Peale).   1, Wales.
Bulwer's Petrel, *Bulweria bulwerii* (Jardine and Selby).   About 7 records.
Blackbrowed-Albatros, *Diomedea melanophris* Temminck.   **1,** Cambridge.

F.C.R.J.

PRINTED IN GREAT BRITAIN AT
THE PRESS OF THE PUBLISHERS

TH